Optical Rotatory Dispersion
and Circular Dichroism
in Organic Chemistry

HOLDEN-DAY SERIES IN PHYSICAL TECHNIQUES IN CHEMISTRY

Carl Djerassi, Advisor

APPLICATIONS OF NMR SPECTROSCOPY IN ORGANIC CHEMISTRY:
Illustrations from the steroid field
Bhacca and Williams

COMPUTATION OF MOLECULAR FORMULAS FOR MASS SPECTROMETRY
Lederberg

INFRARED ABSORPTION SPECTROSCOPY
Nakanishi

INTERPRETATION OF MASS SPECTRA OF ORGANIC COMPOUNDS
Budzikiewicz, Djerassi, and Williams

OPTICAL ROTATORY DISPERSION AND CIRCULAR DICHROISM IN
ORGANIC CHEMISTRY
Pierre Crabbé

PHYSICAL METHODS IN ORGANIC CHEMISTRY
Edited by J. C. P. Schwarz

STRUCTURE ELUCIDATION OF NATURAL PRODUCTS BY MASS
SPECTROMETRY
Vol I: Alkaloids
Vol II: Steroids, terpenoids, sugars, and miscellaneous classes
Budzikiewicz, Djerassi, and Williams

Optical Rotatory Dispersion and Circular Dichroism in Organic Chemistry

PIERRE CRABBÉ

SYNTEX, S.A., AND
IBEROAMERICAN UNIVERSITY (MEXICO)

HOLDEN-DAY

San Francisco, London, Amsterdam

1965

Library of Congress Catalog Card Number: 65-16746

Printed in the United States of America

Foreword

Physical methods have had an enormous impact on organic chemistry, but the number of such tools which have gained entry into the permanent armamentarium of the organic chemist is relatively small. One must surely list among this group optical rotatory dispersion and the closely related circular dichroism.

In 1959 it was still possible for me to cover in one book all of the developments that had occurred in the field of chemical applications of optical rotatory dispersion. Since then, spectropolarimeters and, more recently, dichrographs have become so common that nearly one thousand publications have appeared dealing with applications of these two techniques in organic and biological chemistry.

Clearly the time is ripe for this new book, which investigates the more recent developments in optical rotatory dispersion and compares this method with circular dichroism. Dr. Crabbé is admirably suited to the task of discussing and comparing the two techniques and their applications. As an expert in the terpene and steroid fields, he has not only employed these methods in his investigations of such natural products but has, since the late fifties, done research on optical rotatory dispersion. More recently, he has published numerous papers on stereochemical applications of optical rotatory dispersion and circular dichroism; as a result much of his book bears the imprint of personal experience.

Dr. Crabbé's book is addressed first to the graduate student or professional chemist who is unacquainted with these two methods but would like to learn what these techniques can do for him in the pursuit of his own work. It will also be very useful to the experienced organic chemist who has employed one or both of these tools and would like to have a handy reference volume which contains literature citations and detailed coverage of all recent advances in the field. To write a book for the uninitiated as well as for the expert is a difficult task, and Dr. Crabbé is to be congratulated for his obvious success. Organic chemists, notably those interested in stereochemistry and in natural products, will be grateful to the author for having lightened their load.

Stanford University   Carl Djerassi
December 1964

Preface

"Les conceptions les plus hardies, les spéculations les
plus légitimes, ne prennent un corps et une âme que
le jour où elles sont consacrées par l'observation et
l'expérience."

Louis Pasteur

The classical contribution of Pasteur to organic stereochemistry was
truly the crowning of the venerable and fertile period of discoveries with which
the names of Biot and Fresnel, among others, are associated.

Despite Le Bel and van't Hoff's fundamental observations at the end of the
last century, the stereochemistry of carbon compounds made little progress
during the first part of the twentieth century. However, the last twenty years
have seen a marked resurgence of the organic chemist's interest in stereochemical problems.[1] The elucidation of the configuration of numerous natural
products, the stereospecific syntheses in the alkaloid, terpene and steroid fields,
the ascertainment of absolute configuration, and the birth of conformational
analysis constitute some examples of recent progress in the stereochemistry
of organic compounds.

The remarkable advances realized in organic stereochemistry are attributable mainly to the rapid development of physical techniques. The contribution
of such methods as infrared, ultraviolet, and nuclear magnetic resonance spectroscopy, as well as mass spectrometry and X-ray crystallography, is undoubtedly
fundamental in this respect. Still more dramatic is the explosive development
of modern stereochemistry as a result of recent improvements in instrumentation for optical rotatory dispersion and circular dichroism.

While great credit is due to the pioneer work of Kuhn, Levene, Lowry,
Mitchell, and Rothen for their perspicacity in applying these techniques to
organic chemical problems, it is mainly thanks to Djerassi that use of optical
rotatory dispersion and, more recently, circular dichroism has become so

widespread. Klyne and Ourisson have also played a prominent role in the actual development and applications of these methods. In a way, this book is an homage to all these scientists who have contributed to the rapid progress in this important branch of organic chemistry.

In view of the fundamental contribution of both optical rotatory dispersion and circular dichroism to the advancement of modern organic stereochemistry, it was felt that a descriptive monograph offering the basic principles of these methods and at the same time giving an idea of their broad possibilities of application would be welcome.

A student or a newcomer to the field of organic stereochemistry obviously cannot in a short time assimilate and keep up with all the literature being published in this field. Hence, the purpose of the present book is to illustrate, with specific examples chosen from the most recent, the wide possibilities of optical rotatory dispersion and circular dichroism for investigating organic stereochemical problems. Moreover, it is hoped that this book will also be of interest to the research chemist, since not only the basic principles and classical work are reviewed, but mention is made of recent applications, many of them still unpublished.

It is not the purpose of the present monograph to cover all the published work on either optical rotatory dispersion or circular dichroism; very complete studies on both the theoretical and practical aspects have already been published by authorities in these fields.[2-10] Nevertheless, almost five years have elapsed since the appearance of Djerassi's classical book[7] and Klyne's detailed chapter[8] on optical rotatory dispersion. Furthermore, while Velluz and Legrand's review[11] on circular dichroism appeared only four years ago, many new applications of this technique have since been reported. Under such circumstances a monograph on both optical rotatory dispersion and circular dichroism, covering the recent aspects and applications of both methods, seemed desirable.

Since comparative studies on the applications of optical rotatory dispersion and circular dichroism to organic chemical problems have already appeared,[12,13,14] the present monograph will not analyze these methods from a critical point of view. Rather, it will suggest how to handle specific structural and stereochemical problems, giving the technique which should be used and the reason for that choice.

Mexico City, December 1964   Pierre Crabbé

REFERENCES

1. E. L. Eliel, Stereochemistry of Carbon Compounds, McGraw-Hill, New York, 1962.

2. W. Kuhn in Stereochemie (K. Freudenberg, ed.), Deuticke, Leipzig, 1933.

3. T. M. Lowry, Optical Rotatory Power, Longmans, Green, London, 1935.

4. S. Mitchell, The Cotton Effect, G. Bell, London, 1933.

5. P. A. Levene and A. Rothen in Organic Chemistry (H. Gilman, ed.), vol. 2, Chap. 21, Wiley, New York, 1938.

6. W. Heller in Physical Methods of Organic Chemistry (A. Weissberger, ed.), vol. I, Part 2, Chap. 13, p. 1491, Interscience, New York, 1949.

7. C. Djerassi, Optical Rotatory Dispersion: Applications to Organic Chemistry, McGraw-Hill, New York, 1960.

8. W. Klyne in Advances in Organic Chemistry (R. A. Raphael, E. C. Taylor, and H. Wynberg, eds.), vol. I, p. 239, Interscience, New York, 1960.

9. Symposium on Rotatory Dispersion: Related Theory and Application (B. H. Levedahl and T. W. James, eds.), Tetrahedron, 13, 1–240 (1961).

10. G. G. Lyle and R. E. Lyle in Determination of Organic Structures by Physical Methods (F. C. Nachod and W. D. Phillips, eds.), vol. 2, Chap. 1, p. 1, Academic Press, New York, 1962.

11. L. Velluz and M. Legrand, Angew. Chem., 73, 603 (1961).

12. C. Djerassi, H. Wolf, and E. Bunnenberg, J. Am. Chem. Soc., 84, 4452 (1962).

13. P. Crabbé, Tetrahedron, 20, 1211 (1964).

14. C. Djerassi, Proc. Chem. Soc., 314 (1964).

Acknowledgments

A book of this type could not be up-to-date without the help of many colleagues, who very kindly informed me about their new results and observations. I therefore wish to express my sincere gratitude for their collaboration. I want to thank especially Professor D. Arigoni (E.T.H. Zürich), Dr. E. Blossey (Wabash College, Crawfordsville, Indiana), Professor E. R. Blout and Mr. J. P. Carver (Harvard Medical School), Dr. J. I. Brauman and Mr. G. J. Elman (Stanford University), Dr. I. T. Harrison (Syntex Research Laboratories), Professor W. Herz (Florida State University), and Professor A. Moscowitz (University of Minnesota), who provided very helpful and constructive comments on the manuscript. Professor J. M. Conia (University of Caen), Professor C. Djerassi (Stanford University), Dr. K. Kuriyama (Shionogi Research Laboratory), Professor J. Levisalles (University of Nancy), Professor K. Mislow (Princeton University), Professor G. Ourisson (University of Strasbourg), Professor K. Schreiber (German Academy of Sciences, Berlin), and Dr. G. Snatzke (University of Bonn) informed me of many unpublished results from their laboratories. I should like to express my warmest thanks to Professor W. Klyne (University of London), who not only read the entire book and made a number of detailed suggestions, but also informed me of his most recent observations and obtained many optical rotatory dispersion curves reported in this monograph. I also express my special gratitude to Mr. H. Carpio for drawing the figures and formulas. Finally, I am indebted to authors, editors, and publishers who cooperated fully in giving the permission to reproduce numerous figures.

Table of Contents

Note to the Reader

Six-membered rings, such as cyclohexane, usually — but not always — exist in the chair conformation (1) which is, in general, much more stable than any of the conformations of the flexible forms. Of the latter, usually the boat conformations (2) are the least stable and the twist conformations (3) the most stable.[1]

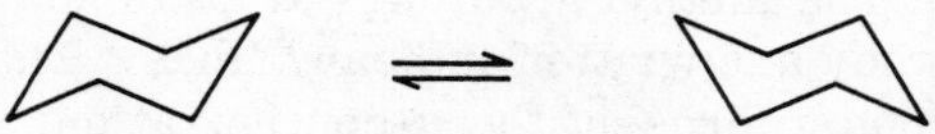

1

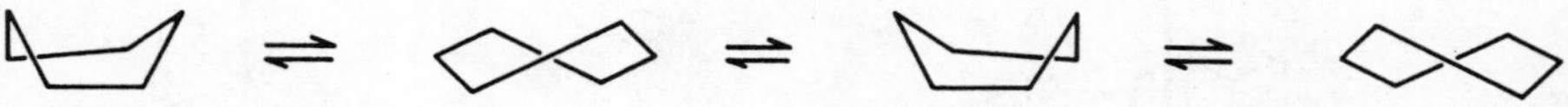

2   3   2   3

In the chair form (1) the substituents may be divided into two categories. They may exhibit the <u>axial</u> or the <u>equatorial</u> configuration. The six axial substituent (4a) are those which lie parallel to the ternary axis of the ring, while the six equatorial substituents (4e) are roughly in the plane of the molecule.

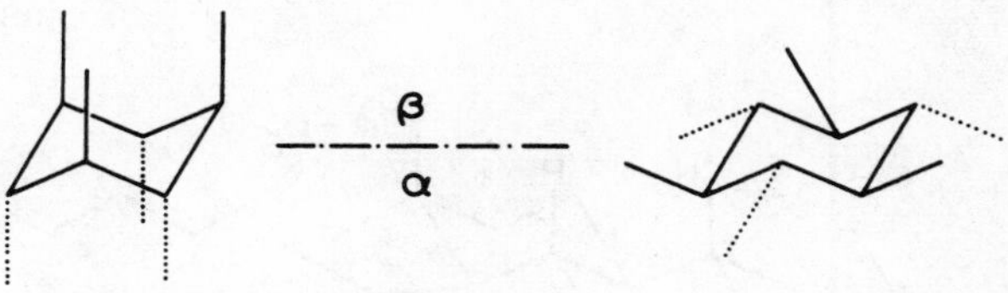

4 a   4 e

The axial and equatorial substituents are alternately up (heavy lines) and down (dotted lines). The heavy lines indicate a β-configuration (above the plane of the molecule). The dotted lines indicate an α-configuration (below the plane of the ring system).

In polycyclic compounds, the rings usually follow the rules of cyclohexane stereochemistry.[1,2] Hence, in such substances mentioned in this monograph thick lines are used for β-substituents, dotted lines for α-substituents. Hydrogen atoms are usually not shown on the carbon atoms of the skeleton.[3] They are considered to be α at the ring junctions unless a heavy dot is used to indicate a β-hydrogen. In the present volume the heavy dot is only used to imply a β-hydrogen atom. In all other cases a thick line is used to indicate a β-bond.

These conventions,[3] as well as the numbering system used throughout this book for polycyclic compounds, are illustrated below with a specific example. The stereochemical representation (structure, configuration, and conformation) of lophanol (5) is as shown in (6). The polycyclic system adopts a chair-chair-chair-quasi-chair conformation for rings A, B, C, and D.[1,2] Moreover, the ring junctures are <u>trans</u>, e.g., at the A/B ring junction the hydrogen atom at C-5 is axial α (down: dotted line in formulas (5) and (6)) and the methyl group at C-10 is axial β (up: heavy line in formulas (5) and (6)). In this monograph, lophanol will be represented as shown in formula (7). <u>In extenso</u>, the 5-hydrogen atom has the α-configuration and thus is not represented. The same is true for C-9, and C-14 hydrogen atoms. The β-configuration of the 8-hydrogen atom is made explicit by a heavy dot. The methyl groupings at C-10 and C-13 have the β-configuration, hence they are written in heavy lines. The dotted line at C-4 indicates the methyl group to present the α-configuration. Finally, the 3-hydroxyl grouping is β, as is the 17-side chain: they are written in thick lines.

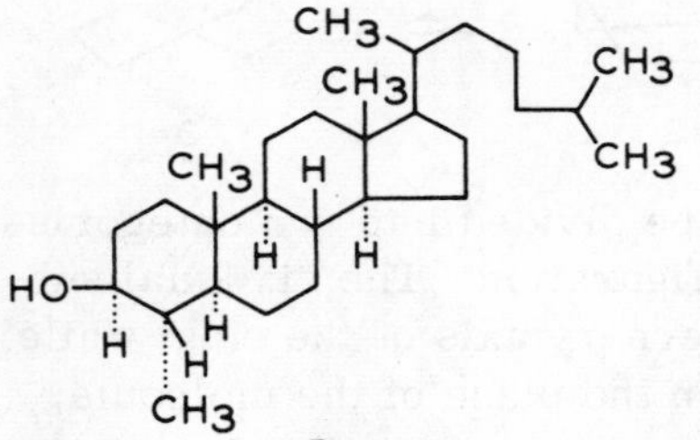

5

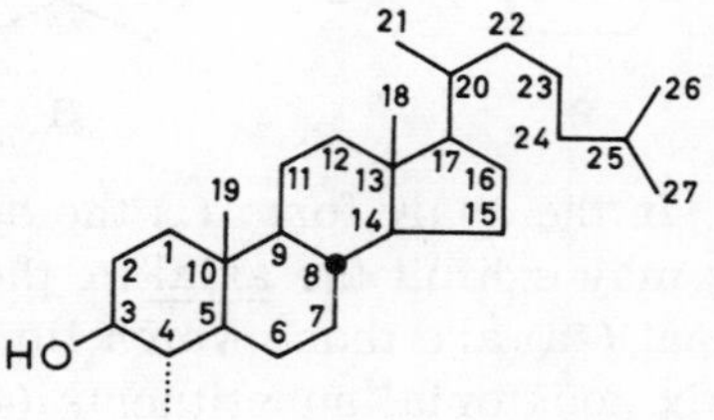

7

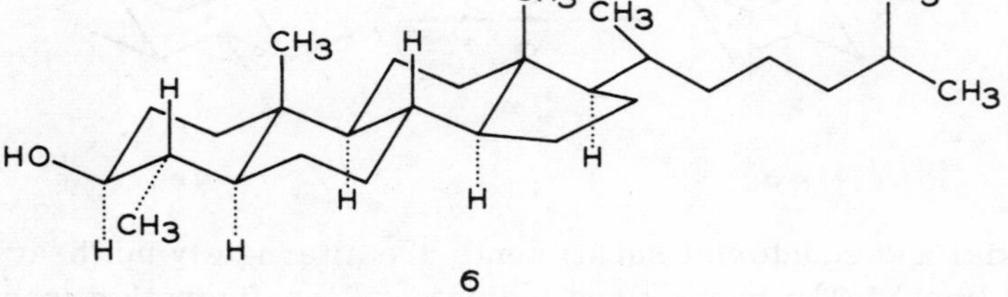

6

REFERENCES

1. E. L. Eliel, Stereochemistry of Carbon Compounds, McGraw-Hill, New York, 1962.

2. L. F. Fieser and M. Fieser, Steroids, Reinhold Publ. Corp., New York, 1959.

3. G. Ourisson, P. Crabbé, and O. R. Rodig, Tetracyclic Triterpenes, Holden-Day, San Francisco, 1964.

To My Parents

1

Optical Activity

1-1. HISTORICAL INTRODUCTION

The phenomenon of changes in optical activity with wavelength of a polarized beam of light has been known since the beginning of the nineteenth century. Hence the pioneer work of Biot, Fresnel, and Pasteur may be considered the base of modern stereochemistry.[1]

As early as 1811, Arago[2] discovered that a quartz plate produces unequal rotation values for different radiations. Biot[3] and Fresnel[4] later showed that the rotatory power of an optically active medium increases with the decreasing wavelength of the incident light. However, apart from a few theoretical studies, this observation received little attention for more than a century. That it was neglected for so long seems to be due partly to the discovery of electromagnetic phenomena, which absorbed the physicists' attention, and probably partly to the discovery of the Bunsen burner.[5] The Bunsen burner provided the organic chemist with a convenient and nearly monochromatic source of light: the sodium flame. Thus for a long time optical activity was measured at one wavelength only, usually the sodium D line (5893 Å). It is worth noting how much information the organic chemist deduced from this single measurement.[1]

Nevertheless, apart from the pioneer work of Tschugaeff[6] and Rupe,[7] it was not until the 1930's that the phenomenon of optical rotatory dispersion, i.e., the change of optical rotation with wavelength, took on a new importance, due to the studies of Kuhn,[8] Lowry,[9] Mitchell,[10] and Levene and Rothen.[11]

Less than 30 years after the basic phenomenon of optical rotatory dispersion was discovered, Haidinger[12] reported his observation about differences in absorption of the components of circularly polarized light, known as circular dichroism (see Sec. 2-3). That phenomenon, observed by Haidinger in crystals of amethyst quartz, was later found by Cotton[13] with solutions of copper and chromium tartrate.

Mitchell,[14] Lowry,[15] and Kuhn[16] were also the first to use circular dichroism for organic chemical problems. Credit should be given to these distinguished scientists, who, in spite of the technical difficulties, had the foresight to apply both these physical chemical methods to organic chemical problems.

The studies undertaken in the early 1930's on the applications of optical rotatory dispersion[17] and circular dichroism to organic chemical problems were often hampered by technical difficulties. Hence the use of these techniques for stereochemical purposes encountered obvious limitations at that time. Fortunately, in the middle of the 1950's, optical rotatory dispersion measurements were facilitated when a photoelectric spectropolarimeter became available.[18] Furthermore, shortly thereafter, convenient circular dichroism studies were made possible by the construction of more flexible instruments.[19]

These improvements in instrumentation were immediately followed by numerous applications of optical rotatory dispersion and circular dichroism techniques to organic chemical problems. Among the most dynamic and productive groups working in these fields are Djerassi's (Stanford University), Klyne's (University of London), and Ourisson's (University of Strasbourg), as well as the Roussel-Uclaf Company (Paris). As will be shown in subsequent chapters, optical rotatory dispersion and circular dichroism have proved to be of fundamental help in structural, configurational, and conformational problems encountered in the organic chemist's everyday life. Some of these problems can now be solved in days, whereas in the mid-1950's they would have taken months or even years to solve.

1-2. OPTICALLY ACTIVE SUBSTANCES

Although the basic mechanism in optical rotation cannot be discussed here,[20] the question "why does an optically active medium rotate the plane of linearly polarized light" will be dealt with in Chapter 2. In this section brief mention will be made of the various classes of compounds which show optical activity, i.e., the molecules to which optical rotatory dispersion and circular dichroism methods could be applied.

In summary, one can say that the optical rotatory dispersion technique can be applied to **any kind of optically active** molecule, even outside of absorption regions. Circular dichroism gives information only about compounds having one or several **optically active chromophores in the spectral range under examination.**

While the optically active chromophores will be examined in Section 2-4, attention will be focused here on the more general concept of optically active compounds.

According to Pasteur[21] a molecule, to show optical activity, should be able to exist in two isomeric forms related as nonsuperimposable mirror images. This criterion has subsequently been modified into three stereochemical symmetry conditions.[22] To have optical rotatory power the molecule should be devoid of a center of inversion, a plane of symmetry, and an alternating rotation-reflection axis of symmetry. Hence the absence of a rotation-reflection symmetry axis is the basic stereochemical requirement for optical activity, since a "onefold alternating axis is equivalent to a plane of symmetry and a twofold

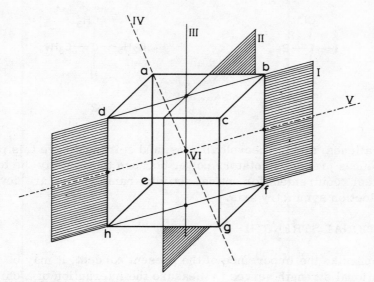

Fig. 1. Elements of symmetry of the cube: I represents a diagonal plane of symmetry passing through b, d, h, and f; II is a rectangular plane of symmetry; III shows one axis of fourfold symmetry; IV is an axis of threefold symmetry, passing through the opposite corners a and g. One axis of twofold symmetry, emerging from opposite edges, is represented in V. The center of symmetry VI is situated at the center of the geometrical model.

alternating axis is identical with a center of inversion."[23] The significance of such elements of symmetry is illustrated in Figure 1-1 for the cube.

In a molecule which satisfies the above requirements for optical activity, the center of optical activity may be described as an asymmetric screw pattern of polarizability.[24]

Such a pattern may originate[1] either in the difference in polarizability of the groups attached to the asymmetric atom or in a dissymmetry of polarizability caused by spatial arrangements of the groups in the molecule. Chlorobromoiodomethane (1), in which the dissymmetry of polarizability (sometimes called "atomic asymmetry") is due to the difference in electronegativity of the various groups attached to the asymmetric carbon atom, is typical of the first class. The second class of compounds, in which the optical activity is attributable to "conformational asymmetry," is exemplified by 3-methylhexane (2), in which the dissymmetry arises from the spatial arrangement of the hydrogen, methyl, ethyl, and propyl group on the asymmetric carbon. In compounds (1) and (2) the central carbon atom, bearing four **different** groups, is called an "asymmetric carbon atom."

From the theoretical point of view, it is worth noting that by applying the molecular orbital method for the calculation of optical rotatory power, it has been shown[25] that the molecular rotation originates essentially from the active **bonds** of the molecule and **not** from the asymmetry centers.[26]

Finally, it should also be mentioned that some organic molecules, although devoid of any asymmetric carbon atom, can show optical activity. Some skewed

$$Cl$$

$$I—C—Br$$

$$H$$

1

$$CH_3$$

$$C_2H_5—C—C_3H_7$$

$$H$$

2

biphenyls,[27] allenes, alkylidenecycloalkanes, and spiranes[1] have this property. These compounds present a rotatory power because they satisfy the fundamental stereochemical requirement for optical activity; namely, they are devoid of a rotation-reflection symmetry axis.

1-3. ROTATIONAL STRENGTH

To emphasize the importance of the present concept, it may be mentioned that the rotational strength serves to measure the interaction of a chromophore (such as a carbonyl group) with its asymmetric environment. Conversely, the concomitant asymmetry induced in the electron distribution within the chromophore can also be deduced from the rotational strength.[5, 20, 28]

In Chapter 2, it will be seen that both absorption and dichroism phenomena have their origin in the charge displacements induced by a perturbing light wave. Such movements of charge lead to the production of induced electric and magnetic dipoles. The rotational strength R_k of a chromophore is related to these induced electric and magnetic dipole moments by equation [1]:

$$[1] \qquad\qquad R_k = \mu_e^k \cdot \mu_m^k$$

where μ_e^k and μ_m^k have the dimensions of electric and magnetic dipole moments, respectively.[28]

If a molecule possesses either a center of inversion or a reflection plane of symmetry, the rotational strength will be equal to zero, and no optical activity will be found.[28] Indeed, if $\mu_e^k \neq 0$, but $\mu_m^k = 0$, equation [1] refers to an "electric dipole allowed, magnetic dipole forbidden" transition, and the product is 0. If $\mu_e^k = 0$, but $\mu_m^k \neq 0$, it refers to a transition designated as "electric dipole forbidden, magnetic dipole allowed," and the product is again zero. Finally, if the vectors μ_e^k and μ_m^k are at right angles to each other, their scalar product is also zero.[28]

Hence the rotational strength, expressed in equation [1], is a direct reflection of the asymmetry characterizing the surrounding of a chromophore. It is the purpose of Chapter 2 to show that such an asymmetric environment of a chromophore will lead to a "Cotton effect," easily detected by optical rotatory dispersion and circular dichroism.

REFERENCES

1. E. L. Eliel, Stereochemistry of Carbon Compounds, McGraw-Hill, New York, 1962.

2. F. Arago, Mém. Inst., 12, 93 and 115 (1811).

3. J. B. Biot, Mém. Acad. Sci., 2, 41 (1817).

4. A. Fresnel, Ann. Chim. Phys., 28, 147 (1825).

5. C. Djerassi, Optical Rotatory Dispersion: Applications to Organic Chemistry, McGraw-Hill, New York, 1960.

6. L. Tschugaeff and W. Pastanogoff, Z. Physik. Chem., 85, 553 (1913), and earlier references from these authors.

7. A complete bibliography of the works of H. Rupe can be found in H. Dahn and T. Reichstein, Helv. Chim. Acta, 35, 1 (1952).

8. W. Kuhn in Stereochemie, (K. Freudenberg, ed.), Deuticke, Leipzig, 1933.

9. T. M. Lowry, Optical Rotatory Power, Longmans, Green, London, 1935.

10. S. Mitchell, The Cotton Effect, G. Bell, London, 1933.

11. P. A. Levene and A. Rothen in Organic Chemistry (H. Gilman, ed.), vol. 2, Chap. 21, Wiley, New York, 1938.

12. W. Haidinger, Ann. Phys., 70, 531 (1847).

13. A. Cotton, Comptes rendus, 120, 989 and 1044 (1895); Ann. Chim. Phys., 8, 347 (1896).

14. (a) S. Mitchell, J. Chem. Soc., 3258 (1928); (b) S. Mitchell and S. B. Cormack, J. Chem. Soc., 415 (1932); (c) S. Mitchell and R. R. Gordon, J. Chem. Soc., 853 (1936); (d) S. Mitchell and K. Schwarzwald, J. Chem. Soc., 889 (1939); (e) S. Mitchell and G. K. Simpson, J. Chem. Soc., 784 (1940); (f) See also ref. 10.

15. See, for example, T. M. Lowry and H. S. French, J. Chem. Soc., 2654 (1932), and references therein; see also ref. 9.

16. (a) W. Kuhn and H. K. Gore, Z. physik. Chem., 12, 389 (1931), and later publications from this author; (b) W. Kuhn, Tetrahedron, 13, 1 (1961); (c) See also ref. 8.

17. The classical work is reviewed by W. Klyne in Advances in Organic Chemistry (R. A. Raphael, E. C. Taylor, and H. Wynberg, eds.), vol. I, p. 239, Interscience, New York, 1960.

18. H. C. Rudolph, J. Opt. Soc. Am., 45, 50 (1955).

19.   (a) S. Mitchell, J. Sci. Instr., 34, 89 (1957); (b) S. Mitchell, Unicam Spectro-vision, No. 6 (1958); (c) M. Grosjean and M. Legrand, Comptes rendus, 251. 2150 (1960).

20.   (a) A. Moscowitz in Advances in Chemical Physics (I. Prigogine, ed.), vol. IV, p. 67, Interscience, New York, 1962; (b) B. Carroll and I. Blei, Science, 142, 200 (1963).

21.   L. Pasteur, Ann. Chim. Phys., 24, 443 (1848).

22.   W. Voigt, Ann. Phys., 18. 645 (1905).

23.   S. F. Mason, Quart. Rev., 17, 20 (1963).

24.   J. H. Brewster, J. Am. Chem. Soc., 81, 5475, 5483, and 5493 (1959), Tetrahedron, 13, 106 (1961).

25.   A. Julg, Tetrahedron, 12, 146 (1961).

26.   (a) W. Kauzmann, F. B. Clough, and I. Tobias, Tetrahedron, 13, 57 (1961); (b) A. D. Liehr, J. Phys. Chem., 68, 665 (1964), and subsequent papers by Liehr.

27.   See, for example, K. Mislow, E. Bunnenberg, R. Records, K. Wellman, and C. Djerassi, J. Am. Chem. Soc., 85, 1342 (1963), and related papers from New York University and Stanford University.

28.   E. U. Condon, W. Altar, and H. Eyring, J. Chem. Phys., 5, 753 (1937); see also A. Moscowitz, ref. 5, p. 167.

2

Theoretical Considerations

2-1. INTRODUCTION

Any beam of light has associated with it electric and magnetic fields vibrating at right angles and perpendicular to the direction of propagation of the beam.[1-3] The interaction of these fields with a material medium produces various phenomena included under the generic name "spectroscopy." Some basic spectroscopic properties of a given medium are its absorption spectrum, related to the absorption coefficient (ϵ), and its dispersion curve, associated with the index of refraction (n). Phenomenologically, there is a close relationship between light absorption and dispersion measurements. The important aspect of this relationship is that a small anomalous dispersion will generally—but not always—be associated with a weak absorption band, while a stronger absorption band will give rise to a large anomaly of the dispersion.[3]

If one selects only one wavelength from the beam of light and sends it through a polarizer, an electric field E oscillating sinusoidally along a determined direction of space is associated with the monochromatic polarized beam. This wave of plane polarized light, the variable vector E, may be considered to be made up of two vectors, one corresponding to right circularly polarized wave E_R and one to left circularly polarized wave E_L. In a circularly polarized wave, the head of the vector rotates continuously around the axis of propagation of the wave. Hence a right circularly polarized light wave may be compared to a right-handed helix, as shown in Figure 2-1.

Electric field

Direction of propagation

Fig. 2-1. Right-handed helix described by a right circularly polarized light wave.

Vector E becomes the resultant of two vectors of equal length, called E_R and E_L. If E_R rotates clockwise and E_L counterclockwise with the same frequency, the two vectors make equal angles ($\omega = \omega'$), and their resultant E translates the motion of a plane polarized wave along the direction of the vibration axis X (see Fig. 2-2).

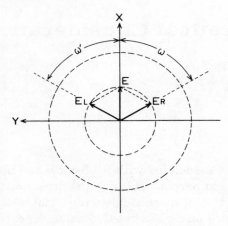

Fig. 2-2. The electric field vector E as the resultant of two rotating vectors, E_R and E_L.

2-2. ROTATORY DISPERSION

If the waves associated with E_R and E_L rotate at **different speeds**, the angles become different ($\omega \neq \omega'$), and although the resultant E is still plane polarized, its electric vector, and thus its plane of polarization, is rotated through an angle α. More explicitly, if the right circularly polarized ray E_R travels faster than the left circularly polarized ray E_L ($\omega > \omega'$), as indicated on Figure 2-3, the resultant wave E still pulsates in a plane. However, the plane of polarization is no longer the X plane. Rather, the plane of polarization makes an angle α with the X plane, since the plane of polarization **has rotated by such an angle.** If the right circularly polarized ray travels faster ($\omega > \omega'$ and α is positive), the medium is dextrorotatory. Conversely, the medium is levorotatory when the plane polarized wave makes a negative angle with the X plane ($\omega < \omega'$).

Since the **speed** of a light wave traveling through a material medium is a function of its index of refraction (n),[4] it becomes apparent that a specific medium will be optically active (see Sec. 1-2)[5-7] if it has different indices of refraction for the left and right circularly polarized light, and in extenso n_L has to be different from n_R. As early as the beginning of the nineteenth century, Fresnel[4] attributed the optical rotation of an active medium to the different refractive indices for left and right circularly polarized light, as shown in equation [1]:

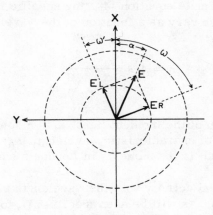

Fig. 2-3. Optical activity α resulting from circular birefringence.

[1]
$$\alpha = \frac{\pi}{\lambda} (n_L - n_R)$$

where α is the rotation in radians per unit length (measured with the same units as λ), λ is the wavelength of the incident light, and n_L and n_R are the indices of refraction for left and right circularly polarized light, respectively.

To obtain the specific rotation $[\alpha]$, where α is given in the more common experimental units of degrees per decimeter, equation [1] must be converted into equation [2]:

[2]
$$[\alpha] = \frac{\alpha}{c} \cdot \frac{1800}{\pi}$$

where c is the concentration in grams per milliliter of solution, and $1800/\pi$ is the conversion factor giving the specific rotation in degrees per decimeter.

The molecular rotation $[\Phi]$ is defined in equation [3]:

[3]
$$[\Phi] = \frac{[\alpha] \cdot M}{100}$$

where M is the molecular weight of the optically active substance.

The molecular rotation is the most suitable experimental quantity for comparing rotations of different substances, since comparison is then made on a mole-for-mole basis. Hence only this unit will be used throughout the following discussions.

To be optically active, a material medium has to show different indices of refraction (n_L and n_R) for the left and right circularly polarized light. If this is the case, the medium is **circularly birefringent**. Furthermore, since the indices of refraction (n_L and n_D) are not constant, but vary differently with the wavelength, as indicated in the approximate equation [4],[8] the specific rotation $[\alpha]$ and the molecular rotation $[\Phi]$ also vary as a function of the wavelength. Hence

$$[4] \qquad\qquad n = 1 + \frac{k \cdot \lambda^2}{\lambda^2 - \lambda_0^2}$$

where λ is the wavelength of the incident light, k is a constant function of the strength of the oscillator of characteristic wavelength λ_0; λ_0, which is a constant for a given compound, is the same as in London's equation for intermolecular attraction.[8]

The variation of optical activity with the wavelength gives an **optical rotatory dispersion curve.** As will be seen (Sec. 2-5A), for a compound containing no chromophore (a substance which does not absorb light in the region of wavelengths in which it is being examined), the optical activity progressively decreases in magnitude as the wavelength increases. A **plain positive** or **plain negative** dispersion curve is obtained, depending upon whether it rises or falls with decreasing wavelength. For a compound presenting one or several optically active absorption bands within the spectral range under experimental observation, the dispersion curve is **anomalous** and shows one or several "extrema" (peaks or troughs) in the spectral region in which the chromophores absorb light. **Outside** the region where optically active absorption bands are observed, Drude[9] proposes a mathematical expression relating the optical activity with the wavelength of the incident light. The first term of the Drude equation is as follows:

$$[5] \qquad\qquad [\alpha] = \frac{A}{\lambda^2 - \lambda_0^2}$$

where A is a constant, λ is the incident light, and λ_0 is the wavelength of the closest absorption maximum.

In terms of molecular rotation, equation [5] becomes:

$$[6] \qquad\qquad [\Phi] = \frac{K}{\lambda^2 - \lambda_0^2}$$

where K is equal to A multiplied by the molecular weight of the optically active compound, divided by 100.

If λ_0 cannot be determined experimentally (e.g., the plain dispersion curves in which λ_0 lies below 200 mμ), then λ is much greater than λ_0 and equation [6] is reduced to

$$[7] \qquad\qquad [\Phi] = \frac{K}{\lambda^2} \cdot$$

This relation, proposed by Biot,[10] clearly indicates a decrease of molecular rotation with increasing wavelength.

A two-term equation such as [8] must be used for compounds presenting two absorption maxima:

[8]
$$[\Phi] = \frac{K_1}{\lambda^2 - \lambda_0^2} + \frac{K_2}{\lambda^2 - \lambda_1^2}$$

where the first term expresses the rotatory contribution of a chromophore absorbing at λ_0 and the second term refers to the second optically active absorption band at λ_1, farther toward the ultraviolet. Since the mathematical treatment of such equations, or more complicated ones, is rather difficult, these expressions are usually not of convenient application for experimental organic chemists, and the present discussion will be limited to their bare mention.

2-3. CIRCULAR DICHROISM

After passing through an optically active medium, both constituents (E_L and E_R) of a circularly polarized ray not only show **circular birefringence** (different speeds due to the inequality between the refractive indices n_L and n_R) but, as might be anticipated, they are also **differentially absorbed**.

Thus in the spectral region in which optically active absorption bands are present, the length of vector E_R is no longer equal to E_L, and their resultant E no longer oscillates along the circumference of a circle (see Fig. 2-3). Instead, the head of the resultant vector E now traces out an ellipse, as shown in Figure 2-4. Hence when an optically active medium is traversed by a plane polarized light in the spectral range in which an optically active chromophore absorbs, not only does the plane of polarization rotate at an angle α, but the resulting light is also **elliptically polarized**: the medium exhibits **circular dichroism**. In terms of quantum mechanics, this means that the transition probabilities are different for left and right circularly polarized light.[11]

In Figure 2-4, the angle of rotation α is given by the angle between the incident linearly polarized light (axis X) and the major axis b of the emergent elliptically polarized light. Moreover, the ratio of the minor axis a of the ellipse to the major one b measures the tangent of the angle of ellipticity Ψ.

Since the major axis b and the minor axis a of the ellipse are the sum and difference, respectively, of the amplitudes p of both circular components upon emerging from the optically active medium, the tangent of the angle of ellipticity Ψ corresponds to

[9]
$$\tan \Psi = \frac{(p_R - p_L)}{(p_R + p_L)} .$$

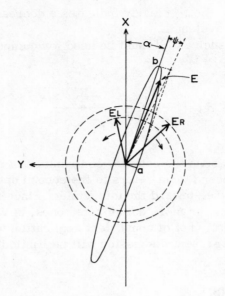

Fig. 2-4. The rotation α and ellipticity Ψ of plane polarized light emerging from an optically active medium in the absorption wavelength range.

The amplitudes p are related to the absorption indices k by

[10]
$$p = p_o \cdot e^{-\frac{2\pi k}{\lambda}}$$

where λ is the wavelength of incident light.

Since the angle of ellipticity Ψ and the difference between the absorption coefficients for the left and right circularly polarized lights $(k_L - k_R)$ are small, a quantitative treatment shows that equations [9] and [10] give, in good approximation,

[11]
$$\Psi = \frac{\pi}{\lambda}(k_L - k_R)$$

where Ψ is measured in radians per unit length and λ is the wavelength of incident light.

In equation [11], reminiscent of the Fresnel equation [1] for optical activity, one may substitute for the absorption coefficients k_L and k_R the more common molecular extinction coefficients ϵ_L and ϵ_R, using equation [12] for the conversion:

[12]
$$k \cong 2.303 \cdot \epsilon \cdot C$$

where C is the concentration of absorbing substance in moles per liter.

By analogy with the specific rotation $[\alpha]$ in equation [2], the specific ellipticity $[\Psi]$ is defined by

$$[13] \qquad\qquad [\Psi] = \frac{\Psi}{1 \cdot c}$$

where Ψ is measured in degrees, 1 is the path length in decimeters, and c is the concentration in grams per cubic centimeter of solution.

Similarly, the molecular ellipticity $[\Theta]$ is defined by [12]

$$[14] \qquad [\Theta] = \frac{[\Psi] \cdot M}{100} = 2.303 \left(\frac{4500}{\pi}\right) (\epsilon_L - \epsilon_R) = 3300 \, (\epsilon_L - \epsilon_R) \, .$$

Since the differential dichroic absorption $\epsilon_L - \epsilon_R$ [13] is also given as $\Delta\epsilon$, equation [14] may be written as:

$$[15] \qquad\qquad [\Theta] = 3300 \cdot \Delta\epsilon \, .$$

Since any medium that exhibits circular birefringence also shows circular dichroism, both effects occur simultaneously in a molecule which has optically active absorption bands.

2-4. COTTON EFFECT

The combination of unequal absorption (circular dichroism) and unequal velocity of transmission (optical rotation) of left and right circularly polarized light in the region in which optically active absorption bands are observed is a phenomenon called the "Cotton effect."

Cotton[14,15] observed that an optically active compound showed in this spectral region an abnormal behavior of its rotatory power. Thus the basic information which can be deduced from rotatory dispersion and circular dichroism curves is obtained most easily in the immediate vicinity of the spectral region of maximal absorption.

What is an optically active chromophore? According to Moscowitz, [1,16-20] optically active chromophores can be classified into two extreme types: (a) the inherently dissymmetric chromophore, and (b) the inherently symmetric, but asymmetrically perturbed, chromophore.

The optical activity of compounds belonging to the first class is **inherent** in the intrinsic geometry of the chromophore. As examples of this type, hexa-helicene[17] and twisted biphenyls[20,21] may be cited (see Chap. 8). In these compounds, the molecular amplitude of the optical rotatory dispersion curve and the maximum value of the circular dichroism curve (see Sec. 2-5) are generally quite high in comparison with the corresponding quantities observed for the second type of chromophore.

A typical example of the second group is the carbonyl function. For an isolated carbonyl group there are two orthogonal reflection planes of symmetry, and to a first approximation the chromophore should be optically **inactive**, as indeed it is in formaldehyde. Only when the chromophore is placed in some dissymmetric molecular environment, e.g., in a terpene or steroid, do its transitions become optically active. The optical activity manifests itself because the erstwhile inherently symmetric electronic distribution of the carbonyl group is now asymmetrically perturbed by the rest of the molecule in such a way that the symmetry of this electron distribution is lowered sufficiently to permit optical activity. However, since this optical activity is **induced** in the chromophore by its environment, rather than being inherent (as in the first type), the magnitude of the associated Cotton effect is often considerably smaller than in the first type of chromophore.

It might be added that the optical activity associated with the type (b) chromophore is typified by the presence of an asymmetric carbon atom. In such instances, the inherently symmetric chromophore acts like a molecular probe with which to explore the extra chromophoric geometry, since the magnitude of the induced optical activity depends on the geometry of the extra chromophoric portion of the molecule relative to the symmetry elements of the chromophore. However, in molecules containing type (a) chromophores, there frequently is no asymmetric carbon atom (e.g., in twisted biphenyls), since no asymmetric environment is necessary to produce the requisite conditions of asymmetry.

In conclusion, the Cotton effect associated with an optically active absorption band of a given compound manifests itself by a circular dichroism curve and an anomalous optical rotatory dispersion curve.

2-5. NOMENCLATURE

A. In Optical Rotatory Dispersion[22-24]

The rotatory dispersion curves can be divided into three different groups: plain curves, single Cotton effect curves, and multiple Cotton effect curves. All curves are plotted with the wavelengths in millimicrons (mμ) on the abscissa against molecular rotations [Φ] (given by equation [3]) on the ordinate. Furthermore, optical rotatory dispersion curves are usually run from high wavelengths (700 mμ) toward low wavelengths (200 mμ).

A plain rotatory dispersion curve exhibits no maximum or minimum within the spectral range under observation. Such a curve is typical of compounds devoid of optically active absorption bands within the wavelength range under consideration.

Plain dispersion curves are called **positive** or **negative** according to their tendency toward more positive or more negative values with <u>decreasing</u> wavelength.

The positive plain rotatory dispersion curve of 17β-hydroxy-5α-androstane (1) and the **negative plain curve** of 17α-hydroxy-5α-androstane (2)[25] are represented in Figure 2-5.

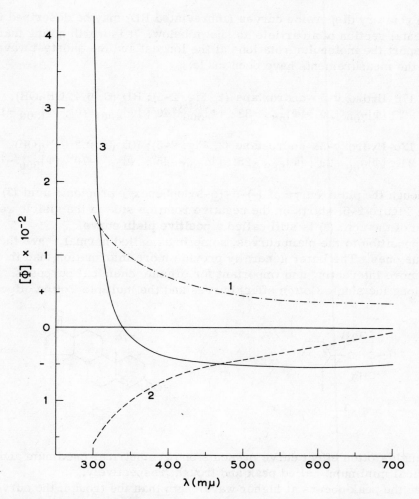

Fig. 2-5. Positive plain dispersion curves of 17β-hydroxy-5α-androstane (1) and (-)-α-(o-iodophenoxy)-propionic acid (3); negative plain curve of 17α-hydroxy-5α-androstane (2).

Such rotatory dispersion curves (abbreviated RD) may be described in the experimental section of an article as shown below. It is worth noting that one should report the molecular rotations at the longest and the shortest wavelengths at which the measurements have been made.

17β-Hydroxy-5α-androstane (1, Fig. 2-5); RD (C, 0.4; CH_3OH), 22°; $[\Phi]_{700}$ +20°; $[\Phi]_{589}$ +32°; $[\Phi]_{500}$ +40°; $[\Phi]_{400}$ +70°; $[\Phi]_{300}$ +155°.

17α-Hydroxy-5α-androstane (2, Fig. 2-5); RD (C, 0.2; CH_3OH), 21°; $[\Phi]_{700}$ -20°; $[\Phi]_{589}$ -25°; $[\Phi]_{500}$ -45°; $[\Phi]_{400}$ -70°; $[\Phi]_{300}$ -151°.

Although the plain curve of (-)-α-(o-iodophenoxy)-propionic acid (3),[24] shown in Figure 2-5, starts on the negative rotation side in the visible region, the curve of the acid (3) is still called a **positive plain curve**.

In opposition to the plain curves, sometimes called **normal**,[23] are the **anomalous** ones. The latter generally provide more information than the former, and are more interesting and important for organic chemical purposes. To this class belong the single Cotton effect curves and the multiple Cotton effect curves.

3   4

A single Cotton effect curve presents one geometrical maximum and one geometrical minimum, called **peak** and **trough**, respectively.

When the peak occurs at higher wavelength than the trough, the curve is a **positive Cotton effect curve**. Conversely, when the trough occurs first, the curve is a **negative Cotton effect curve**.

Figure 2-6 shows[26] the positive Cotton effect curve of 3β-hydroxy-5α-androstan-17-one (4). The first extremum observed at the longer wavelength is the peak at 312 mμ (Fig. 2-6). It is followed at a lower wavelength (276 mμ) by a **trough**, giving the symmetrical S shape typical of dispersion curves of many saturated ketones. The point λ_0 (295 mμ), of rotation $[\Phi]$ = 0, where the curve inverts its sign, corresponds roughly to the wavelength of the ultraviolet absorption band.

The vertical distance (a in Fig. 2-6) between the peak and the trough is called the **molecular amplitude**.[22] The molecular amplitude, a, is defined as the difference between the molecular rotation at the extremum (peak or trough) of longer wavelength $[\Phi]_1$ and the molecular rotation at the extremum of shorter wavelength $[\Phi]_2$, divided by 100. Hence equation [16] expressed the molecular amplitude in hundreds of degrees.

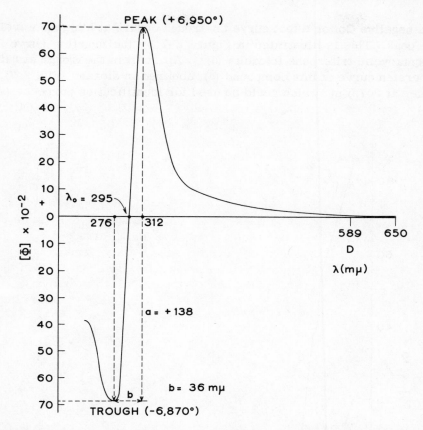

Fig. 2-6. Positive Cotton effect curve of 3β-hydroxy-5α-androstan-17-one (4)..

[16]
$$a = \frac{[\Phi]_1 - [\Phi]_2}{100}$$

In the present example (Fig. 2-6), the molecular amplitude a = +138. The
horizontal distance (b in Fig. 2-6) is called the **breadth** of the Cotton effect
curve. It is expressed in millimicrons (mμ), and b = 36 for compound (4) in Figure 2-6. While the latter notion is very seldom used, the former is important
for it constitutes a characteristic of a given compound.

The description of a single Cotton effect curve in the experimental section
of an article could be as follows:

3β-Hydroxy-5α-androstan-17-one (4, Fig. 2-6)[26]; RD (C, 0.7; CH$_3$OH),
20°; $[\Phi]_{700}$ +90°; $[\Phi]_{589}$ +270°; $[\Phi]_{312}$ +6,950°; $[\Phi]_{276}$ -6,870°; $[\Phi]_{235}$
-3,860°.

The molecular amplitude could also be mentioned, although in the example
it can be deduced easily from the above data.

In a **negative Cotton effect curve** the trough occurs at a higher wavelength than the peak. This is illustrated in Figure 2-7 by the negative curve of the pentacyclic triterpene friedelin (5).[27] Apart from the trough at 315 mμ, the dispersion curve of this compound (5), obtained in dioxane (Fig. 2-7), shows a shoulder at 307.5 mμ which could be used for identification purposes (see Chap. 4).

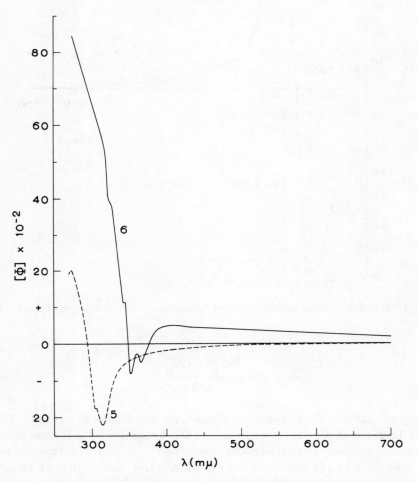

Fig. 2-7. Negative Cotton effect curve of friedelin (5); multiple Cotton effect curve of testosterone (6).

The last type of dispersion curve is characterized by a multiple Cotton effect. In this type of curve two or more peaks with a corresponding number of troughs will be observed.

In Figure 2-7 the rotatory dispersion curve of testosterone (6)[24] is shown. It will be noted that, apart from the multiple Cotton effect around 360 mμ

5

6

indicating entrance into the optically active absorption band, there is a broad peak between 420 and 405 mμ. This peak represents the superposition of contributions from all high-lying transitions with the 300 mμ transition.

The rotatory dispersion data of an α,β-unsaturated ketone is best summarized for an experimental section as follows:[24]

Testerone   (4, Fig. 2-7); RD (C, 0.10; dioxane), 25-26°; $[\Phi]_{700}$ +176°, $[\Phi]_{589}$ +297°; $[\Phi]_{420-405}$ +518° (broad peak); $[\Phi]_{366}$ -509°; $[\Phi]_{360}$ -274°; $[\Phi]_{352}$ -812°; $[\Phi]_{340-337}$ +1,123° (shoulder); $[\Phi]_{325}$ -3,858° (inflection); $[\Phi]_{275}$ +8,440°.

B. In Circular Dichroism[12,13,28,29]

The circular dichroism curves are plotted with the wavelengths in millimicrons (mμ) as abscissa against either differential dichroic absorption $\epsilon_L - \epsilon_R$,[13] dichroic absorption $\Delta\epsilon$,[28] or molecular ellipticity[12,29] $[\Theta]$ (given by equations [14] and [15]: $[\Theta] = 3300 \cdot \Delta\epsilon$) as ordinate. The circular dichroism curves plotted in molecular ellipticity units have the advantage of allowing an easy comparison of the intensity of the Cotton effect with the rotatory dispersion molecular rotation, since approximately equal orders of magnitude are always encountered.

As a corollary of the Kronig-Kramers theorem,[17,30] an expression has been proposed which relates the molecular amplitude a of a rotatory dispersion curve to the dichroic absorption $\Delta\epsilon$ of a circular dichroism curve:

[17] $$a = 40.28 \cdot \Delta\epsilon \; .$$

In terms of molecular ellipticity $[\Theta]$, equation [17] becomes

[18] $$a = 0.0122 \cdot [\Theta] \; .$$

Such expressions as [17] and [18] are of obvious interest since they allow correlations to be established between rotatory dispersion and circular dichroism results. However, while such relationships should only be considered as semi-quantitative, it should also be emphasized that they were obtained for the n - π^* transition of saturated carbonyl groupings and should be used only with caution for other chromophores.

Finally, the use of relation [19], called the "optic anisotropy" or "dissymmetry factor," has also been suggested.[13,31]

[19]
$$\frac{\Delta\epsilon}{\epsilon} = g$$

The terms "peak" and "trough" were suggested[22] to define the extrema of a Cotton effect of an optical rotatory dispersion curve in order to avoid any possible confusion with the words "maximum" and "minimum" of absorption spectroscopy. Indeed, it has been shown previously (see Sec. 2-5A) that the midpoint between the extrema of a positive or negative Cotton effect curve coincides roughly with the absorption maximum of the chromophore and **not** with the peak or the trough of the rotatory dispersion curve.

In circular dichroism the problem is different, since the wavelength of the extremum of a circular dichroism curve almost coincides with the position of the maximum in absorption spectroscopy. It should be noted, however, that in general the mean frequency of the ellipticity does not coincide exactly with the mean frequency of absorption; moreover, the shape of the curve is not completely symmetrical. The theoretical reason for these facts is known.[32] Furthermore, circular dichroism extrema being necessarily quantities requiring a sign, the circular dichroism data should be expressed[29] as **positive (or negative) maximum**, **positive (or negative) minimum**, and **positive (or negative) point of inflection**.

The circular dichroism curve and the ultraviolet spectrum of 3β-hydroxy-5α-androstan-17-one (4) are reproduced in Figure 2-8.[33,34]

As in the optical rotatory dispersion curve of ketone (4) (Fig. 2-6) the Cotton effect is positive; hence the circular dichroism curve (Fig. 2-8) is said to show a <u>positive maximum</u>. Furthermore, the wavelength of the positive maximum corresponds almost exactly with the wavelength of the absorption band of the 17-keto chromophore in ultraviolet spectroscopy. Finally, application of equation [18] to the Cotton effect observed by circular dichroism ($[\Theta]$ = +11440)[34] leads to a rotatory dispersion molecular amplitude a = +140, which is in good agreement with the value obtained by rotatory dispersion measurements (a = +138; see Fig. 2-6).

The description of this circular dichroism (abbreviated CD) curve in the experimental portion of an article can be condensed as follows:

3β-Hydroxy-5α-androstan-17-one (4, Fig. 2-8);[34] CD (C, 0.08; C$_2$H$_5$OH), 22°; $[\Theta]_{340}$ 0; $[\Theta]_{298}$ +11440; $[\Theta]_{240}$ 0.

When circular dichroism curves are not reproduced, the bandwidth Γ, or $\Gamma/2$ when the band is not well isolated at half maximum, should be reported, as indicated in Figure 2-8.

Finally, the term <u>negative circular dichroism minimum</u> is used for the negative Cotton effect associated with a minimum of absorption in the ultraviolet spectrum. For more complex cases, reference 29 should be consulted.

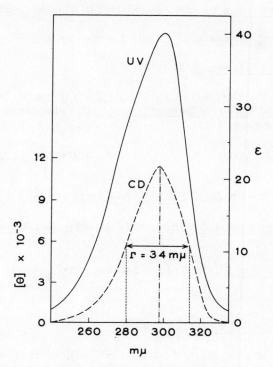

Fig. 2-8. Ultraviolet spectrum (UV) and circular dichroism curve (CD) of 3β-hydroxy-5α-androstan-17-one (4).

REFERENCES

1.   (a) A. Moscowitz, chap. 12 in C. Djerassi, <u>Optical Rotatory Dispersion: Applications to Organic Chemistry</u>, McGraw-Hill, New York, 1960; (b) W. Heller in <u>Physical Methods of Organic Chemistry</u> (A. Weissberger, ed.), vol. I, part 2, chap. 13, p. 1491, Interscience, New York (1949).

2.   (a) S. F. Mason, <u>Molec. Phys.</u>, <u>5</u>, 343 (1962); (b) S. F. Mason, <u>Quart. Rev.</u>, <u>17</u>, 20 (1963).

3.   J. G. Foss, <u>J. Chem. Educat.</u>, <u>40</u>, 592 (1963).

4.   A. Fresnel, <u>Ann. Chim. Phys.</u>, <u>28</u>, 147 (1825).

5.   E. L. Eliel, <u>Sterochemistry of Carbon Compounds</u>, McGraw-Hill, New York, 1962.

6.   J. H. Brewster, <u>J. Am. Chem. Soc.</u>, <u>81</u>, 5475, 5493 (1959), <u>Tetrahedron</u>, <u>13</u>, 106 (1961).

7.   A. Julg, <u>Tetrahedron</u>, <u>12</u>, 146 (1961).

8.   S. Glasstone, Textbook of Physical Chemistry, D. Van Nostrand, New York, 1948.

9.   P. Drude, Lehrbuch der Optik, S. Hirzel, Leipzig, 1906.

10. J. B. Biot, Mém. Acad. Sci., 2, 41 (1817).

11. (a) E. U. Condon, W. Altar and H. Eyring, J. Chem. Phys., 5, 753 (1937); (b) A. Moscowitz in Advances in Chemical Physics (I. Prigogine, ed.), vol. IV, p. 67, Interscience, New York, 1962.

12. E. Bunnenberg, C. Djerassi, K. Mislow, and A. Moscowitz, J. Am. Chem. Soc., 84, 2823 (1962).

13. T. M. Lowry and H. S. French, J. Chem. Soc., 2654 (1932).

14. A. Cotton, Comptes rendus, 120, 989 and 1044 (1895); Ann. Chim. Phys., 8, 347 (1896).

15. S. Mitchell, The Cotton Effect, G. Bell, London, 1933.

16. Private communication from Prof. A. Moscowitz, University of Minnesota.

17. A. Moscowitz, Tetrahedron, 13, 48 (1961).

18. A. Moscowitz, K. Mislow, M. A. W. Glass, and C. Djerassi, J. Am. Chem. Soc., 84, 1945 (1962).

19. K. Mislow, Ann. N. Y. Acad. Sci., 93, 457 (1962).

20. K. Mislow, M. A. Glass, R. E. O'Brien, P. Rutkin, D. H. Steinberg, J. Weiss, and C. Djerassi, J. Am. Chem. Soc., 84, 1455 (1962).

21. (a) K. Mislow, M. A. Glass, R. E. O'Brien, P. Rutkin, D. H. Steinberg, and C. Djerassi, J. Am. Chem. Soc., 82, 4740 (1960); (b) K. Mislow and C. Djerassi, J. Am. Chem. Soc., 82, 5247 (1960); (c) E. Bunnenberg, C. Djerassi, K. Mislow, and A. Moscowitz, J. Am. Chem. Soc., 84, 2823 (1962); (d) K. Mislow, E. Bunnenberg, R. Records, K. M. Wellman, and C. Djerassi, J. Am. Chem. Soc., 85, 1342 (1963); (e) G. M. Badger, R. J. Drewer, and G. E. Lewis, J. Chem. Soc., 4268 (1962).

22. C. Djerassi and W. Klyne, Proc. Chem. Soc., 55 (1957), J. Chem. Soc., 4929 (1962).

23. W. Klyne in Advances in Organic Chemistry (R. A. Raphael, E. C. Taylor, and H. Wynberg, eds.), vol. I, p.239, Interscience, New York, 1960.

24. C. Djerassi, Optical Rotatory Dispersion: Applications to Organic Chemistry, McGraw-Hill, New York, 1960.

25. P. M. Jones and W. Klyne, J. Chem. Soc., 871 (1960).

26. This curve was obtained through the courtesy of Professor W. Klyne, University of London.

27. C. Djerassi, R. Riniker, and B. Riniker, J. Am. Chem. Soc., 78, 6362 (1956).

28. L. Velluz, M. Legrand, and M. Grosjean, Comptes rendus, 256, 1878 (1963).

29. C. Djerassi and E. Bunnenberg, Proc. Chem. Soc., 299 (1963).

30. (a) R. de L. Kronig, J. Opt. Soc. Am., 12, 547 (1926); (b) H. A. Kramers, Atti congr. intern. fisici, Como, 2, 545 (1927); (c) W. Kuhn in Stereochemie (K. Freudenberg ed.), Deuticke, Leipzig, 1933; (d) W. Kuhn, Ann. Rev. Phys. Chem., 9, 417 (1958).

31. W. Kuhn, Trans. Faraday Soc., 46, 293 (1930).

32. W. Moffit and A. Moscowitz, J. Chem. Phys., 30, 648 (1959).

33. R. E. Ballard and S. F. Mason, J. Chem. Soc., 1624 (1963).

34. This curve has been provided through the courtesy of Professor C. Djerassi, Stanford University.

3

Technical Considerations

3-1. INSTRUMENTATION IN ROTATORY DISPERSION

Although several instruments have been constructed in the past which allow laborious rotatory dispersion measurements in the ultraviolet region of the spectrum, mainly by photographic methods,[1] attention will be focused here on the equipment available since the middle of the 1950's.

About ten years ago, Brand[2] and Rudolph[3] introduced the first commercial photoelectric spectropolarimeter. This instrument is essentially a polarimeter which has a monochromator to provide light at different wavelengths (from 700 mμ to 250 mμ) and a phototube and photomultiplier to measure the angle of rotation.

The Rudolph photoelectric spectropolarimeter which is shown schematically in Figure 3-1 has been described by Djerassi[4] as consisting of four components: a Rudolph circular scale high-precision polarimeter, a Beckman DU quartz monochromator, the light sources, and a photovolt multiplier tube. The light sources are a concentrated arc zirconium lamp (700-300 mμ) and a xenon arc lamp (below 300 mμ).

Most of the optical rotatory dispersion measurements reported during the past decade (1950's) have been obtained with this instrument. More recently, however, Rudolph made available an automatic recording spectropolarimeter.

The interest of the organic chemist in the broad possibilities of these instruments has had a stimulating effect on many companies interested in optics. Hence the last five years have seen a proliferation of new apparatus on the market. A new spectropolarimeter has been designed by the Roussel-Uclaf Laboratories.[5] An automatic spectropolarimeter, Model ORD-UV-5, has been made by the Japan Spectroscopic Company, Ltd., (JASCO). The Applied Physics Cary Recording Spectropolarimeter, Model 60,[6] and the Bellingham and Stanley (London), also called Bendix-Ericsson U.K. Ltd., (New Basford, Nottinghamshire) or Bendix-Gillham-King Spectropolarimeter (Polarmatic 62),[7] are also recently designed instruments. They offer the important advantage of permitting

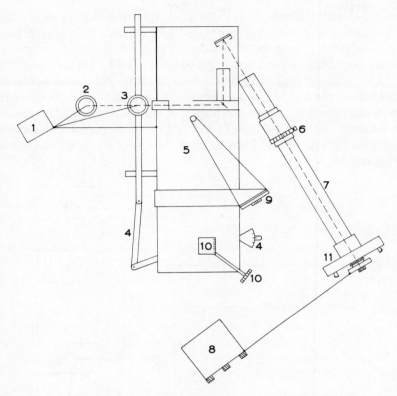

Fig. 3-1. The Rudolph spectropolarimeter: (1) power-supply unit for light sources; (2) xenon lamp; (3) zirconium lamp; (4) traveling bar and device for lamps adjustment; (5) monochromator; (6) symmetrical angle adjuster; (7) polarimeter; (8) photometer; (9) slit-width adjuster; (10) wavelength adjuster and scale; (11) analyzer. The dashed line indicates the path of light [from C. Djerassi, Optical Rotatory Dispersion: Applications to Organic Chemistry, McGraw-Hill Book Company, New York (1960); reproduced by permission of the publisher].

measurements down to 200 mμ, and even to 185-190 mμ with nitrogen flushing. Recently, two instruments with wide spectral range have been described.[8] At least one other apparatus will soon appear on the market, the Rouy Spectropolarimeter, probably to be available from Weston Schlumberger (Newark, N.J.).[7b]

Each of these apparatus presents specific advantages; a number of critical studies dealing with the detailed properties of these instruments have appeared.[5-10]

3-2. INSTRUMENTATION IN CIRCULAR DICHROISM

Since commercial instrumentation in circular dichroism is more recent than in optical rotatory dispersion, fewer types of apparatus are available so far.[11-14]

The Roussel-Jouan Dichrograph,[12] the principle of which is described in Figure 3-2, is based on an oscillating crystal technique. This apparatus is best described as consisting of a monochromator, a polarizer, and a crystal of monoammonium phosphate submitted to an electric field. Under these conditions, when the crystal is correctly oriented, the plane polarized beam of light can be divided into right and left components. These constituents are then passed through the optically active medium. When these unequally absorbed circular components are recombined in the region of electronic absorption, they give elliptically polarized light. This light is then sent to an electron multiplier and finally registered.

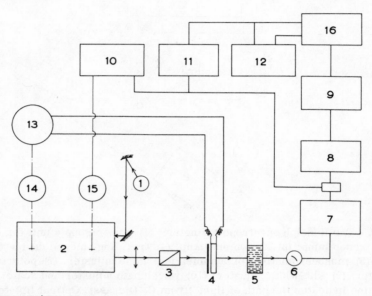

Fig. 3-2. The Roussel-Jouan dichrograph: (1) light source; (2) monochromator; (3) Rochon prism; (4) oscillating crystal; (5) cell; (6) electron multiplier; (7, 8) amplifiers; (9) detector; (10, 11, 12) amplifiers; (13) power-supply unit for the oscillating crystal; (14, 15) wavelength and slit-width adjusters; (16) automatic recording device [from M. Grosjean and M. Legrand, <u>Comptes rendus</u>, **251**, 2150 (1960); reproduced by permission of the editor].

Very recently a new automatic recording dichrograph has been reported.[15] This instrument, possessing greater brightness and precision, is claimed to permit circular dichroism measurements between 185 mμ and 600 mμ, whereas the earlier Roussel-Jouan Dichrograph covered only the 220-600 mμ spectral range.[15 bis]

Finally, the Japan Spectroscopic Company Ltd. is making available a new accessory to their spectropolarimeter ORD-UV-5 which will also permit circular dichroism measurements.[16] This apparatus seems to be the ideal combination and should be a useful and flexible tool for the organic chemist.

3-3. CHOICE OF SOLVENTS

The choice of solvents should be directed by the nature of the chromophore under investigation and depends on the wavelength at which it absorbs. Of course, the broader the spectral range which can be covered, the more instructive the curve will be. Moreover, for low wavelength absorbing chromophores, solvents with high ultraviolet penetration will be chosen. Unfortunately, very often one is then limited by solubility problems. For many purposes and for normal accuracy, dioxane has been found to be the proper solvent for circular dichroism and optical rotatory dispersion studies.

It should be noted that sizable variations in the circular dichroism curves have sometimes been noted merely with a change of solvent.[12c] Furthermore, in some cases (mainly ketones showing a weak Cotton effect in circular dichroism), solute-solvent interactions or changes of conformation, or both have been observed. Such interactions have been detected and discussed in recent studies;[17,18] these studies have found confirmation in circular dichroism measurements in an acid medium[17,19] (see Chap. 6).

Furthermore, special solvents or mixtures of solvents may be used for specific studies. Some recent examples of the use of a mixture of solvents (ether-isopentane-ethanol) in low-temperature circular dichroism have been published[20,21] and will be commented on in Chapter 6.

It has been known for a long time that in monochromatic polarimetry variations in solvents may affect the rotatory power.[22] These variations, which are a function of the polarity of the solvent (e.g., solvation and association phenomena), will be reflected in the rotatory dispersion and circular dichroism curves.

Methanol, although a polar solvent, shows good transparency through the normal spectral range and is therefore the solvent chosen for examination of saturated ketones or any other chromophore devoid of fine structure. Methanol is also used for detection of (hemi) ketal formation, which sometimes provides the organic chemist with useful information.[23,24] Some specific examples of solvent effects will be reported in Chapters 6, 7, and 9.

Since most of the fine structure of multiple Cotton effect curves (as in the α, β-unsaturated keto chromophore) is revealed in nonpolar solvents, octane, hexane, cyclohexane (if the compound is soluble), or dioxane will be the solvent chosen in such studies.

Dioxane may also be used for saturated ketones, but it should be noted that the change in going from methanol to dioxane is accompanied in rotatory dispersion by a bathochromic shift of about 8 mμ.[24]

As in the case of circular dichroism measurements, other solvents may be used in optical rotatory dispersion studies. Since these are more often the exception than the rule, references should be consulted for special cases.[24-26]

Before closing this chapter, it is worth noting that an important advantage of both optical rotatory dispersion and circular dichroism is the sample requirement of only one to two milligrams (frequently less) for an accurate determination. The sample can be recovered after measurement, an important advantage in natural products chemistry, since often little material is available.

REFERENCES

1. (a) R. Descamps, Trans. Faraday Soc., 26, 357 (1930); (b) W. Heller in Physical Methods of Organic Chemistry, A. Weissberger, ed., vol. 1, part 2, chap. 13, p. 1491, Interscience, New York, 1949; (c) M. K. Hargreaves, J. Chem. Soc., 2953 (1953).

2. E. Brand, E. Washburn, B. F. Erlanger, E. Ellenbogen, J. Daniel, F. Lippmann, and M. Scheu, J. Am. Chem. Soc., 76, 5037 (1954).

3. H. C. Rudolph, J. Opt. Soc. Am., 45, 50 (1955).

4. (a) C. Djerassi, E. W. Foltz, and A. E. Lippman, J. Am. Chem. Soc., 77, 4354 (1955); (b) A. N. James and B. Sjöberg, chap. 3 in C. Djerassi, Optical Rotatory Dispersion: Applications to Organic Chemistry, McGraw-Hill, New York, 1960.

5. M. Grosjean, A. Lacam, and M. Legrand, Bull. Soc. Chim. France, 1495 (1959).

6. H. Cary, R. C. Hawes, P. B. Hooper, J. J. Duffield, and K. P. George, Appl. Optics, 3, 329 (1964).

7. (a) E. J. Gillham and R. J. King, J. Sci. Instr., 38, 21 (1961); (b) B. Carroll and I. Blei, Science, 142, 200 (1963); (c) Private communication from Prof. W. Klyne on Polarmatic 62-Spectropolarimeter.

8. (a) J. P. Dirkx, P. J. Van Der Haak, and F. L. J. Sixma, Anal. Chem., 36, 1988 (1964); (b) B. Jirgensons, Makromol. Chem., 72, 119 (1964).

9. J. P. Jennings, Biochem. J., 86, 16P (1963).

10. H. Wolf, E. Bunnenberg, C. Djerassi, A. Lüttringhaus, and A. Stockhausen, Ann. Chem., 674, 62 (1964).

11. (a) S. Mitchell, J. Sci. Instr., 34, 89, (1957); (b) S. Mitchell, Unicam Spectro-vision, No. 6, 6 (1958).

12. (a) J. Badoz, M. Billardon, and J. P. Mathieu, Comptes rendus, 251, 1477 (1960); (b) M. Grosjean and M. Legrand, Comptes rendus, 251, 2150 (1960); (c) L. Velluz and M. Legrand, Angew. Chem., 73, 603 (1961).

13. See also: (a) R. Deen, Ph. D. Thesis, University of Leiden, Holland, 1961; (b) G. Holzwarth, W. B. Gratzer, and P. Doty, J. Am. Chem. Soc., 84, 3194 (1962); (c) S. F. Mason, Mol. Phys., 5, 343 (1962).

14. A. I. Scott, F. McCapra, F. Comer, S. A. Sutherland, D. W. Young, G. A. Sim, and G. Ferguson, Tetrahedron, 20, 1339 (1964).

15. M. Grosjean and M. Tari, Comptes rendus, 258, 2034 (1964).

15bis. See also: P. F. Arvedson and E. M. Larsen, Proceedings of the 8th. International Conference on Coordination Chemistry, (V. Gutman, ed.), Vienna, September 1964, p. 101, Springer-Verlag, Vienna, 1964.

16.   Private communication from Mr. Shigeru Honma, Japan Spectroscopic Co., Ltd., Tokyo.

17.   (a) H. P. Gervais and A. Rassat, Bull. Soc. Chim. France, 743 (1961); (b) C. Coulombeau and A. Rassat, Bull. Soc. Chim. France, 2673 (1963).

18.   A. Moscowitz, K. M. Wellman, and C. Djerassi, Proc. Nat. Acad. Sci. U.S., 50, 799 (1963).

19.   P. Witz and G. Ourisson, Bull. Soc. Chim. France, 627 (1964).

20.   A. Moscowitz, K. M. Wellman, and C. Djerassi, J. Am. Chem. Soc., 85, 3515 (1963).

21.   K. M. Wellman, R. Records, E. Bunnenberg, and C. Djerassi, J. Am. Chem. Soc., 86, 492 (1964), and related papers.

22.   T. M. Lowry, Optical Rotatory Power, Longmans, Green, London, 1935.

23.   C. Djerassi, L. A. Mitscher, and B. J. Mitscher, J. Am. Chem. Soc., 81, 947 (1959).

24.   C. Djerassi, Optical Rotatory Dispersion: Applications to Organic Chemistry, McGraw-Hill, New York, 1960.

25.   C. Djerassi, R. Riniker, and B. Riniker, J. Am. Chem. Soc., 78, 6377 (1956).

26.   (a) N. C. Knelen, N. J. Krause, T. O. Carmichael, and O. E. Weigang, J. Am. Chem. Soc., 84, 1738 (1962); (b) C. Tanford, J. Am. Chem. Soc., 84, 1747 (1962); (c) J. L. Mateos and D. J. Cram, J. Am. Chem. Soc., 81, 2756 (1959); (d) V. M. Potapov and A. P. Terentev, Zh. Obshch. Khim., 34, 516 (1964).

4

Applications of Optical Rotatory Dispersion and Circular Dichroism in Structural Problems

4-1. INTRODUCTION

The organic chemist who faces the problem of the structural elucidation of a new compound has many physico-chemical tools at his disposal. The purpose of this chapter is to show that optical rotatory dispersion and circular dichroism measurements sometimes provide structural information not readily available from other sources or methods. Some stereochemical aspects will be treated in subsequent chapters, but often the optical rotatory dispersion or the circular dichroism curve, or both, of an unknown optically active compound will give valuable information about the position of a function (e.g., double bond, hydroxyl, or carbonyl) in a specific molecule.

Since most of the work on optical rotatory dispersion and circular dichroism has been performed in the terpene and steroid series, many examples will be chosen among these groups of natural products. However, it should be mentioned that other classes of optically active natural products have also shown the broad possibilities these optical methods offer in structural problems.

4-2. PLAIN ROTATORY DISPERSION CURVES

Plain, or normal, rotatory dispersion curves, being rather simple, offer less scope than anomalous curves for structural and stereochemical studies. However, valuable information about the structure of a new substance devoid of a chromophore in the spectral range under examination can sometimes be gained by simple examination of its plain rotatory dispersion curve.

The main difference between an anomalous rotatory dispersion curve and a circular dichroism curve is that the former is typified by a "background curve," attributed to the background rotations, deduced from the Drude equation (equations [5] and [6], Sec. 2-2).[1] An interesting example is shown in Figure 4-1. The Cotton effect curve of 5α-spirostan-3-one (tigogenone) (1) is **positive**, but

30

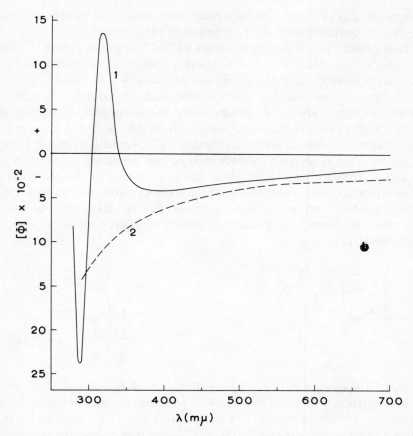

Fig. 4-1. Positive Cotton Effect curve of 5α-spirostan-3-one (1) superimposed on the negative plain curve of 5α-spirostan (2) [from C. Djerassi, <u>Optical Rotatory Dispersion:Applications to Organic Chemistry</u>, McGraw-Hill, New York (1960); reproduced by permission of the publisher].

the "background curve" of the parent compound, devoid of chromophore, 5α-spirostan (deoxytigogenin) (2) is a **negative** plain curve.[2]

The background rotations, sometimes called "skeleton effect,"[3] of an optical rotatory dispersion curve are due to rotational contribution of more distant absorption bands of a chromophore present in a molecule or of other atoms (i.e., asymmetric centers and the like) or both. Hence any optically active molecule, even devoid of chromophore in the spectral range in which it is examined, will have a background curve. It should be noted however, that in the future, improvements in instrumentation will permit a broader examination of this spectral range, as well as detection of new rotatory dispersion peaks and troughs, and will thus ultimately reduce the importance of the plain curves.

The common organic compounds which exhibit plain curves are hydrocarbons, nonconjugated olefins, alcohols, amines, and the like. Ketones and aldehydes far removed from an asymmetric center also give plain curves (e.g., compound 7).

3   4

The plain dispersion curves of four different cholestene double–bond isomers are collected in Figure 4–2. While the curve of 5α–cholest-1-ene (3) is weakly positive, its Δ^2-isomer (4) is much more positive. Similarly, the differentiation between cholest-5-ene (5) and 5α–cholest-6-ene (6) is easy, since the plain curve of the Δ^6 isomer is much more negative.[4]

5   6

As is clearly indicated in Figure 4-2, the molecular rotations [Φ] are much higher around 300 mμ than at the sodium D line (589 mμ), hence it follows that structural differences will be easier to detect from the rotatory dispersion curve than from the specific rotation value at the sodium D line.

So far, circular dichroism has been of no help for the study of the asymmetry around an isolated double bond, since the available instruments have not enabled one to reach the wavelength of the chromophore absorption band. It is conceivable, however, that a recently announced[5] circular dichroism apparatus reaching the 185 mμ region will permit such measurements in the future.

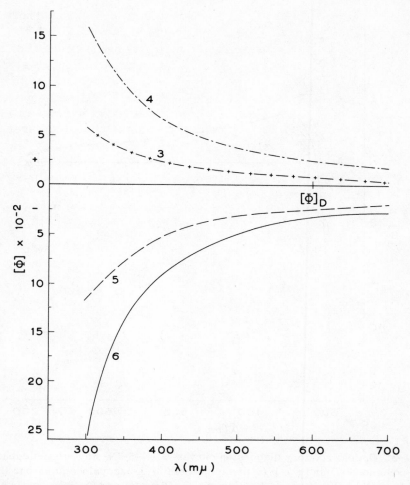

Fig. 4-2. Plain positive rotatory dispersion curves of 5α–cholest–1–ene (3) and 5α–cholest–2–ene (4). Plain negative rotatory dispersion curves of cholest–5–ene (5) and 5α–cholest–6–ene (6).

The next example shows the application of optical rotatory dispersion for detection of transannular nitrogen–carbonyl interaction in cyclic aminoketones.[6] The positive plain dispersion curve of the open-chain aminoketone (+)-5-(N-ethyl-α-methylphenethyl-amino)-2-pentanone (7) is shown in Figure 4-3. In contrast, the rotatory dispersion curve of the cyclic aminoketone (+)-1-(α-methylphenethyl)-1-aza-cycloöctan-5-one (8) shows a strong negative Cotton effect superimposed on a positive plain curve[6] (see Fig. 4-3). The Cotton effect curve of the cyclic aminoketone (8) has been attributed to significant nitrogen-carbon (C=O) electronic interaction.[6]

Finally, optical rotatory dispersion may be used to recognize the optical activity in compounds of negligible molecular rotation value at the sodium D

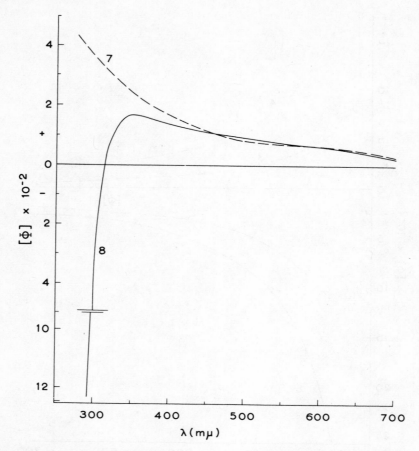

Fig. 4-3. Optical rotatory dispersion curves of (+)-5-(N-ethyl-α-methylphenethyl-amino)-2-pentanone (7) and (+)-1-(α-methylphenethyl)-1-azacycloöctan-5-one (8) [modified from N. J. Leonard, J. A. Adamcik, C. Djerassi and O. Halpern, <u>J. Am. Chem. Soc.</u>, **80**, 4858 (1958)].

line. Two tetrahydroionanediols (9), isolated from animal urines,[7] showed no measurable specific rotation at 589 mμ. However, the dispersion curves of their diacetates and dibenzoates exhibited appreciable optical activity.[8] Another example is the bicyclic compound (10) obtained by degradation of vitamin B_{12}.[9] The acid (10) showed a molecular rotation $[\Phi]_D = +1°$, but at a lower wavelength $[\Phi]_{365} = -165°$, indicating unambigously that the molecule was not racemic.[8]

9

10

4-3. RECOGNITION AND LOCATION OF A CARBONYL GROUP IN AN ASYMMETRIC ENVIRONMENT

The carbonyl function is an inherently symmetric chromophore which can be asymmetrically perturbed (Sec. 2-4). Hence the rotatory dispersion method may be used to recognize the presence of a carbonyl group in an optically active molecule. Although the dispersion curve often confirms the observations gained by other spectroscopic methods, in some special cases rotatory dispersion provides valuable structural information. For example, the carbonyl group of a five-membered ring ketone absorbs at nearly the same frequency as an acetoxy function. Since many compounds containing both functions show only one peak in the infrared, near 1740 cm^{-1}, and since the nuclear magnetic resonance spectrum would mainly confirm the presence of the acetoxy group, rotatory dispersion or circular dichroism might be the simplest way to identify the carbonyl chromophore in such cases.

Furthermore, the location of the carbonyl chromophore in different positions of a polycyclic molecule with various asymmetric centers, such as a steroid or a polyterpene, gives rise to different Cotton effect curves. This consideration led Djerassi[1,4,10,11] to examine the Cotton effect associated with a keto group in the various positions of the steroid molecule. Steroid ketones were chosen as a perfect example of the application of rotatory dispersion to structural problems, because the conformation of these molecules is fixed by the cyclic system, and comparison of the various curves becomes possible.

Keeping the stereochemistry as undisturbed as possible and locating alternatively a keto group in various positions of the steroid skeleton with the "normal" $(5\alpha,8\beta,9\alpha,10\beta,13\beta,14\alpha)$ stereochemistry, eleven suitable nuclear possitions are possible (e.g., 11-21) and pertinent examples were studied. The rotatory dispersion curves of most of these ketones, characterized by a single Cotton effect, are reproduced in Figures 4-4 to 4-6.[1]

Figure 4-4 shows the rotatory dispersion curves of 5α-cholestan-1-one (11), 5α-cholestan-2-one (12) and 5α-cholestan-3-one (13). While the 2-keto (12) and 3-keto (13) steroids exhibit a positive curve, the 1-keto isomer (11) shows an unusual Cotton effect curve. In the latter case, the dispersion curve is considerably affected by the skeleton effect. This background effect, presumably due to varying contribution associated with the π - π^* absorption of the carbonyl chromophore below 200 mμ,[12] is quite useful in structural work. In this case, for example, it permits easy differentiation between 1-keto and any other keto steroid (see Sec. 6-4).

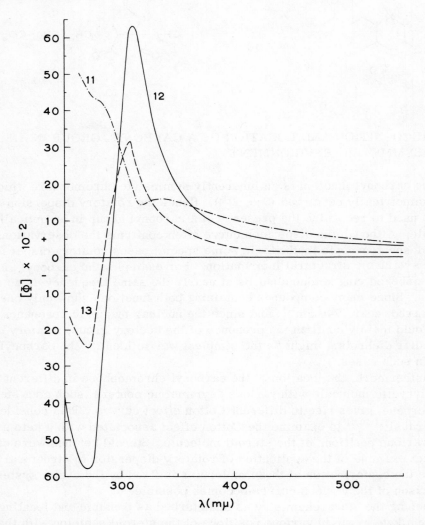

Fig. 4-4. RD curves of 5α-cholestan-1-one (11), 5α-cholestan-2-one (12), and 5α - cholestan-3-one (13).

Differentiation between a 2-keto (12) and a 3-keto 5α-steroid (13) is impossible by ultraviolet or infrared spectroscopy. However, as shown in Figure 4-4, both compounds exhibit a positive Cotton effect curve with very distinct amplitudes (12, a = +121 and 13, a = +56). Another convenient way to distinguish

11

12

13

14

between the two possibilities (12) and (13) is by formation of the ketal of the carbonyl group.[1,13] Experimentally, this is performed by determining the change in amplitude of the dispersion curve in methanol solution produced by the addition of a drop of hydrochloric acid, which catalyzes the formation of the ketal. With 2-keto steroids, such as (12), only approximately 10 percent of the ketal is formed because of steric interaction with the 10β-substituent. Hence the rotatory dispersion curves of these compounds suffer minor reduction in amplitude in the presence of hydrochloric acid. In contrast, 3-keto steroids, such as 5α - cholestan-3-one (13), show a decrease of around 70 percent of the amplitude. This observation is fortunate, for it permits another easy differentiation between a 2- and a 3-keto steroid.

As shown in Figure 4-5, 5α-cholestan-4-one (14) and 5α-cholestan-6-one (15) produce similar negative Cotton effect curves, with a small difference in amplitude. The dispersion curve of a 7-keto-5α-steroid, such as 3β-hydroxy-5α- cholestan-7-one acetate (16), also gives a negative Cotton effect. However, the general shape of the curve, seriously affected by the background rotations, is characterized by the peak appearing near the zero rotation line.

Both 11-keto (17) and 12-keto (18) steroids have a positive Cotton effect. In this case also, differentiation will be possible, since the 12-keto isomer (18, a = +22!)[†] usually has a stronger positive Cotton effect than the 11-keto steroid (17, a = +11) (see also Fig. 7-8).

15

16

_____

† The sign ! means that the second extremum was not reached.

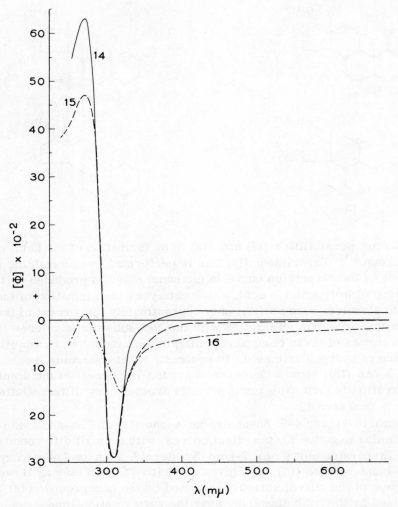

Fig. 4-5. RD curves of 5α–cholestan–4–one (14), 5α–cholestan–6–one (15) and 3β –hydroxy–5α–cholestan–7–one–acetate (16)[modified from C. Djerassi, <u>Optical Rotatory Dispersion:Applications to Organic Chemistry</u>, McGraw–Hill, New York (1960)].

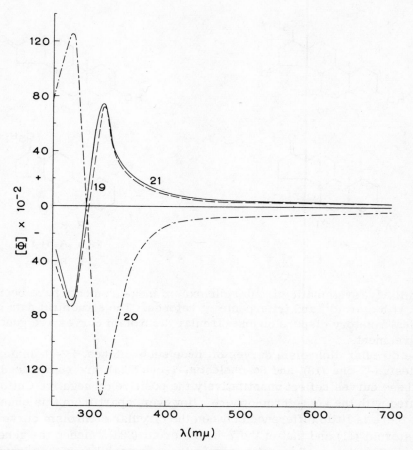

Fig. 4-6. RD curves of 3β-hydroxy-5α-cholestan-15-one (19), 3β-hydroxy-5α-androstan-16-one (20), and 5α-androstan-17-one (21).

The rotatory dispersion curves of the keto group in the three possible locations of ring D of a steroid are represented in Figure 4-6. Although the characteristic infrared carbonyl frequency of the cyclopentanone system permits one to locate easily the keto group in ring D of a steroid, the very strong Cotton effects associated with a 16- and 17-keto group not only confirm the infrared information but also establish the position of the function. As shown in Figure 4-6, 3β-hydroxy-5α-androstan-16-one (20) exhibits a strong negative Cotton effect, while 5α-androstan-17-one (21) has an intense positive Cotton effect. Finally, 15-keto steroids, such as 3β-hydroxy-cholestan-15-one (19), exhibit a positive Cotton effect whose amplitude is reminiscent of their 17-isomers. Differentiation between both possibilities (15- or 17-ketone) is possible by obtaining the dispersion curve in a basic medium, which, in most 15-keto derivatives, will lead to an inverted 14βH-15-ketone exhibiting a negative Cotton effect (see Sec. 6-5).

19

20

21

22 a, R= H

b, R= CH$_3$

Similarly, systematic circular dichroism measurements have been performed with steroid[14] and triterpenic[3,15] ketones. The structural data gained by the optical rotatory dispersion and circular dichroism curves are generally in good agreement.

The circular dichroism curves of three such ketones, 5α-cholestan-1-one (11), 5α-cholestan-3-one (13), and 5α-cholestan-7-one (22a), are reproduced in Figure 4-7. These curves reflect **quantitatively** the positive or negative Cotton effect associated with the keto-chromophore. However, apart from this quantitative aspect, there is little difference between the circular dichroism curve of the 1-keto steroid (11) and that of the 7-keto steroid (22a). Hence the general shape of the optical rotatory dispersion curves is more useful than the circular dichroism for locating a keto group in the steroid skeleton.[16]

Nevertheless, it may be mentioned that recent circular dichroism measurements[17] have indicated that low temperatures sometimes produce curves with increased vibrational fine structure. The acquired fine structure may differ sensibly from another circular dichroism curve of the same sign, and hence serve for identification purposes and structural studies.

Rotatory dispersion has found useful applications in structure determination of natural products other than steroids and terpenes. The following example is taken from the group of macrolide antibiotics. During the structure elucidation of neomethymycin, two possible structures (23) and (24) were in agreement with the chemical and physical evidence.[18] However, the possible structure (24) could be excluded by rotatory dispersion. As indicated in Figure 4-8, the dispersion curve of neomethymycin (23) shows a general similarity to that of methymycin (25). This would not be expected from a structure based on (24), in which the environment around the carbonyl chromophore is completely different. Thus the latter structure (24) could be eliminated, a conclusion which proved to be in accord with other evidence.[18]

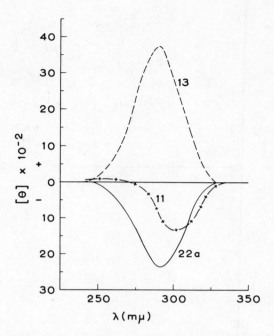

Fig. 4-7. CD curves of 5α-cholestan-1-one (11), 5α-cholestan-3-one (13) and 5α-cholestan-7-one (22a) [from C. Djerassi, H. Wolf, and E. Bunnenberg, J. Am. Chem. Soc. **84**, 4552 (1962); reproduced by permission of the editor].

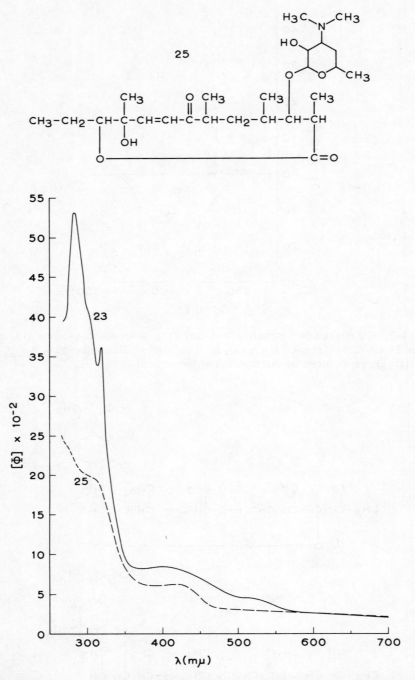

Fig. 4-8. RD curves of neomethymycin (23) and methymycin (25) [modified from C. Djerassi and O. Halpern, <u>Tetrahedron</u>, **3**, 255 (1958)].

4-4. INFLUENCE OF METHYL GROUPS ON THE COTTON EFFECT ASSOCIATED WITH 3-KETO STEROIDS AND TERPENES

The Cotton effect curves of cyclic or polycyclic ketones are very sensitive to conformational modifications (see Chap. 6). This property is useful in structure determination studies, since the rotatory dispersion and circular dichroism curves provide valuable information about the environment of the carbonyl group in an unknown compound.

It has already been mentioned that a 3-keto-5α-steroid, such as 5α-cholestan-3-one (13), exhibits a positive Cotton effect. Furthermore, when the dispersion curve is taken in methanol with a drop of hydrogen chloride, approximately 70 percent of the ketal is formed.[13] Introduction of another methyl group in position 2 or 4 (i.e., α to the carbonyl group), each of them with both possible configurations (α and β), does not modify the sign of the Cotton effect. However, studies in acid solution[13] indicate that introduction of an alkyl substituent next to the keto group reduces the hemiketal formation to less than 10 percent. This observation has been used with success in locating the unknown methyl group in the cactus sterol lophenol.[19]

The steroid bis-methylated at position 2, namely, 2,2-dimethyl-5α-cholestan-3-one (26), also shows a positive Cotton effect which is **not altered** in methanolic acid medium.

26   27

When two methyl groups are introduced into position 4 of the steroid nucleus the situation is completely different: an inversion of the Cotton effect occurs. Thus 4,4-dimethyl-5α-cholestan-3-one (27) exhibits a negative Cotton effect (see Fig. 4-9).[1] Since most tetracyclic[20,21] and pentacyclic[21] triterpenes possess a 3-oxygenated 4,4-dimethyl A/B trans pattern, this particularity became important in structural studies of alkylated steroids and in the terpene series. When ring A is five-membered, however, as in A-nor-3,3-dimethyl-5α-cholestan-2-one, there is no inversion of the Cotton effect. Thus the A-nor dimethylated steroid (28) shows a strong positive Cotton effect curve (Fig. 4-9).[22]

28   29

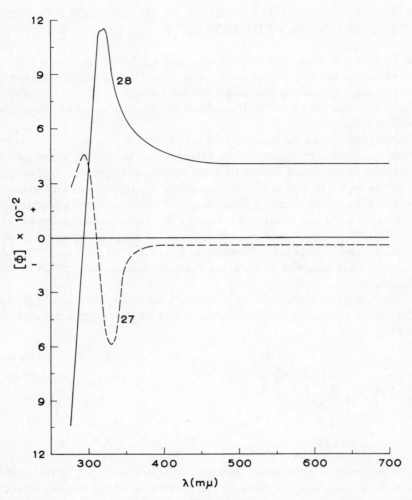

Fig. 4-9. RD curves of 4,4-dimethyl-5α-cholestan-3-one (27) and A-nor-3,3-dimethyl-5α-cholestan-2-one (28).

Introduction of a third methyl group at position 8, to give the 4,4,8-trimethyl structure common to many tetra- and pentacyclic triterpenes once again inverts the Cotton effect. Figure 4-10 shows the dispersion curve of hydroxy-dammarenone-II (29), β-amyrone (30), and lupanone (31).[23] Similarly, while 5α-cholestan-7-one (22a; a = -31) exhibits a negative Cotton effect, the introduction of a gem-dimethyl group at C-6, as in (22b; a = +93), inverts the Cotton effect.[24] These changes in sign of Cotton effects are best interpreted as resulting from conformational transmission occurring in the ring system (see Chap. 6).

Circular dichroism measurements of tetracyclic and pentacyclic triterpenes have not only confirmed previous rotatory dispersion findings but also allowed

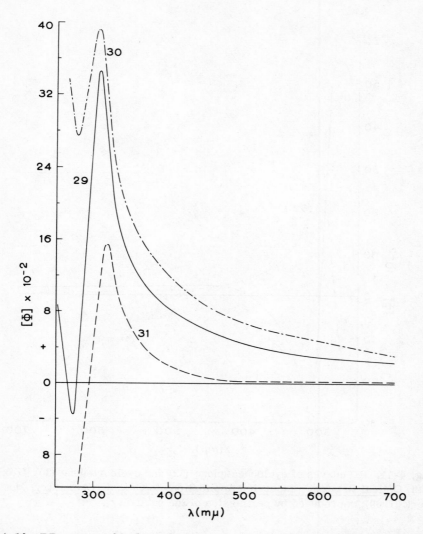

Fig. 4-10. RD curves of hydroxydammarenone-II (29), β-amyrone (30), and lupanone (31).

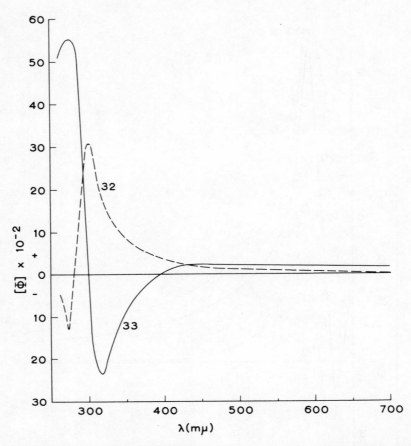

Fig. 4-11. RD curves of cycloeucalenone (32) and cycloartenone (33) [from C. Djerassi, <u>Optical Rotatory Dispersion:Applications to Organic Chemistry</u>, McGraw-Hill, New York (1960); reproduced by permission of the publisher].

the detection of subtle conformational interactions not always identified by rotatory dispersion.[15]

It should be pointed out that while the presence of a cyclopropane ring between positions 9 and 10 does not alter the general feature of the rotatory dispersion curve of a 4-mono or dimethylated compound, the introduction of a double bond in ring B may have a drastic influence of the Cotton effect associated with the 4,4-dimethyl-3-keto pattern.[25] This is shown in Figures 4-11 and 4-12. The 4α-monomethyl triterpene cycloeucalenone (32) shows a positive Cotton effect curve, while the dimethylated triterpene cycloartenone (33) presents the typical negative Cotton effect of the 4,4-dimethyl-3-keto-steroids (see Fig. 4-11). In contrast, while lanostan-3-one (34) displays a mild negative Cotton effect (see Fig. 4-12), Δ^7-lanosten-3-one (35) shows a much stronger negative curve, and its double bond isomer Δ^8-lanosten-3-one (36) exhibits a positive Cotton effect curve. These observations have proved very useful for structural studies of new triterpenes.

A recent example is posed by the structure elucidation of the triterpene shionone (37).[26] The strongly negative Cotton effect exhibited by this new triterpene is different from that of all known tetracyclic triterpenic 3-ketones. Moreover, the rotatory dispersion curve of shionone is reminiscent of the curve of friedelin (see Fig. 2-7). This observation, together with chemical evidence, allowed the assignment of the structure and stereochemistry represented in formula (37) for the A/B ring junction of this new tetracyclic triterpene.[26]

4-5. DETECTION OF OVERLAPPING ABSORPTION BANDS

The identification of the absorption band of α-iodo keto steroids, around 300 mμ, constitutes another interesting application of circular dichroism and rotatory dispersion to structural problems.

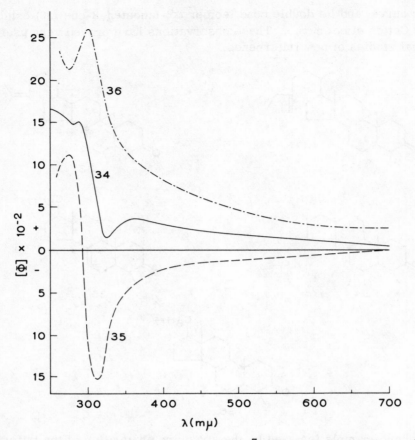

Fig. 4-12. RD curves of lanostan-3-one (34), Δ^7-lanosten-3-one (35), and Δ^8-lanosten-3-one (36) [modified from C. Djerassi, <u>Optical Rotatory Dispersion Applications to Organic Chemistry</u>, McGraw-Hill, New York (1960)].

The strong absorption at 255 mμ, due to the iodine of 2α-iodo-5α-cholestan-3-one (38), hides the weak n - π^* carbonyl transition around 300 mμ, so that this absorption band cannot be detected by ultraviolet spectroscopy. However, being highly optically active, the latter band is neatly detected by circular dichroism.[27] As indicated in Figure 4-13, where the ultraviolet spectrum, circular dichroism, and optical rotatory dispersion curves of 2α-iodo-5α-cholestan-3-one (38) are shown, the dispersion curve[28] of this iodo-steroid confirmed the earlier observations. Similar findings have been made with other α-iodo keto steroids.[28]

These observations may find an explanation[27] in Eyring's theory[29] of rotational strength (see Sec. 1-3). The greater the induced electric dipole moment μ_e^k (in equation [1], Sec. 1-3), the greater the intensity of ultraviolet transition will be. Hence one may assume that in 2α-iodo-5α-cholestan-3-one (38) the induced electrical dipole moment is small, and conversely, the magnetic dipole moment is rather large.

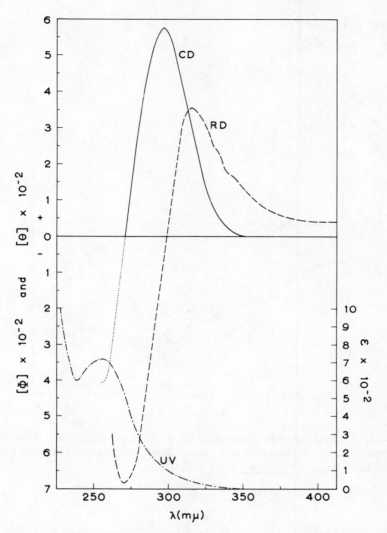

Fig. 4-13. Circular dichroism (CD), optical rotatory dispersion (RD), and ultraviolet absorption (UV) curves of 2α-iodo-5α-cholestan-3-one (38) [from C. Djerassi, H. Wolf, and E. Bunnenberg, J. Am. Chem. Soc., **85**, 324 (1963); reproduced by permission of the editor].

Another example of overlapping absorption bands is proposed by (+)-1,2-diselenane-3,6-dicarboxylic acid (39), whose ultraviolet absorption, circular dichroism, and optical rotatory dispersion curves are reproduced in Figure 4-14.[16] While the ultraviolet spectrum of this compound (39) is ill-defined, the rotatory dispersion and circular dichroism curves furnish much more information about the structure of this heterocyclic derivative. In particular, the

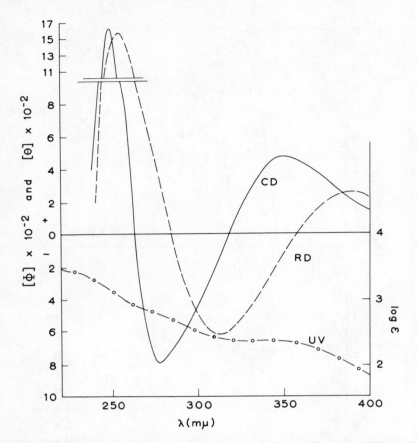

Fig. 4-14. Optical rotatory dispersion (RD), circular dichroism (CD), and ultra-violet absorption (UV) curves of (+)-1,2-diselenane-3,6-dicarboxylic acid (39) [adapted from C. Djerassi, <u>Proc. Chem. Soc.</u>, 314 (1964)].

$$\text{HO}_2\text{C} \qquad \text{Se-Se} \qquad \text{CO}_2\text{H}$$

39

circular dichroism curve (see Fig. 4-14) shows three Cotton effects centered at 351 mμ, 277 mμ, and 249 mμ. The rotatory dispersion curve clearly indicates a positive Cotton effect only near 350 mμ, the resolution of the other Cotton effects being much poorer.[16] Thus this example shows the advantage of circular dichroism over ultraviolet for structural purposes and over rotatory dispersion for selectivity between several absorption bands. In multiple Cotton effect curves, circular dichroism quite often offers advantages over optical rotatory dispersion, since overlapping optically active absorption bands are usually better resolved by the former method.[30]

In the next chapters, dealing with stereochemical problems, other applications of optical rotatory dispersion and circular dichroism to structural studies will be mentioned. However, from the examples reported above, where the stereochemical aspects have been deliberately omitted, it is obvious that in many cases these physical tools will provide valuable structural information not readily available from other spectroscopic methods.

REFERENCES

1. C. Djerassi, Optical Rotatory Dispersion: Applications to Organic Chemistry, McGraw-Hill, New York, 1960.

2. C. Djerassi and R. Ehrlich, J. Am. Chem. Soc., 78, 440 (1956).

3. P. Witz, H. Herrmann, J. M. Lehn, and G. Ourisson, Bull. Soc. Chim. France, 1101 (1963).

4. C. Djerassi, W. Closson, and A. E. Lippman, J. Am. Chem. Soc., 78, 3163 (1956).

5. M. Grosjean and M. Tari, Comptes rendus, 258, 2034 (1964).

6. N. J. Leonard, J. A. Adamcik, C. Djerassi, and O. Halpern, J. Am. Chem. Soc., 80, 4858 (1958).

7. (a) V. Prelog, J. Führer, R. Hagenbach, and R. Schneider, Helv. Chim. Acta, 31, 1799 (1948); (b) W. Klyne and A. A. Wright, J. Endocrinol., 18, 32 (1959).

8. W. Klyne in Advances in Organic Chemistry R. A. Raphael, E. C. Taylor, and H. Wynberg, (eds.), vol. I, p. 239, Interscience, New York, 1960.

9. V. M. Clark, A. W. Johnson, I. O. Sutherland, and Sir A. R. Todd, J. Chem. Soc., 2383 (1958).

10. C. Djerassi and W. Closson, J. Am. Chem. Soc., 78, 3761 (1956).

11. C. Djerassi, J. Osiecki, R. Riniker, and B. Riniker, J. Am. Chem. Soc., 80, 1216 (1958).

12. C. Djerassi, Proc. Chem. Soc., 314 (1964).

13. C. Djerassi, L. A. Mitscher, and B. J. Mitscher, J. Am. Chem. Soc., 81, 947 (1959).

14. L. Velluz and M. Legrand, Angew. Chem., 73, 603 (1961).

15. (a) P. Witz and G. Ourisson, Bull. Soc. Chim. France, 627 (1964); (b) P. Witz, Ph.D. Thesis, University of Strasbourg, May 1964.

16. C. Djerassi, H. Wolf, and E. Bunnenberg, J. Am. Chem. Soc., 84, 4552 (1962).

17.   K. M. Wellman, R. Records, E. Bunnenberg, and C. Djerassi, *J. Am. Chem. Soc.*, 86, 492 (1964).

18.   C. Djerassi and O. Halpern, *Tetrahedron*, 3, 255 (1958).

19.   C. Djerassi, G. W. Krakower, A. J. Lemin, L. H. Liu, J. S. Mills, and R. Villotti, *J. Am. Chem. Soc.*, 80, 6284 (1958).

20.   G. Ourisson, P. Crabbé, and O. Rodig, *Tetracyclic Triterpenes*, San Francisco, Holden-Day, 1964.

21.   (a) J. Simonsen and W. C. J. Ross, *The Terpenes*, vols. IV and V, Cambridge University Press, Cambridge, 1957; (b) P. de Mayo, *The Higher Terpenoids*, Interscience, New York, 1959.

22.   R. Hanna, C. Sandris, and G. Ourisson, *Bull. Soc. Chim. France*, 1454 (1959).

23.   C. Djerassi, J. Osiecki, and W. Closson, *J. Am. Chem. Soc.*, 81, 4587 (1959).

24.   F. Lederer and G. Ourisson, *Bull. Soc. Chim. France*, 1078 (1962).

25.   C. Djerassi, O. Halpern, V. Halpern, and B. Riniker, *J. Am. Chem. Soc.*, 80, 4001 (1958).

26.   (a) Y. Tanahashi, T. Takahashi, F. Patil, and G. Ourisson, *Bull. Soc. Chim. France*, 584 (1964); (b) G. Ourisson, F. V. Patil, T. Takahashi, and Y. Tanahashi, Abstracts of Papers, p. 64, International Symposium on the Chemistry of Natural Products, Kyoto, April 1964; (c) F. Patil, G. Ourisson, Y. Tanahashi, and T. Takahashi, *Bull. Soc. Chim. France*, 1422 (1964).

27.   (a) A. K. Bose, M. S. Manhas, R. C. Cambie, and L. N. Mander, *J. Am. Chem. Soc.*, 84, 3201 (1962); (b) R. C. Cambie, L. N. Mander, A. K. Bose, and M. S. Manhas, *Tetrahedron*, 20, 409 (1964).

28.   C. Djerassi, H. Wolf, and E. Bunnenberg, *J. Am. Chem. Soc.*, 85, 324 (1963).

29.   E. V. Condon, W. Altar, and H. Eyring, *J. Chem. Phys.*, 5, 753 (1937).

30.   P. Crabbé, *Tetrahedron*, 20, 1211 (1964).

5

Plain Rotatory Dispersion Curves in Stereochemistry

5-1. INTRODUCTION

The comprehension of the behavior of an organic compound results from Kekulé's constitutional theory, which was significantly improved by the concepts of classical stereochemistry set forth by Le Bel and van't Hoff at the end of the nineteenth century. The theory of conformational analysis, introduced by Barton[1] at the beginning of the 1950's, further improved the understanding of the structure of organic substances. Hence an organic molecule is completely known when specification has been made of its **constitution**, its **configuration**, and its **conformation.**

By constitution one means the carbon skeleton of the compound as well as the location of the various groupings and functions in the molecule. The configuration of a specific group may be defined as its spatial orientation, limited by the principles of free rotation about single bonds and restricted rotation about double bonds. The various conformations of a molecule are the spatial arrangements, not superimposable upon each other,[1] of the atoms representing one configurationally defined species, i.e., the arrangements of atoms that can be made by twisting bonds but **not** by making or breaking them.

Moreover, the importance of the existence of **preferred** conformations in organic molecules is now generally accepted. The fundamental tenet of this concept, recognized under the title of "conformational analysis," is that the physical and chemical properties of a molecule can be related to its preferred conformation.[1]

On the basis of these premises and the fact, already mentioned, that any optically active compound (with or without a chromophore within the spectral range under investigation) will exhibit a dispersion curve (see Sec. 4-2), it will be shown in this chapter that plain rotatory dispersion curves sometimes provide valuable information about the configuration of specific functions and groupings in an organic molecule. Chapters 6 through 12 will deal with the influence of configuration and conformation on the Cotton effect of optically active compounds possessing one or several chromophores in their molecule.

5-2. PLAIN DISPERSION CURVES AND RELATIVE CONFIGURATION

The relative stereochemistry of two or more asymmetric centers in the same molecule can often be successfully investigated by rotatory dispersion. An examination of steroid hydrocarbons indicates small differences between the plain curves of the androstane, pregnane, and cholestane skeletons with both 5αH and 5βH configurations.[2] These differences are summarized in Table 5-1.

Table 5-1

OPTICAL PROPERTIES OF SOME STEROID HYDROCARBONS

Series		Molecular Rotations (deg)		
(steroid structure, R at C-17, 5 position marked)		$[\Phi]_{600}$	$[\Phi]_{500}$	$[\Phi]_{300}$
Androstane	5αH	+5	+10	+40
R = H	5βH	+5	+5	−10
Pregnane	5αH	+55	+75	+280
R = CH$_2$—CH$_3$	5βH	+45	+65	+210
Cholestane	5αH	+100	+150	+550
R = CH—[CH$_2$]$_3$—CH(CH$_3$)CH$_3$ with CH$_3$	5βH	+110	+160	+530

Various steroidal sapogenins were also examined by rotatory dispersion.[3] It was observed that nearly all nonketonic sapogenins having the 22a-spirostan configuration, such as deoxytigogenin (1), exhibit a strong **negative** plain curve. However, the sapogenins possessing the 22b configuration, as exemplified by cyclosarsa-sapogenin (2), show a **positive** plain curve. The difference between these curves has been attributed[3] to the inverted stereochemistry of the spiroketal side chain at C-22. Such an interpretation was proposed because changes in the A/B ring juncture do not affect the rotatory dispersion curve to any appreciable extent (see Table 5-1).

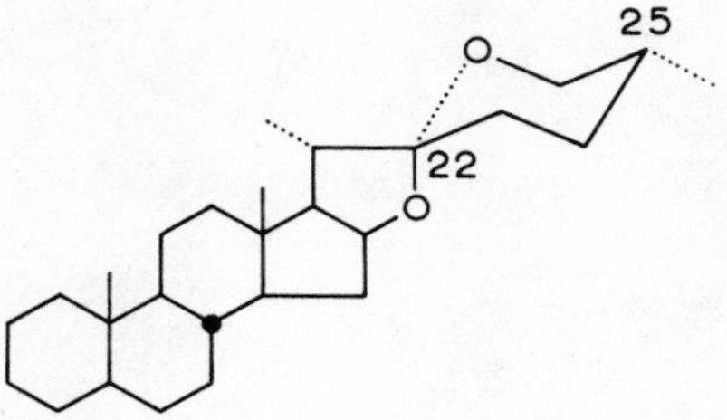

Optical rotatory dispersion may be used to assign the relative configuration of a secondary hydroxyl group in the steroid molecule. Figure 5-1 shows the plain **negative** dispersion curve of 17α-hydroxy-5α-androstane (3a) and plain **positive** dispersion curve exhibited by 17β-hydroxy-5α-androstane (4a).[2] The configuration of these steroids at C-17 could also be deduced from the dispersion curves of the acetates (3b, 4b) and the benzoates (3c, 4c), which show opposite signs (see Fig. 5-1).[2]

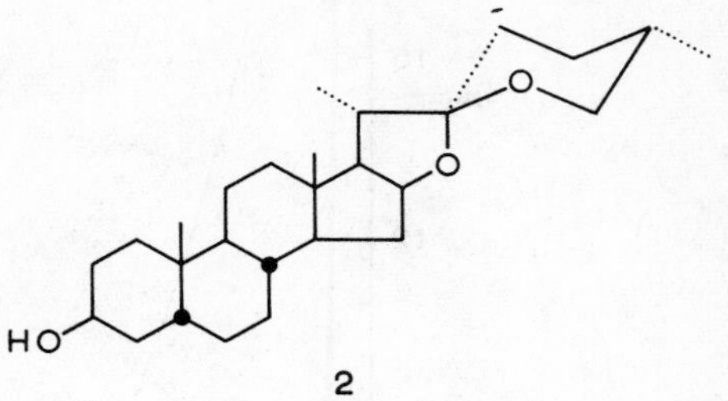

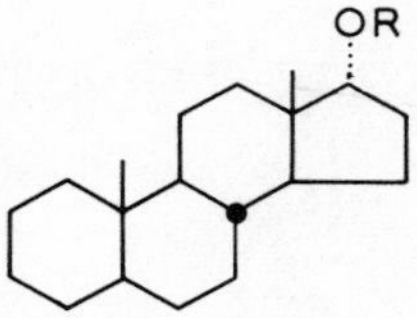

3 a, R = H
   b, R = Ac
   c, R = Bz

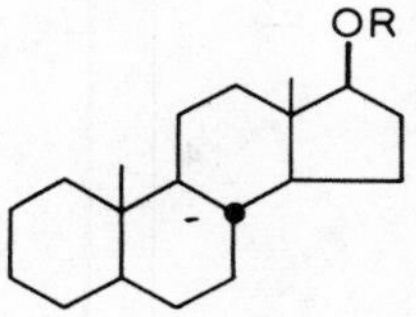

4 a, R = H
   b, R = Ac
   c, R = Bz

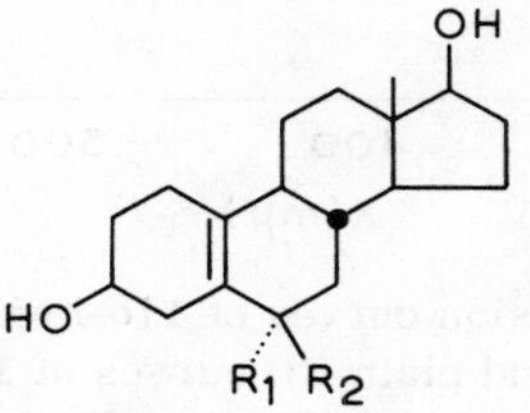

5 a, R_1 = OH; R_2 = H
   b, R_1 = H; R_2 = OH

In connection with the curves of acetates and benzoates reported in Fig. 5-1, it should be mentioned that recent improvements in instrumentation now allow the measurement of Cotton effects associated with the carbonyl n - π* transition of an ester group around 220 mμ[4,5] (see Chap. 11).

The configuration of other secondary alcohols has successfully been assigned by optical rotatory dispersion,[5] and this method has also been applied to allylic alcohols. The difference in relative configuration which distinguishes the 6α- (5a) from its 6β-hydroxy epimer (5b)[6] is much more easily deduced from their plain rotatory dispersion curves than from their specific rotations at the sodium

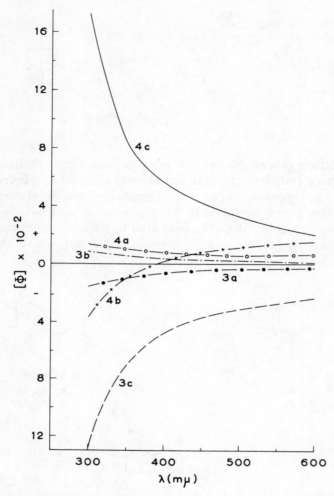

Fig. 5-1. Plain rotatory dispersion curves of 17α–hydroxy-5α–androstane (3a), its acetate (3b), and benzoate (3c), and plain RD curves of 17β–hydroxy-5α–androstane (4a), the corresponding acetate (4b) and benzoate (4c) [from P. M. Jones and W. Klyne, <u>J. Chem. Soc.</u>, 871 (1960); reproduced by permission of the editor].

D line. The values reported in Table 5-2 clearly indicate that when the difference in specific rotation is only 25° at 589 mμ, a molecular rotation difference of more than 500° permits an easy differentiation at 295 mμ. Furthermore, the application of Mills' rule for allylic alcohols[7] permits the assignment of the correct stereochemistry to such compounds.

The configurations not only of secondary but also of tertiary hydroxyl groups can be deduced from their plain dispersion curves. This can be seen in Figure 5-2, which shows the plain dispersion curves of 17α-ethynyl-5α-androstan-3,17β-diol-3-acetate (6), its 17-stereoisomer (7), as well as their Δ⁵-analogs

Table 5-2

OPTICAL ROTATORY PROPERTIES OF ALLYLIC ALCOHOLS

Compounds	Specific Rotations	Molecular Rotations (deg)		
	$[\alpha]_D$	$[\Phi]_{589}$	$[\Phi]_{400}$	$[\Phi]_{295}$
5a	+71	+207	+304	+992
5b	+96	+280	+508	+1577

(8) and (9).[8] While the curves of the epimeric compounds (6) and (7) are of opposite sign, the difference between the plain curves of (8) and (9), both negative, is only a matter of intensity. This is due to the strong negative rotatory power associated with the Δ^5-double bond (see Sec. 4-2).

Sjöberg[9] has undertaken an extensive rotatory dispersion study of various types of aryl substituted carboxylic acids, summarized by the general formulas (10) to (12). From the plain curves which were obtained, many interesting observations have been made, and stereochemical correlations could be established between different series. However, the new rotatory dispersion and circular dichroism instrumentation now allows measurement of Cotton effects associated with the n - π* transition of such optically active carboxylic acids.[10] Hence more precise and reliable conclusions based on the Cotton effects can be obtained (see Chap. 11).

The optical rotatory dispersion of diastereomeric open-chain alcohols of the type represented in formula (13) have been determined,[11] and careful examination of these dispersion curves led to some interesting conclusions. For the alcohols in which two asymmetric centers are substituted with the

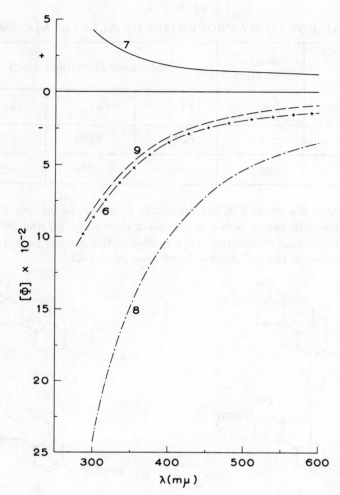

Fig. 5-2. Plain rotatory dispersion curves of 17α-ethynyl-5α-androstan-3,17β-diol-3-acetate (6), 17β-ethynyl-5α-androstan-3,17α-diol-3-acetate (7), 17α-ethynyl-androst-5-en-3,17β-diol-3-acetate (8), and 17β-ethynyl-adrost-5-en-3,17α-diol-3-acetate (9) [modified from L. Mamlok, A. M. Giroud, and J. Jacques, <u>Bull. Soc. Chim. France,</u> 1806 (1961)].

same alkyl groups, the dispersion curves of the <u>threo</u> isomers[†] pass through a peak in the 340-310 mμ region, whereas the <u>erythro</u> isomers[†] exhibit no extremum in the spectral range. This is illustrated in Figure 5-3, where the plain positive dispersion curve of <u>erythro</u>-4-phenyl-3-hexanol (14) and the positive extremum of <u>threo</u>-4-phenyl-3-hexanol (15) are represented.

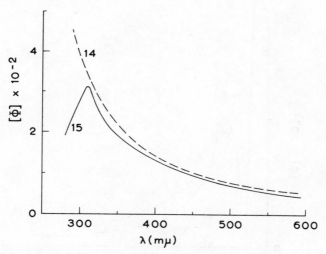

Where R = alkyl group, etc.
       X = CH$_2$
    or hetero group (NH, O, S, Se)

12

Where R$_1$, R$_2$, R$_3$, and R$_4$
may be alkyl, aryl, or hydrogen

13

Fig. 5-3. RD curves of <u>erythro</u>-4-phenyl-3-hexanol (14) and <u>threo</u>-4-phenyl-3-hexanol (15) [adapted from J. L. Mateos and D. J. Cram, <u>J. Am. Chem. Soc.</u>, **81**, 2756 (1959)].

[†]For any system of type R$_1$—C$_{ab}$—C$_{ac}$—R$_2$ containing two asymmetric centers, such as compounds (14) and (15), the terminology "erythro" and "threo" has been suggested. If both like groups in the projection formula are on the same side, as are the ethyl side chains in (14), the stereoisomer has the <u>erythro</u> form. Conversely, if both groups are on opposite sides, as in (15), the stereoisomer has the <u>threo</u> form.[12]

The situation is different for alcohols in which one asymmetric carbon atom carries a methyl and the other an ethyl group, as in <u>erythro</u>- and <u>threo</u>-2-phenyl-3-pentanols (16). One can see in Figure 5-4 that while the <u>erythro</u>-isomer shows a peak around 310 mμ, the <u>threo</u>-isomer exhibits an inflection in the same spectral region.

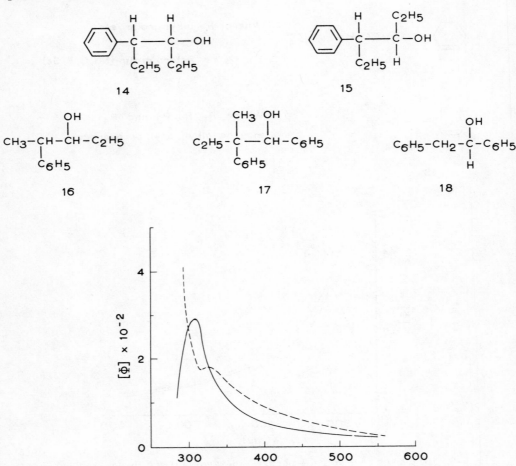

Fig. 5-4. RD curves of <u>erythro</u>-2-phenyl-3-pentanol (———) and <u>threo</u>-2-phenyl-3-pentanol (------) (16) [modified from J. L. Mateos and D. J. Cram, <u>J. Am. Chem. Soc.</u>, **81**, 2756 (1959)].

Moreover, all optically active alcohols in which a phenyl group is attached to each asymmetric carbon atom exhibit only plain positive curves in the spectral range which has been examined. Nevertheless, the plain curve of the <u>threo</u>-isomer, being much more positive than that of the <u>erythro</u>-isomer, affords an easy differentiation between these optical isomers. This can be seen in

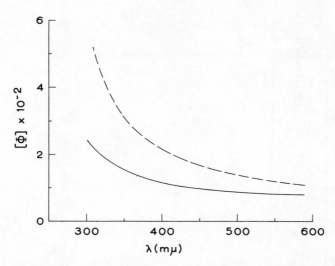

Fig. 5-5. Plain RD curves of <u>threo</u>-1,2-diphenyl-2-methyl-1-butanol (------) and <u>erythro</u>-1,2-diphenyl-2-methyl-1-butanol (———) (17) [adapted from J. L. Mateos and D. J. Cram, <u>J. Am. Chem. Soc.</u>, **81**, 2756 (1959)].

Figure 5-5, where the plain curves of <u>threo</u>- and <u>erythro</u>- 1,2-diphenyl-2-methyl-1-butanol (17) are shown.

It is remarkable that all the compounds examined in this study[11] gave plain or anomalous **positive** dispersion curves. Finally, in some of these compounds notable changes were observed when the rotatory dispersion curves were obtained in solvents of different polarity (ethanol, dioxane, and chloroform), indicating probable variations in hydrogen bonding occurring with the solvents.

Somewhat connected with this work is the recent observation[13] that the rotatory dispersion curves of 1,2-diphenylethanol (18) and the related benzoyl 1,2-diphenylethanol vary considerably with the nature of the solvent in which they are examined. This is illustrated in Figure 5-6, where appreciable variations in the shape of the plain positive dispersion curve associated with (18) can be noted.[13]

Recent improvement in rotatory dispersion and circular dichroism instrumentation (see Chap. 3) will soon permit access to the Cotton effect of most of these compounds, allowing correlations to be made between the various series and thus permitting more valuable conclusions to be drawn.

This difference between the optical rotatory dispersion curves which could be obtained a few years ago and the information which can be deduced from newer instruments is best illustrated in the next two figures. Figures 5-7 and 5-8 show the changes observed in the dispersion curves during the stepwise reduction of the ethylenic bonds in the epimeric enol-lactones (19) and (20).[14]

Figure 5-7 reproduces the "plain" curves obtained two years ago with an automatically recording Rudolph spectropolarimeter, and Figure 5-8 gives the tracings made recently[15] on the Bellingham and Stanley/Bendix-Ericsson automatic recording spectropolarimeter.

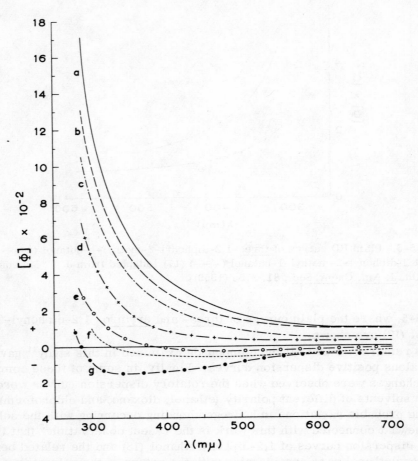

Fig. 5-6. Plain RD curves of 1,2–diphenylethanol (18) in (a) ethyl alcohol; (b) methanol; (c) acetic acid; (d) dioxane; (e) benzene; (f) pyridine, and (g) isoöctane [modified from V. M. Potapov and A. P. Terentev, Zh. Obshch. Khim., **34**, 516 (1964)].

21a, R = H
b, R = Ac

22

23a, R = H
b, R = Ac

24

Complete reduction of compound (19) into (23b) results in an inversion of the sign of the plain curves in Figure 5-7, while a positive Cotton effect is observed for (23b) in Figure 5-8. Conversely, complete reduction of its stereo-isomer (20) into the saturated lactone (24) leads to a less negative plain curve. Moreover, in the curve (24) shown in Figure 5-8, a negative Cotton effect is suggested around 228 mμ. The difference in stereochemistry which character-izes the lactone group in these compounds is thus more clearly reflected in their optical rotatory dispersion curve than by their specific rotation value at the sodium D line.

Finally, while the background curve of the 3β-acetoxy derivative (21b) is shown to be slightly more negative than that of the corresponding alcohol (21a), it is also apparent in Figure 5-8 that the unsaturation at C-5 in compounds (21a, b) and (22) introduces a large negative background (see Sec. 4-2) on which the lactone Cotton effect is superimposed.

5-3. PLAIN DISPERSION CURVES AND ABSOLUTE CONFIGURATION

Even the general trend of the plain dispersion curve of a new substance may sometimes give sufficient information to allow assignment of its absolute configuration.[16] Hence this constitutes an important application of the rotatory dispersion technique, for the determination of absolute configuration, which is the differentiation between mirror-image representations, has been of concern since the earliest days of stereochemistry.[12,16]

Almost ten years ago, an extensive study of α-amino acids was undertaken by rotatory dispersion.[17] The information which was gained from these mea-surements later permitted a careful analysis of the dispersion data obtained from natural octopin (25). This substance, which is α,α'-amino-(δ-guanidovaleric

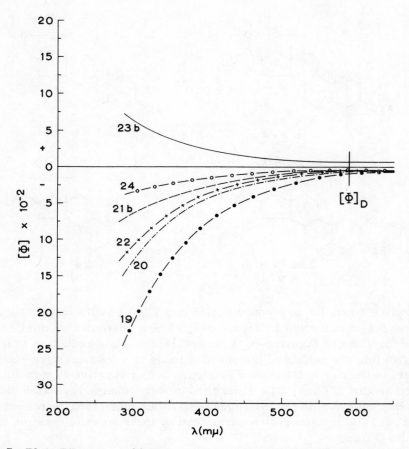

Fig. 5-7. Plain RD curves of lactones (19) to (24) obtained with the Rudolph spectropolarimeter.

acid)-propionic acid (25),[18] was shown to consist of D-alanine and L-arginine units.

The absolute configuration of alkaloids belonging to the yohimbane (26)[19,20] and aporphine (27)[21] series has also been successfully investigated by rotatory dispersion. This is shown in Figure 5-9, in which the plain dispersion curves of corydine (28), isocorydine (29), norisocorydine hydrobromide (30), and magnoflorine iodide (31) are reproduced [21] (see also Chap. 11).

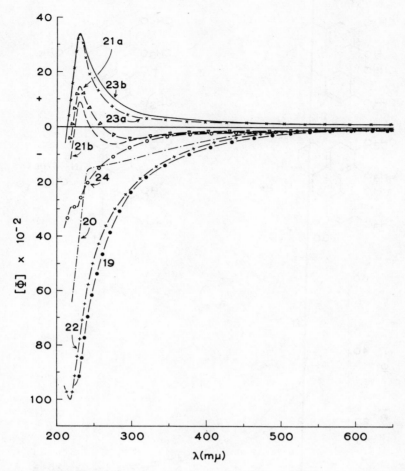

Fig. 5-8. RD curves of lactones (19) to (24) measured recently with the Bellingham and Stanley/Bendix-Ericsson spectropolarimeter.

26   27

As early as the 1930's a fairly extensive series of rotatory dispersion investigations was undertaken. The plain dispersion curves which were obtained, exhibiting increased rotation values in the ultraviolet spectral range[22] (for instance, in the sugar series), led to conclusions in agreement with deductions made from the specific rotations.[23,24]

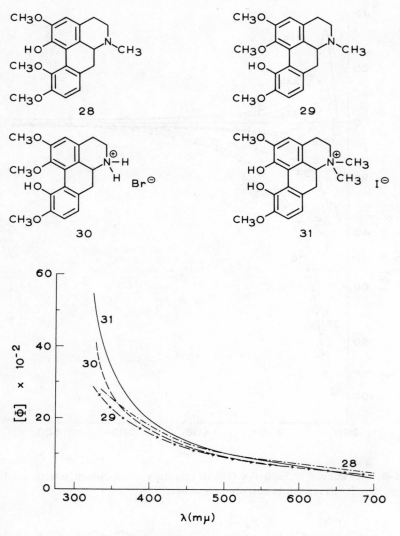

Fig. 5-9. Plain RD curves of corydine (28), isocorydine (29), norisocorydine hydrobromide (30), and magnoflorine iodide (31) [modified from C. Djerassi, K. Mislow, and M. Shamma, Experientia, **18**, 53 (1962)].

The absolute configuration of toxol (32) was recently deduced from the plain negative dispersion curve exhibited by its degradation derivative d-dimethyl-tartrate.[25] Since the sign of this plain curve was in agreement with previous findings,[26] the configuration at C-2 in toxol (32) was shown to be the same as at C-5', the corresponding center, in rotenone (33).[27]

The last examples will be chosen from the terpene series. The similarity between the plain **positive** dispersion curves of the tricyclic sesquiterpene

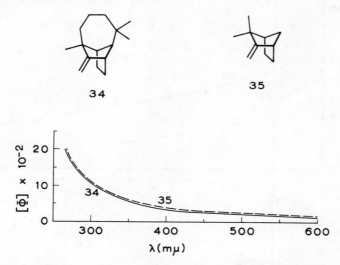

32   33

longifolene (34) and the bicyclic monoterpene (+)-camphene (35) permitted
Ourisson et al.[28] to conclude that the ring system in both terpenes had the same
absolute configuration (see Fig. 5-10).

34   35

Fig. 5-10. Plain RD curves of longifolene (34) and (+)-camphene (35) [modified
from G. Jacob, G. Ourisson, and A. Rassat, <u>Bull. Soc. Chim. France</u>, 1374 (1959)].

Examination of the plain dispersion curves of the isomeric pimaric acids
provides a convenient way to assign the absolute configuration at C-9† in these
diterpenes.[29] Since dihydropimaric acid (36) exhibits a **positive** plain curve
similar to the dispersion curve of cholest-4-ene (37),[23,30] and dihydroisopimaric
acid (38) shows a negative plain curve reminiscent of cholest-5-ene (39) (see
Fig. 5-11), the 9α- and 9β-configurations respectively, were assigned to the
angular hydrogen atom in these compounds. This conclusion also leads to the
absolute stereochemistry at C-9 for these diterpenes. Indeed, the absolute
configuration of the steroids is known,[31] and their rotatory dispersion curves,
therefore, can be used for such reference purposes.

_____

† Steroid numbering.

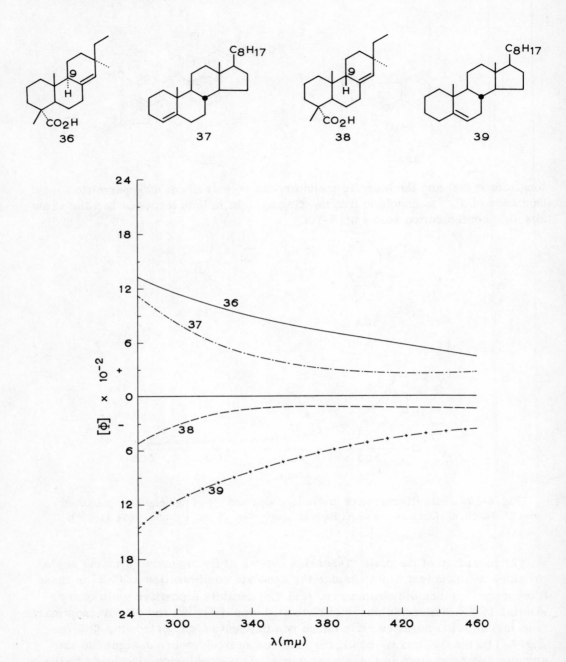

Fig. 5-11. Plain RD curves of dihydropimaric acid (36), cholest-4-ene (37), dihydroisopimaric acid (38), and cholest-5-ene (39).

The double bond isomers (40), (41), and (42) belong to the pentacyclic β-amyrin series[32] (see Fig. 5-12). From a structural point of view, the plain dispersion curves exhibited by these isomers allow an easy differentiation.[32]

From the stereochemical viewpoint, using again the plain curves of cholest-4-ene (37) and cholest-5-ene (39) as reference standards (see Fig. 5-11), the absolute configuration at the C/D and D/E ring junctures of these double-bond isomers [(40) to (42)] can easily be deduced by correlation.

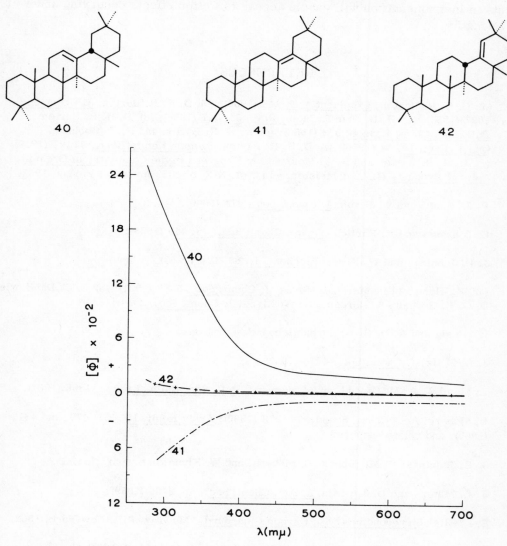

Fig. 5-12. Plain RD curves of Δ^{12}-oleanene (40), $\Delta^{13(18)}$-oleanene (41), and Δ^{18}-oleanene (42).

Many other examples of plain curves have been reported in the literature.[33] However, as will be seen in the next chapters, most of these curves are indeed anomalous dispersion curves whose Cotton effect could not be detected by the instruments available at the time they were obtained. Virtually, all plain curves are Cotton effect curves whose optically active absorption bands occur at lower wavelengths. Hence, the definition "plain" applies only to a specified wavelength range. Thus, as mentioned previously (see Sec. 4-2), the importance of such "plain curves" will decrease considerably in the future, for improvements in instrumentation will enable access to Cotton effects occurring at lower wavelengths.

REFERENCES

1. (a) D. H. R. Barton, Experientia, 6, 316 (1950); (b) D. H. R. Barton, J. Chem. Soc., 1027 (1953); (c) H. D. Orloff, Chem. Rev., 54, 347 (1954); (d) D. H. R. Barton, Bull. Soc. Chim. France, 973 (1956); (e) D. H. R. Barton and R. C. Cookson, Quart. Rev., 10, 44 (1956); (f) D. H. R. Barton, Suomen Kemistilehti, 32, 27 (1959); (g) D. H. R. Barton and G. A. Morrison in Progress in the Chemistry of Organic Natural Products (L. Zechmeister, ed.), vol. XIX, p. 165, Springer, Vienna, 1961.

2. P. M. Jones and W. Klyne, J. Chem. Soc., 871 (1960).

3. C. Djerassi and R. Ehrlich, J. Am. Chem. Soc., 78, 440 (1956).

4. J. P. Jennings and W. Klyne, Biochem. J., 86, 12P (1963).

5. (a) W. Klyne and P. Marshall-Jones, J. Chem. Soc., 5415 (1961); (b) J. C. Danilewicz, D. C. F. Garbutt, A. Horeau, and W. Klyne, J. Chem. Soc., 2254 (1964).

6. R. Ginsig and A. D. Cross, unpublished observations.

7. J. A. Mills, J. Chem. Soc., 4976 (1952).

8. L. Mamlok, A. M. Giroud, and J. Jacques, Bull. Soc. Chim. France, 1806 (1961).

9. B. Sjöberg, Acta Chem. Scand., 14, 273 (1960); Arkiv Kemi, 15, 451, 473, and 481 (1960), and related papers.

10. J. P. Jennings, P. M. Scopes, B. Sjöberg, and W. Klyne, in preparation.

11. J. L. Mateos and D. J. Cram, J. Am. Chem. Soc., 81, 2756 (1959).

12. E. L. Eliel, Stereochemistry of Carbon Compounds, McGraw-Hill, New York, 1962.

13. V. M. Potapov and A. P. Terentev, Zh. Obshch. Khim., 34, 516 (1964).

14. P. Crabbé, L. M. Guerrero, J. Romo, and F. Sánchez-Viesca, Tetrahedron, 19, 25 (1963).

15. These curves were obtained through the courtesy of Professor W. Klyne and Dr. P. M. Scopes at the University of London.

16. J. M. Bijvoet, Endeavour, 14, 71 (1955).

17.   M. C. Otey, J. P. Greenstein, M. Winitz, and S. M. Birnbaum, J. Am. Chem. Soc., 77, 3112 (1955).

18.   N. Izumiya, R. Wade, M. Winitz, M. C. Otey, S. M. Birnbaum, R. J. Koegel, and J. P. Greenstein, J. Am. Chem. Soc., 79, 652 (1957).

19.   C. Djerassi, R. Riniker, and B. Riniker, J. Am. Chem. Soc., 78, 6362 (1956).

20.   J. A. D. Jeffreys, J. Chem. Soc., 3077 (1959).

21.   C. Djerassi, K. Mislow, and M. Shamma, Experientia, 18, 53 (1962).

22.   (a) N. A. Sörensen and B. Trumpy, Z. Physik. Chem. (Leipzig) , (B) 28, 135 (1935); (b) T. L. Harris, E. L. Hirst, and C. E. Wood, J. Chem. Soc., 848 (1937), and earlier papers in this series.

23.   C. Djerassi, Optical Rotatory Dispersion: Applications to Organic Chemistry, McGraw-Hill, New York, 1960.

24.   W. Klyne in Advances in Organic Chemistry (R. A. Raphael, E. C. Taylor, and H. Wynberg, eds.). Interscience, vol. 1, p. 239, New York, 1960.

25.   (a) L. H. Zalkow and N. Burke, Chem. and Ind., 292 (1963); (b) W. A. Bonner, N. I. Burke, W. E. Fleck, R. K. Hill, J. A. Joule, B. Sjöberg, and L. H. Zalkow, Tetrahedron, 20, 1419 (1954).

26.   T. M. Lowry and H. H. Abram, J. Chem. Soc., 1187 (1915).

27.   (a) G. Büchi, L. Crombie, P. J. Godin, and J. S. Kaltenbronn, J. Chem. Soc., 2843 (1961); (b) M. Nakazaki and H. Arakawa, Bull. Chem. Soc., Japan, 34, 1246 (1961); (c) C. Djerassi, W. D. Ollis, and R. C. Russell, J. Chem. Soc., 1448 (1961).

28.   G. Jacob, G. Ourisson, and A. Rassat, Bull. Soc. Chim. France, 1374 (1959).

29.   (a) A. K. Bose and W. A. Struck, Chem. and Ind., 1628 (1959); (b) O. E. Edwards and R. Howe, Chem. and Ind., 537 (1959).

30.   C. Djerassi, W. Closson, and A. E. Lippman, J. Am. Chem. Soc., 78, 3163 (1956).

31.   L. F. Fieser and M. Fieser, Steroids, Reinhold, New York, 1959.

32.   C. Djerassi, J. Osiecki, and W. Closson, J. Am. Chem. Soc., 81, 4587 (1959).

33.   Inter alia: (a) refs. 23 and 24; (b) C. Djerassi, E. W. Foltz, and A. E. Lippman, J. Am. Chem. Soc., 77, 4354 (1955); (c) A. E. Lippman, E. W. Foltz, and C. Djerassi, J. Am. Chem. Soc., 77, 4364 (1955); (d) C. Djerassi and W. Closson, J. Am. Chem. Soc., 78, 3761 (1956); (e) C. Djerassi, O. Halpern, V. Halpern, O. Schindler, and C. Tamm, Helv. Chim. Acta, 41, 250 (1958).

Cotton Effect of Carbonyl-Containing Saturated Compounds

6-1. THE OCTANT RULE

The presence of a carbonyl function in a saturated ketone guarantees the existence of a weak ultraviolet absorption band in the vicinity of the 280–300 mμ region.[1] The transition observed in such instances consists in the promotion of one electron from a nonbonding $2 p_y$ orbital of the oxygen atom to an antibonding π orbital involving both the carbon and the oxygen atoms of the carbonyl group, as shown in Figure 6-1 for the acetone molecule.[2] Whatever perturbations the rest of the molecular framework may induce on the chromophoric electrons,

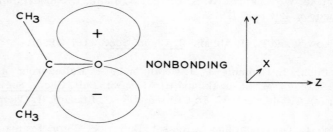

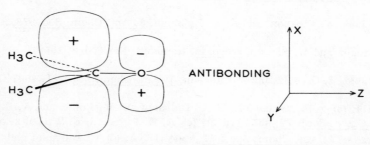

Fig. 6-1. Schematic representation of the orbitals involved in the ~ 290 mμ transition in acetone [modified from A. Moscowitz, in <u>Advances in Chemical Physics</u>, I. Prigogine, Ed., Interscience Publishers, New York (1962)].

they are not significant for the dipole strength of the transitions (see Chaps. 1-3). However, while the rotational strength of an n - $\pi *$ transition must be zero in a symmetrical molecule like acetone, this strength has some nonzero value when the carbonyl is asymmetrically surrounded, as in a steroid or a terpene. Hence the rotational strength of a carbonyl function is quite sensitive to molecular environment and will reflect quantitatively the asymmetry around the chromophore.[3,4]

As a consequence of the aforementioned concept, the carbonyl group, or any symmetric chromophore whose associated optically active transitions are readily amenable to investigation, becomes an ideal probe with which to search out structural, configurational, and conformational subtleties of a particular molecular framework.

Turning now to the octant rule,[5] which is the main object of this chapter, it will be seen that when a carbonyl function is situated in a cyclohexane ring **in the chair conformation**, the n - $\pi *$ transition of the chromophore will lead to a Cotton effect which is directly dependent upon the spatial orientation of the substituents of the ring system. **The octant rule**, which is deduced from symmetry principles, **relates the sign and amplitude of the Cotton effect exhibited by an optically active saturated ketone to the spatial orientation of atoms about the carbonyl function.**[5] Hence this rule permits prediction of the sign and, semiquantitatively, the intensity of the Cotton effect exhibited by saturated ketones.

Since many aspects of this rule have been treated in several detailed articles and reviews,[3-7] the actual discussion will refer to the main practical conclusions and to some of its numerous applications in stereochemistry.

The carbonyl chromophore being the reference point, a cyclohexanone can be divided into eight octants by means of three mutually perpendicular planes.[5,6,7] These are nodal and symmetry planes of the orbitals involved in the n - $\pi *$ transition associated with the absorption of the carbonyl group. The cyclohexanone ring is used as an example only because it is easy to discuss. However, the same concept is applicable to any ring system or side chain carrying a carbonyl grouping.

As shown in Figure 6-2, plane A is vertical, passing through C-1 and C-4. The only substituents in this plane are the ones attached to C-4. The horizontal plane B encompasses the carbon atom bearing the carbonyl group (C-1) and its two adjacent carbon atoms (the carbon atom C-2 to the right, called R_2, and the carbon atom C-6, to the left, called L_6). The equatorially oriented substituents attached to these carbon atoms (C-2 and C-6) lie nearly in the nodal plane B. Therefore these planes A and B (see Fig. 6-2) correspond to the nodal planes xz and yz of the orbitals mentioned in Figure 6-1. These planes (A and B) provide four octants, the back octants, shown in Figure 6-2. A third plane, C, perpendicular to plane A and dissecting the oxygen–carbon atom (C-1) bond, produces four additional octants, called front octants (see Fig. 6-2). It should be emphasized that the exact nature and position of plane C are still uncertain. In any event, the four back octants defined by planes A and B are the most important ones for the practical applications to be discussed below.

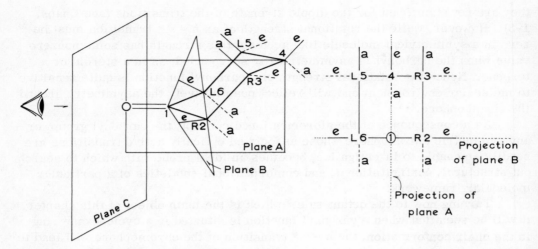

Fig. 6-2. Geometry of cyclohexanone. Three planes, called A, B, and C, create eight octants. The octant projection, shown on the right side of the figure, indicates the spatial orientation of the different groups in respect with the carbonyl function (1). Abbreviations: a = axial, e = equatorial, L = left, R = right (modified from C. Djerassi, <u>Optical Rotatory Dispersion: Applications to Organic Chemistry</u>, McGraw-Hill, 1960).

The octant rule[5] states that substituents lying in planes A and B make no contribution to the Cotton effect associated with the carbonyl. Indeed, a substituent which is in one of the symmetry planes does not **appear** unsymmetrical to the carbonyl chromophore. This includes the equatorial substituents on carbon atoms C-2 and C-6, provided that they are exactly in the plane (vide infra), and both substituents on carbon atom C-4. Furthermore, the atoms or groups of atoms situated in an axial configuration on C-2 (lower-right octant) as well as axial and equatorial substituents on C-5 (upper-left octant) make a positive contribution to the Cotton effect. Finally, the substituents located in an axial configuration on carbon C-6 (lower-left octant), as well the axial and equatorial substituents on carbon C-3, produce a negative effect.

In complex cases, atoms lying in front octants must be taken into consideration. Their rotational contributions are opposite in sign to those which they would have in the corresponding back octants. The position of substituents and thus their respective contribution to the sign and amplitude of the Cotton effect are summarized in simplified octant diagrams, shown in Figure 6-3.

From the historical point of view, it should be emphasized that Djerassi's early work on steroidal and triterpenic ketones,[6] in extenso compounds of fixed conformation, really formed the experimental basis of the octant rule. Later the applicability of the rule to monocyclic compounds grew out of that work. From a theoretical point of view it might seem desirable to choose polycyclic ketones of fixed conformation as first examples for the application of the octant

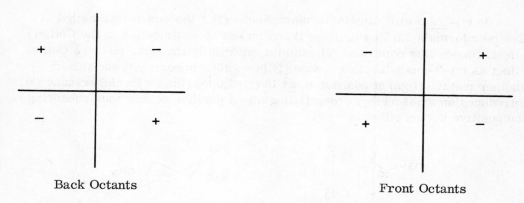

Fig. 6-3. Position and respective contribution of the substituents to the sign and amplitude of the Cotton effect.

rule. However, for pedagogic reasons it has been decided to start with mono-cyclic carbonyl-containing systems, where, nevertheless, conformational mobility often occurs.

The study of the Cotton effect[5] associated with (+)-3-methylcyclohexanone (1)[8] clearly illustrates the octant rule. The carbon atoms C-2, C-4, and C-6 lie in nodal planes and thus make no contribution to the Cotton effect. The contribution of C-3 is canceled by that of C-5, which is equal but opposite. However, the methyl group on C-3, being in a positive octant, is alone responsible for the positive Cotton effect of this substance (1). The molecular amplitude[9] of the dispersion curve of (+)-3-methylcyclohexanone (1) is a = +25.[5, 8] From the quantitative point of view, it should be pointed out that recent low-temperature circular dichroism measurements[10] have indicated the existence of a small amount of another conformer (twisted or with the methyl axial) at room temperature.

In (+)-<u>trans</u>-3,6-dimethylcyclohexanone (2),[5] the equatorial methyl at C-6 (see formula 2a) lies in plane B and makes no contribution to the Cotton effect. Hence this compound (2) exhibits essentially the same positive Cotton effect as (+)-3-methylcyclohexanone (1) (a = +25). In contrast, addition of another methyl group at position 6, as in (+)-3,6,6-trimethylcyclohexanone (3), introduces an axial methyl group falling into a positive octant, thus enhancing the positive Cotton effect (a = +81).

H3C

6

3

CH3

2

O

H3C

CH3

2a

H3C

H3C

6

3

CH3

3

O

H3C

CH3

CH3

3a

Concrete applications of the octant rule will now be examined in monocyclic, bicyclic, tricyclic, tetracyclic and pentacyclic as well as in aliphatic optically active saturated ketones.[†] The importance of this rule in configurational and conformational problems will be emphasized. From the discussion which follows, it will be apparent that both optical rotatory dispersion and circular dichroism will be appropriate for the examination of the Cotton effect associated with such ketones. It should, however, be kept in mind that the dispersion curve includes the background rotations, while the circular dichroism curve expresses more specifically the asymmetry in the immediate vicinity of the chromophore.

6-2. MONOCYCLIC KETONES

A. Cyclohexanones

The correct application of the octant rule to the Cotton effect exhibited by a ketonic substance, as measured by rotatory dispersion and circular dichroism, will provide stereochemical information not readily available from any other physicochemical method. The main utility of the octant rule may be summarized as follows:

---

†"Saturated" in this case implies only that there is no double bond in close proximity to the carbonyl group.

If the absolute configuration[11] of a ketone is known, its conformation can be determined. Conversely, if the conformation of the compound is established, it can be assigned the correct absolute configuration.[6,14-20]

The above-mentioned (+)-3-methylcyclohexanone (1) can exist in two interconvertible conformations represented by (1a) and (1b). Since the Cotton effect associated with this ketone is positive (vide supra), and since its absolute configuration has been shown to correspond to formulas (1a) or (1b),[12] conformation (1a) represents the correct stereochemistry of this substance. Indeed, the Cotton effect should be negative for conformation (1b). A negative Cotton effect would also be expected from the antipode (1c), thus confirming indirectly the absolute configuration (1a) assigned to (+)-3-methylcyclohexanone.

The octant rule has been quite useful in studying the absolute configuration of the monoterpenes (-)-menthone (4) and (+)-isomenthone (5). (-)-Menthone (4) shows a weak positive Cotton effect curve[6,13,14,15,20] (see Fig. 6-4) whose amplitude is similar to that of trans-3,6-dimethylcyclohexanone (2) (see above). This is best explained[5] by the preferred conformation (4a) in which both alkyl groups are equatorially oriented (as in 2a). Isomerization of (-)-menthone (4a) leads to (+)-isomenthone (5), whose Cotton effect[20] is strongly positive (see Fig. 6-4). For (+)-isomenthone (5), two chair conformations (5a) and (5b) can be drawn. Since the octant rule predicts a positive Cotton effect for conformation (5a) and a negative Cotton effect for (5b), the latter could be excluded. However, a recent quantitative study[16] of the Cotton effect associated with (+)-isomenthone (5) indicates that there are contributions from conformers other than (5a). Although the twist form (5c) would be expected to exhibit a strongly positive Cotton effect,[17] its participation together with conformer (5a) cannot be excluded a priori.[16]

Concomitant quantitative studies of the Cotton effect associated with α-equatorial alkyl cyclohexanones have indicated that in such cases an equatorial methyl,[18] isopropyl,[16] and t-butyl[19] group does not lie exactly in the nodal plane.

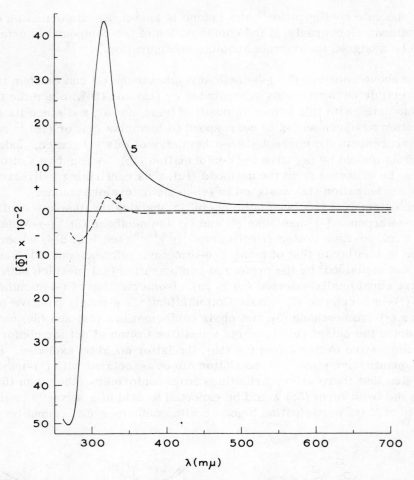

Fig. 6-4. RD curves of (-)-menthone (4) and (+)-isomenthone (5) in methanol (modified from C. Djerassi, <u>Optical Rotatory Dispersion: Applications to Organic Chemistry</u>, McGraw-Hill, 1960).

In these three cases, the equatorial alkyl substituent makes a positive contribution to the Cotton effect, when situated on the right side next to the carbonyl (R_2 in Fig. 6-2). The rotatory contribution has been calculated on a semi-quantitative basis and shown, in terms of molecular amplitude, to be about a < 9, for the equatorial methyl,[18] a = 15 to 21 for the isopropyl,[16] and a = 33 to 39 for an equatorial t-butyl group.[19]

   The stereochemistry of another monoterpene, (+)-isopulegone (7), obtained by thermal isomerization of (+)-pulegone (6), has been assigned recently by simple application of the octant rule. The strong positive Cotton effect exhibited by this compound (7) indicates that it has the same absolute configuration and conformation as (+)-isomenthone (5).[20]

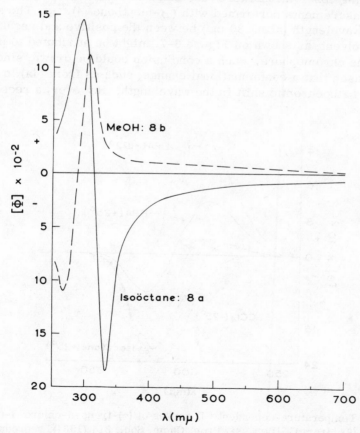

B. α-Haloketone Rule; Conformational Mobility; Solvent- and Temperature-Dependent Cotton Effects

The next example is interesting because it shows an application of the "α-haloketone rule,"[6,7,21-29] a forerunner of the octant rule. It also constitutes a striking example of the value of dispersion curves in conformational mobility studies. Chlorination of (+)-3-methylcyclohexanone (1) afforded (+)-trans-6-chloro-3-methylcyclohexanone (8).[6,24,30] The rotatory dispersion curve of this α-chloro derivative was measured in several solvents. In the nonpolar solvent isoöctane the Cotton effect curve was negative, whereas in methanol (a polar solvent) the curve was positive (see Fig. 6-5). The axial haloketone rule[6,7,21]

Fig. 6-5. RD curves of (+)-trans-6-chloro-3-methylcyclohexanone (8) in methanol and isoöctane [modified from C. Djerassi, Proc. Chem. Soc., 314 (1964)].

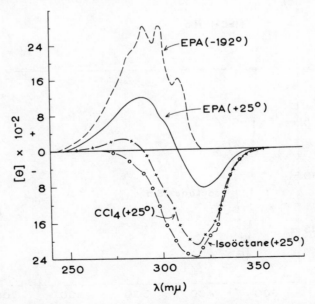

states that an axial halogen (other than fluorine) located on a carbon atom next to the carbonyl of a cyclohexanone affects the sign of the Cotton effect of the parent ketone in the way later established by the octant rule. Therefore the inversion of Cotton effect observed in Figure 6-5 is ascribed to the fact that in isoöctane the chloro-derivative (8) exists predominantly in conformation (8a) (diaxial), while in methanol the main conformer is (8b) (diequatorial).[6,24,30] This conformational equilibrium has been further investigated by low-temperature circular dichroism measurements.[10,31] It has been shown that in ether-isopentane-ethanol mixture (EPA) the diaxial conformer (8a) disappears as the temperature is lowered, in favor of the diequatorial form (8b) (see Fig. 6-6).

Interesting observations were also made by solvent-dependent circular dichroism measurements performed with (-)-menthone (4).[31,32] The substantial difference in wavelength (about 30 mμ) between the positive and negative maxima in any given solvent, as shown on Figure 6-7, might be attributed to possible solvation of the chromophore. Such a conclusion could be drawn, since there is no obvious reason that a conformational change, such as from (4a) to (4b), should cause a large bathochromic shift in the wavelength. However, a recent calcula-

Fig. 6-6. Temperature-dependent CD curves of (+)-<u>trans</u>-6-chloro-3-methyl-cyclohexanone (8) [from C. Djerassi, <u>Proc. Chem. Soc.</u>, 314 (1964), reproduced by permission of the editor].

tion has shown[32] that superposition of two oppositely signed Cotton effects differing in the location of the respective maxima by only one millimicron can give rise to a "double-humped" Cotton effect, as seen in Figure 6-7.[31,32] In this example the two maxima are separated by as much as 28 mμ. As a consequence, the amplitude of the resulting double Cotton effect is much weaker than that of each individual conformer. Hence two conformers differing by a very small value in their circular dichroism maxima can cause the "double-humped" effect shown in Figure 6-7, which thus does not necessarily mean solvation of the chromophore (see below).

Temperature–dependent circular dichroism measurements of (−)-menthone (4) are reported in Figure 6-8.[32] A red shift is observed upon lowering the temperature to −192°, as well as a major increase in rotational strength. This dramatic increase in the positive maximum upon lowering of the temperature is in agreement with an augmentation in population of the diequatorial conformer (4a). In decalin a larger temperature range could be covered. The increase of

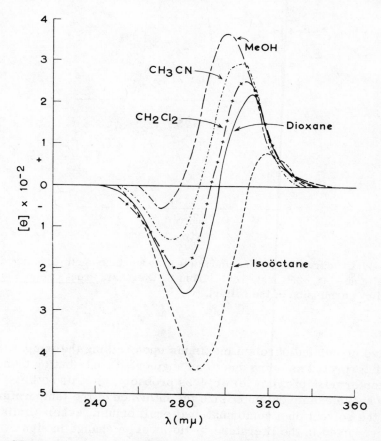

Fig. 6-7. CD curves of (−)-menthone (4) in methanol, acetonitrile, methylene chloride, dioxane, and isoöctane [from C. Djerassi, <u>Proc. Chem. Soc.</u>, 314 (1964), reproduced by permission of the editor].

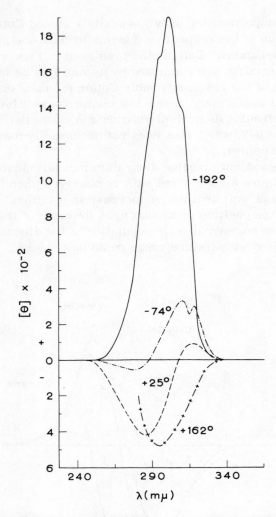

Fig. 6-8. CD curves of (-)-menthone (4) in isopentane–methylcyclohexane at –192°, and in decalin at –74°, +25°, and +162° [from C. Djerassi, <u>Proc. Chem. Soc.</u>, 314 (1964), reproduced by permission of the editor].

the negative circular dichroism maximum upon raising the temperature to +162° has been interpreted as being due to an augmented contribution by negatively rotating conformers of type (4b) or, less probably, (4c), or both.[31,32]

The above examples emphasize the influence of the temperature and the nature of the solvent on a conformational equilibrium. Other similar observations are reported in the literature.[32] However, a change in sign of the Cotton effect does not necessarily denote such a conformational equilibrium. Indeed, the striking observation was made[33] that isofenchone (9) and epiisofenchone (10), although conformationally rigid, exhibit rotatory dispersion curves of <u>sign</u> and

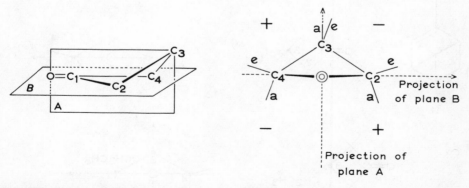

9   10

amplitude which vary according to the nature of the solvent in which they are examined. This observation has been confirmed by circular dichroism and found in several other terpenic and steroidal keto-derivatives.[33-36] The phenomenon has been ascribed[34,35] to asymmetric solvation of the carbonyl group, which leads to varying mixtures of solvated and nonsolvated species in solution. The formation of solute-solvent associations, already observed in specific rotation values[37] and in infrared[38] and nuclear magnetic resonance spectra,[39] can now also be detected by optical rotatory dispersion and circular dichroism.

C. Cyclobutanones; Cyclopentanones; Cycloheptanones

Although the octant rule has been tested mainly through reference to cyclohexanones whose carbonyl function is situated with the cyclohexane ring in the chair conformation, there is no reason to suppose that this rule cannot be generally extended to other cases. However, application of the octant rule to open-chain ketones, to smaller or larger rings than the six-membered cyclohexanone, and finally, to ketones containing six-membered rings in other than a chair conformation is still difficult or impossible. A better understanding of the variations of optical contribution of an atom or group of atoms as they modify their position relative to the origin of the carbonyl group will permit further applications of this rule in the future.

An extension of the octant rule has recently been suggested by Conia et al.[40] for cyclobutanones. This proposal, represented in Figure 6-9, indicates that carbon atoms C-2 and C-4 lie in a nodal plane, while C-3 and its substituents are in a symmetry plane. Hence, while the quasi-equatorial substituents at C-2

Fig. 6-9. The octant rule applied to cyclobutanone (modified from J. Goré, Ph.D. Thesis, University of Caen, July 1964).

and C-4 make a slight or negligible contribution, as in cyclohexanones (vide
supra), the axial substituents at C-2 and C-4 are mainly responsible for the
sign and intensity of the Cotton effect.

This concept has been applied to some optically active substituted
cyclobutanones obtained by chemical degradation of (-)-α-pinene (11) of known
absolute configuration.[41] Hence (+)-2,2,3-trimethyl-cyclobutanone (12), which
belongs to the 3S-series,[42] exhibits a positive Cotton effect in circular dichroism,
while (-)-3-ethyl-4,4-dimethyl-cyclobutanone (13), from the 3R-series,[42] shows
a negative circular dichroism curve. It was concluded that in these compounds
the substituent at C-3 has a quasi-equatorial configuration.[40] Furthermore,
low-temperature circular dichroism measurements clearly indicate conformational mobility in both compounds (12) and (13).[40] However, at -192° these
molecules seem to exist mainly in the conformation represented in the octant
diagrams. Finally, from the above results as well as from circular dichroism
study of other optically active cyclobutanones,[40] it was concluded that in these
compounds the four-membered ring is not planar and that the configuration of
the alkyl group next to the carbonyl is generally quasi-equatorial.

Jacques and collaborators[43] have undertaken a conformational analysis of
flexible cyclopentanone derivatives. This study, based on the earlier work of
Brutcher,[44] who had shown that a cyclopentane ring is generally not planar,
applies the octant rule to cyclopentanones in the way suggested by Klyne[45] (see
Sec. 6-3). The preferred conformations of several optically active cyclopentanones of known absolute configuration (e.g., 2-cyclopentyl-cyclopentanone,
cis-2-methyl-5-isopropyl-cyclopentanone, cis-2-methyl-4-isopropyl-cyclo-
pentanone, and 3-methyl-cyclopentanone) were examined in the light of the
octant rule. The sign or the intensity of the Cotton effects which were obtained
experimentally, or both, did not correspond to the octant diagrams. These
results indicated that the Cotton effect is due mainly to deformations of the
ring system and only secondarily to its substituents. Furthermore, such
studies emphasized the conformational equilibria which characterize these
cyclopentanone derivatives.[10] It was concluded that since conformational

equilibria exist with such compounds, the octant rule is useful in the determination of the relative stability of cis-trans isomers. However, the energy barrier between different conformations of distinct compounds seems to be low enough to preclude quantitative treatments.

It has been shown[6,8] that (-)-3-methyl-cycloheptanone (14) exhibits a negative Cotton effect. If the cycloheptanone ring is examined in the light of the octant rule, the chair conformation (14a) would lead to a positive Cotton effect, and the boat form (14b) should exhibit a negative Cotton effect. Thus (-)-3-methyl-cycloheptanone seems to exist in the boat conformation (14b).[6]

Before closing this section, one important additional remark should be made. Until the octant rule was stated,[5] the carbon-carbon bonds of a cyclohexanone ring were considered to be of normal length, namely, 1.545 Å,[46] and of shortened length, 1.500 Å,[47] for the bonds involving the trigonal carbon atom (C_1—C_2 and C_1—C_6 in formula 15) as in simple open-chain ketones. The internal angle of the carbonyl group [φ in formula (15)] was assumed to be 120° in such compounds. However, accurate calculations made by Corey[48] indicate this angle to be 116°,[49] all other angles keeping the normal 109°28' value. Thus, it was concluded[5] that the backbone system of any cyclohexanone [C_2—C_3—C_4—C_5—C_6 in formula (15)] is only very slightly distorted from normal cyclohexane geometry.

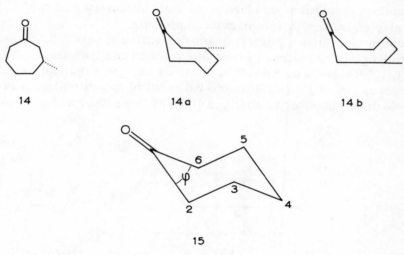

14   14 a   14 b

15

6-3. BICYCLIC KETONES

A. Decalones

The decalones present a rich array of carbonyl groups with differing asymmetric environments. Hence numerous interesting and detailed studies have been made of the Cotton effect which is observed with such cis and trans ketones.[5,6,7,9,14,17,45,50,51] A few of these examples will be examined here, attention being focused on recent results or unusual observations.

A classical example of the application of the octant rule to a bicyclic compound is the study of the Cotton effect of 8β, 9β-dimethyl-trans-decalone-2 (16). The positive Cotton effect which is observed can easily be deduced by examination of the octant projection given with the stereochemical representation of this compound (16a).[5,50] Indeed, carbon atoms 6, 7, and 8, as well as the 8β and 9β methyl groupings, fall into positive octants.

As mentioned earlier, the octant rule is particularly valuable for providing structural and configurational information. The next example shows the unique utility of the rule for studying absolute configuration and establishing subtle conformational details. 9-Methyl-cis-decalone-1 (17) may exist in two alternative conformations (17a) and (17b).[5,50b] If the molecule is to adopt the former conformation (17a), which is the steroid-like form, a strongly negative Cotton effect would be predicted. But if this cis-decalone exists in the non-steroid-like conformation (17b), then a positive Cotton effect is expected. Since this bicyclic ketone (17) exhibits a positive rotatory dispersion curve (a = +51), the non-steroid-like conformation (17b) is preferred. It should be noted, however, that although the latter conformation may be preponderant, this does not necessarily imply that it is the exclusive conformation adopted by the compound.

Optically active antipodes, of known absolute configuration, of cis-decalones of the type discussed above have been synthesized. It has been demonstrated by optical rotatory dispersion measurements that the non-steroid conformation does not play an important role in such compounds.[50c]

Preparation of the appropriate keto derivative of several diterpenes led to substituted trans-decalones of opposite absolute configuration, as summarized in Table 6-1.[9] From these data, it is apparent that the amplitudes of the dispersion curves are of similar absolute value but of opposite sign, thus demonstrating the different absolute configurations of these diterpenes.

16

Octant Projection   a = +52

16a

17   17a   17b

Table 6-1

OPTICAL ROTATORY DISPERSION MOLECULAR AMPLITUDE OF SOME BICYCLIC DITERPENIC KETONES

Series	Molecular amplitude a	Series	Molecular amplitude a
Labdanolic Acid $R_1 = R_2 = CH_3$ $R_3 = [CH_2]_2 - CH - CO_2CH_3$ (with CH_3)	-77	Eperuic Acid $R_1 = R_2 = CH_3$ $R_3 = [CH_2]_2 - CH - CO_2CH_3$ (with CH_3)	$+97 !^{\dagger}$
Agathic Acid $R_1 = CO_2H; R_2 = CH_3$ $R_3 = [CH_2]_2 - CO_2H$	-131	Daniellic Acid $R_1 = CO_2H; R_2 = CH_3$ $R_3 = [CH_2]_2 - CH - CO_2H$ (with CH_3)	$+131$
Neoabietic Acid $R_1 = CH_3; R_2 = CO_2H$ $R_3 = [CH_2]_2 - CO_2H$	-119	Polyathic Acid $R_1 = CH_3; R_2 = CO_2H$ $R_3 = [CH_2]_2 - CO_2H$	$+104$

† The symbol ! indicates that the extremum of shorter wavelength of the Cotton effect curve could not be measured.

Cascarillin, a furanoid diterpene acetate,[52] has been shown by X-ray crystallographic examination[53] to present the relative stereochemistry represented in formula (18) or its mirror image. An appropriate 3-keto† derivative of cascarillin (18) was prepared, and its optical rotatory dispersion curve obtained.[54] The positive Cotton effect which was observed is only compatible with the absolute configuration, as in formula (18), since under such circumstances the 5α-methyl group and the C-6, C-7, and C-8 atoms† fall into positive octants. This assumption was further confirmed when it was observed that the amplitude of the dispersion curve has the same absolute value as, but an opposite sign[54] to, that of 3β-hydroxy-17aβ-methyl-D-homo-5α-androstan-17-one (19),[50a] indicating an opposite absolute configuration of the ring junction in these compounds.

The recently introduced concept[17] of a twist conformation of cyclohexanones has provided an explanation for the unusually strong negative Cotton effect exhibited by trans-tetrahydroeremophilone (20).[17] This compound, which is less stable than its A/B cis-isomer,[55] in the chair conformation (represented in the octant projection 20a), shows a strong 1,3-diaxial interaction between the 9-angular methyl and the 2-isopropyl group. In such a conformation (20a) this ketone would be expected to have a less negative amplitude than 9-methyl-trans-decalone-4 (21) (a = -32). However, trans-tetrahydroeremophilone has in fact a stronger negative Cotton effect (a = -109). This can be rationalized by the twist form adopted by ring A, and shown in the octant projection (20b). In such a conformation the isopropyl-methyl interaction is relieved, and the amplitude should be strongly negative. Indeed, in such a form ring B and all the substituents fall into negative octants.

18

19

20

20a

20b

21

---

†Steroid numbering.

B. Hexahydroindanones

Djerassi and Klyne[17] deduced the concept of twist cyclohexanones from the observation that, as in skewed cyclopentanones, a strong Cotton effect seems to be associated with such systems. Previously, Klyne[45,56] had made a careful study of trans-hexahydroindanones, and the conclusions which were reached will be discussed here, since they are relevant to many stereochemical problems in several series of natural products.

In trans-hexahydroindan-2-ones the cyclopentanone ring is skewed (half-chair), and in such compounds the large amplitude of the rotatory dispersion curve is due to the presence of two out-of-plane, or skewed, ring atoms. Hence the large negative amplitude which characterizes the trans-hexahydroindan-2-ones (22a) and (22b),[45,50,56] has been ascribed to the asymmetry of the carbonyl-carrying ring itself. In contrast with **symmetrical cyclohexanones** in the chair conformation, in such indanones (22a and 22b), the **five-membered ring is not symmetrical,** and in these compounds both C-8 and C-9 are in negative octants. However, the lack of precise knowledge about the exact conformation of the five-membered ring[44,57] still precludes accurate quantitative treatment.

In the 8-methyl-trans-hexahydroindan-1-one (23) a single atom (C-9) of the cyclopentanone ring is **severely skewed** in a positive octant, while C-3 is much less skewed in a negative octant. Furthermore, C-5 and C-6 also make a positive contribution to the Cotton effect. Finally, in such a compound the negative influence of the 8β-methyl substituent is roughly canceled by the positive effect of the C-7 carbon atom.[45] Important applications of these observations will be commented upon in the next sections.

22a, R=H; a= -222

b, R=CH$_3$; a = -219

a= +88

23

C. Influence of Ring Size and Hetero-Atoms

The above-mentioned examples emphasize the importance of ring size in the application of the octant rule to bicyclic ketones. This idea has been further developed by Djerassi and Gurst,[58] who synthesized a series of bicyclic ketones of known absolute configuration in which the carbonyl-containing ring was five- and six-membered and the adjacent ring possessed six, seven, or eight carbon atoms. Optical rotatory dispersion measurements of these bicyclic ketones demonstrated that in saturated bicyclic ketones the sign of the Cotton effect is not affected by the size of the adjacent non-oxygenated ring. However, quantitative variations of the amplitude have been observed. For example, when the cyclohexane ring in 8-methyl-_trans_-hydrindan-2-one (24) is replaced by a cycloheptane (25) or cyclooctane (26) ring, a decrease in amplitude is noted. This could be due to a much greater conformational mobility existing in such medium-sized rings, where many different flexible conformations are possible, one or several of which may project into negative octants. A second possibility is that fusion of a cyclopentanone with a seven- or eight-membered ring reduces the twisting in the cyclopentanone ring.[58]

Before examining the importance these observations have on the Cotton effect of some sesquiterpenic ketones possessing the bicyclo[5.3.0]decane system of compound (25), brief mention will be made of the assignment of absolute configuration to (-)-1-oxoquinolizidine (27) by circular dichroism.[59] The ketone (27) was obtained by resolution of the dl mixture, and was then submitted to circular dichroism examination (see Fig. 6-10). Application of the octant rule to the three most important conformations (28a, b, and c) suggests that (28a) would give a markedly negative Cotton effect, while (28b) would exhibit a negative and (28c) a positive Cotton effect. From the strong negative circular dichroism maximum shown by (-)-1-oxoquinolizidine (27), as illustrated in Figure 6-10, its absolute configuration could be deduced. Furthermore, conformations (28a) and (28b) have been shown greatly to predominate over (28c).[59] This could be expected, because the electronic repulsion exercised between the carbonyl and nitrogen electron pairs would be un-

a = +216   a = +156   a = +161

24   25   26   27

28 a   28 b   28 c

favorable to the latter conformation. Noteworthy also, in Figure 6-10, which reproduces the circular dichroism at two different temperatures, is the fine structure associated with the carbonyl chromophore in the ultraviolet spectrum and reflected in the circular dichroism curves.

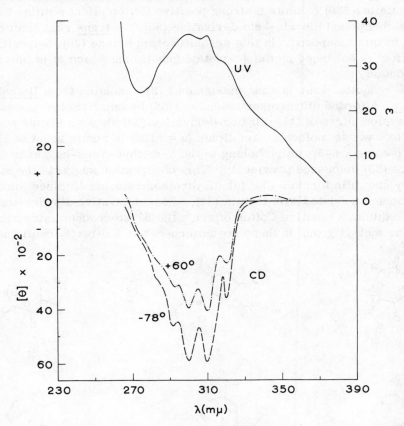

Fig. 6-10. UV and CD curves of (-)-1-oxoquinolizidine (27) in isoöctane [modified from S. F. Mason, K. Schofield, and R. J. Wells, <u>Proc. Chem. Soc.</u>, 337 (1963)].

D. Stereochemistry of some Sesquiterpenes of the Guaianolide Group

Numerous sesquiterpenes containing the bicyclo[5.3.0]decane system have been found recently.[60] Some of these natural products, belonging to the guaianolide series, have already been subjected to rotatory dispersion investigation.[61] Furthermore, recent extensive studies undertaken by Herz and Romo on the sesquiterpenic constituents of <u>Helenium</u> and <u>Artemisia</u> specia have led to the structure elucidation of several new compounds.[62] The rotatory dispersion curves of some of these sesquiterpenes have been obtained and will now be discussed in the light of the above-mentioned applications of the octant rule to hexahydroindanones and related bicyclo-decanones.

Estafiatin (29), a sesquiterpenic constituent of <u>Artemisia mexicana</u> was converted[62d] to tetrahydroestafiatone (30), shown to be identical with a ketone derived from isophoto-α-santonic lactone[63] of known configuration at C–4, C–5, C–6, C–7, and C–11. Since the optical rotatory dispersion curve of tetra-hydroestafiatone (30) exhibits a strong positive Cotton effect similar to that of the above-mentioned bicyclo–keto derivative (25),[58] a <u>trans</u> ring junction was assigned to this compound. In this sesquiterpenic ketone (30) the positive Cotton effect is enhanced by the 4α–methyl substituent which falls into a positive octant.

The sesquiterpenic lactone mexicanin I (31), isolated from <u>Helenium mexicanum</u>, afforded dihydroisomexicanin I (32) by catalytic hydrogenation.[62f] The dispersion curve of this dihydro–derivative (32) shows a strong positive Cotton effect whose molecular amplitude (a = +126) is reminiscent of 17-keto-steroids (see Sec. 6–5), which belong to the 8-methyl-<u>trans</u>-hexahydroindan-1-one series (23) discussed previously. This observation suggests the stereo-chemistry shown in formula (32) for dihydroisomexicanin I. Since mexicanin I (31) has been correlated with tenulin (33), whose derivative dihydroisotenulin (34) also exhibits a positive Cotton effect,[61] the 5β–stereochemistry assigned to the angular methyl group in these sesquiterpenes is indirectly confirmed.

29   30   31

32   33   34

Mexicanin A (35), another constituent of <u>Helenium mexicanum</u>, has been converted to tetrahydromexicanin A (36a) by catalytic hydrogenation.[62c] The weak molecular amplitude of the tetrahydro-compound (36a) (a = –23) has a similar absolute value, but an opposite sign, to that of the <u>cis</u>-hexahydroindan-1-one (37) (a = +20) described by Acklin and Prelog.[64] Hence the <u>cis</u> ring juncture suggested[62c] for tetrahydromexicanin A (36a) is confirmed, because the octant rule[5] would predict a weak negative Cotton effect for this compound. It should be emphasized, however, that the comparison of Cotton effects can only be semiquantitative, since compound (37) very probably exists as a mixture of conformers, while the conformation of the bicyclic system in (36a) is likely to be more rigid. Moreover, the hydroxyl group in (36a) appears to have the

6β-configuration. Indeed, acetylation leads to an acetoxy-derivative (36b) characterized by a molecular amplitude (a = -50) which is more than twice the amplitude of (36a). This indicates the acetoxy-group to be in a negative octant, as suggested in formula (36).

Chemical correlations have been established between the tenulin (33) and helenalin (39) series.[62e] The similar stereochemistry typifying these compounds at positions 1 and 5 is apparent from the dispersion curves of their respective hydrogenated derivatives (34) and (38). Furthermore, the Cotton effects exhibited by these sesquiterpenes and their derivatives have induced Herz, Romo, and their collaborators[62e] to suggest the absolute configuration shown in formulas (31) to (40).

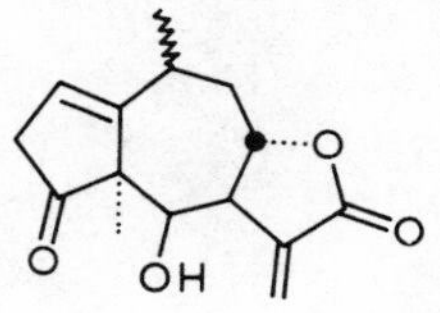

35

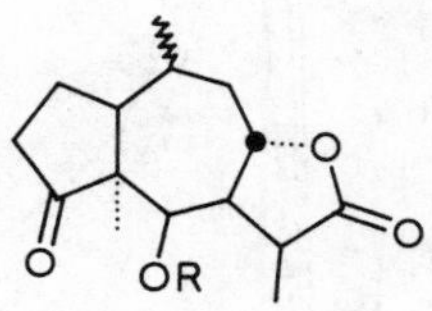

36 a, R = H
 b, R = Ac

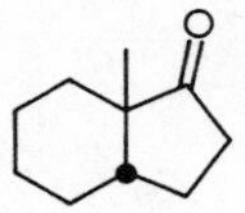

37

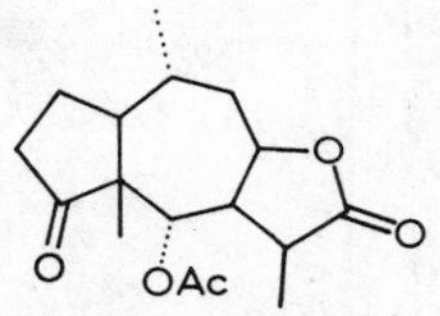

38

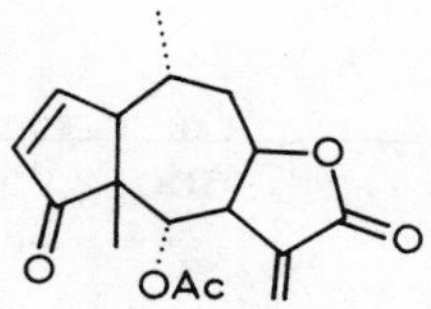

39

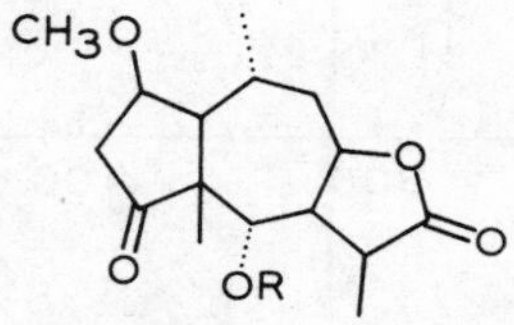

40 a, R = H
 b, R = Ac

Finally, treatment of helenalin acetate (39) with methanolic hydrochloric acid was shown to afford 2-methoxy dihydrohelenalin acetate (40b). The stereochemistry represented in formula (40b) seems to agree with experimental evidence. In Figure 6-11 the rotatory dispersion curve of (40b) exhibits a slightly higher positive Cotton effect than tetrahydrohelenalin (38). This is best interpreted by the suggested stereochemistry shown in formula (40b), since the 2-methoxyl group probably has the β-configuration. The difference between the Cotton effect exhibited by the acetate (40b) and the free alcohol (40a), shown in Figure 6-11, indicates that the 6α-substituent is in a positive octant. This again is in agreement with the absolute configuration proposed for these sesquiterpenes.

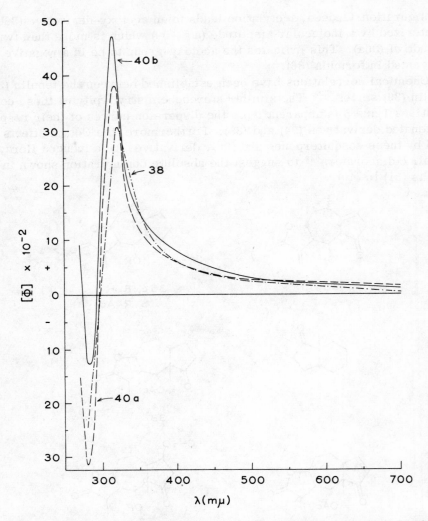

Fig. 6-11. RD curves of tetrahydrohelenalin (38), 2-methoxy-dihydrohelenalin (40a), and 2-methoxy-dihydrohelenalin acetate (40b) in dioxane (courtesy of Prof. J. Romo, Universidad Nacional Autonoma de México).

6-4. TRICYCLIC KETONES

A. Tricyclic Ketones in Steroid Synthesis and Degradation

One of the first publications issued from the laboratories of Djerassi and Klyne dealing with optical rotatory dispersion was devoted to the assignment of absolute configuration[65] to tricyclic ketones of type (41) and (42), obtained after resolution in a total synthesis of steroids.[66] These results have been reexamined recently[9] in the light of the octant rule,[5] and the previous conclusions[65] have been confirmed.

Des-A 5-keto steroids having various configurations at C-8 and C-9 have been examined recently.[9] These substances, obtained by Jones and collaborators[67] by opening of ring A of the corresponding steroids and then removing all or part of this ring, have proved to be stereochemically quite interesting. Table 6-2 gives the rotatory dispersion values for some of these ketones of general formula (43) (where R is a side chain devoid of a chromophore absorbing in the 300 mμ region). It is apparent that good agreement was found between the Cotton effects predicted from the octant rule and the experimental optical rotatory dispersion curves.

Circular dichroism measurements[68] of similar tricyclic ketones, obtained by total syntheses of steroids,[69] have confirmed the previous observations.[9] Thus compound (44) shows a negative circular dichroism curve (Table 6-3) [compare with compound (43a) of Table 6-2], and the positive Cotton effect which characterizes the diketo-benzoate (45) also agrees with the positive dispersion curve of compound (43b) of Table 6-2. From a quantitative point of

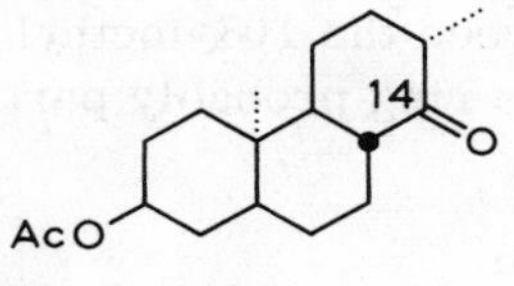

41

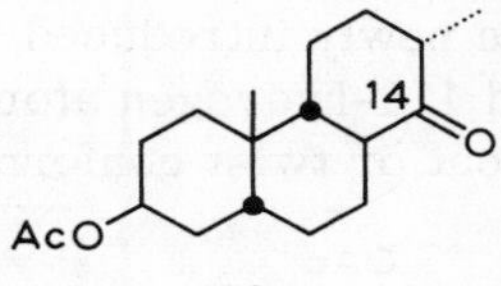

42

Table 6-2

COTTON EFFECT OF TRICYCLIC KETONES DERIVED FROM STEROIDS
WITH VARIOUS CONFIGURATIONS AT C-8 AND C-9

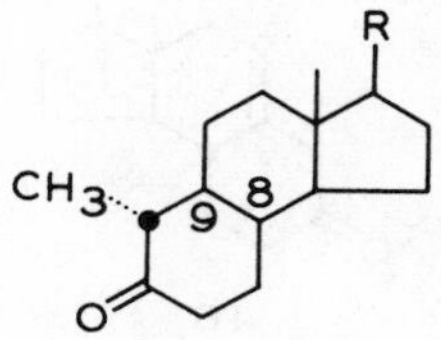

43

Compound	Stereochemistry	Predicted Cotton Effect	Experimental Amplitude
43a	8β, 9α H	Negative	-76
43b	8β, 9β H	Positive	+63 !
43c	8α, 9α H	Small Positive	+21

view, however, it should be noted that the positive Cotton effect of the diketo-benzoate (45) is somewhat reduced by the negative influence of the large 10α-ketonic side chain. In that respect, it was pointed out earlier[5] that atoms or groups of atoms remotely located from the carbonyl group still exert an appreciable influence on the Cotton effect. Moreover, the effect of an atom or group of atoms at a given distance is not constant but varies according to the asymmetry of its position with respect to the nodal surfaces of the n and π^* orbitals of the carbonyl group.†

The circular dichroism of axial alkylated compounds, such as (46) to (51), has also been measured. It was noted,[68] in agreement with the octant rule,[5] that an axial methyl group in an α-position with respect to the carbonyl group has a major influence on the intensity and sometimes the sign of the Cotton effect. For example, in the case of the acids (46) and (47), it has been pointed out[68] that, as expected, the introduction of an axial methyl group at C-10 has a positive effect on the circular dichroism maximum. However, the positive increment is higher than would be expected for a methyl group.[9] In order to release the newly introduced 1,3-interactions between the 10β-methyl and the 6β, 8β, and 11β-hydrogen atoms, the cyclohexanone ring probably partially adopts a boat or twist conformation.

†In the present case (45), the carbonyl group situated in the 10α-side chain, being remote from an asymmetric center, plays a negligible role in the Cotton effect (see Sec. 6-6) and can be ignored in a first approximation.

Furthermore, a bathochromic shift of the circular dichroism maximum has been observed in most compounds having a 10β-alkyl substituent and a large 10α-equatorial side chain (see Table 6-3).[68] The introduction of a double bond between C-9 and C-11 may, in some cases [e.g., compounds (48) and (50)] lead to a fine structure, as indicated in Table 6-3.

Table 6-3

CIRCULAR DICHROISM PROPERTIES OF SOME TRICYCLIC KETONES

Compound	Circular Dichroism Molecular Ellipticity
44	$[\theta]_{293}$ − 5050
45	$[\theta]_{292}$ + 3300
46	$[\theta]_{294}$ + 2080
47	$[\theta]_{302}$ + 1320
48	$[\theta]_{296}$ − 9140
	$[\theta]_{301}$ − 8710
	$[\theta]_{304}$ − 8840
49	$[\theta]_{297}$ − 2165
50	$[\theta]_{296}$ − 6930
	$[\theta]_{302}$ − 6440
	$[\theta]_{306}$ − 6670
51	$[\theta]_{315}$ + 890

B. Diterpene Ketonic Derivatives

The other group of substances which will be examined in this section belongs to the diterpene series. In the strict sense, many of the ketones to be discussed here are not tricyclic but tetra-, penta-, or sometimes even poly-cyclic compounds. In any event, the division of this chapter into mono-, bi-, tri-, and tetracyclic ketones is adopted solely for pedagogic reasons, and is quite arbitrary, since the same octant rule applies to all of them.

Reduction of the aromatic ring of podocarpic acid (52) afforded the B/C trans (53) and B/C cis (54) ketones which were submitted to rotatory dispersion examination.[70] The trans-ketone (53) exhibits a positive Cotton effect (a = +71), while the cis-ketone (54) shows a negative dispersion curve (a = -7). The observed Cotton effects are in agreement with the octant projections of these ketones.

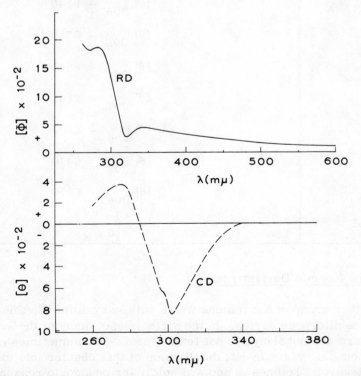

In the course of a stereochemical study of several diterpenes belonging to the agathic acid and podocarpic acid series, the tricyclic ketone (55) was obtained.[71] This keto-ester (55), which has the same stereochemistry at the B/C ring juncture as the tricyclic ketone (41), exhibits a negative Cotton effect, as shown by the rotatory dispersion and dichroism curves reported in Figure 6-12. While the optical rotatory dispersion curve of (55), which may be written

Fig. 6-12. RD and CD curves of the diterpenic keto-ester (55) [modified from S. Bory, M. Fétizon, and P. Laszlo, Bull. Soc. Chim. France, 2310 (1963)].

as (55a), is reminiscent of the curve of 5α-cholestan-1-one (see Fig. 4-4), the circular dichroism curve also exhibits the typical shape of 1-keto steroids, characterized by two maxima of opposite sign and spaced nearly 30 mµ apart. This feature, which is temperature- and solvent-dependent,[72] permits one to assign the equatorial configuration to the methyl group at C-13 as well as a trans B/C ring junction in the keto-compound (55). In such an example, the unusual shape of the rotatory dispersion curve serves to locate the carbonyl group and allows assignment of the correct stereochemistry by simple comparison with the dispersion curve of a 1-keto steroid. However, for a quantitative study of the asymmetry around the chromophore, the circular dichroism curve is preferred. This example thus shows the importance of performing both measurements when possible.

The determination of the absolute configuration of the diterpene cafestol (56) constitutes a classical example for which both rotatory dispersion and circular dichroism techniques have been successfully applied. The most important evidence regarding the stereochemistry of this pentacyclic diterpene (56) was obtained by Djerassi[6,73] from the degradation keto-derivative (57), exhibiting a dispersion curve which was the mirror image of that of 4α-ethyl-5α-cholestan-3-one (58) (see Fig. 6-13). This indicated that cafestol (56) possesses the antipodal absolute stereochemistry at the A/B ring junction of the steroids and hence also of most diterpenes known at that time.[73] Further insight into the stereochemistry of cafestol (56) at position 9[†] was gained by a circular dichroism study of another derivative (59).[74] As indicated in Figure 6-14, this ketone (59) was shown to exhibit a slight bathochromic shift of its positive circular dichroism maxima when compared with a ketone (60) obtained by degradation of phyllocladene (61), a diterpene of known absolute stereochemistry.[73,75] This observation, by correlation with similar ones in other series, permitted assignment of the β-stereochemistry to the hydrogen atom at C-9 in (59) and hence in cafestol (56), a point of important biogenetic significance.[74]

[†]Steroid numbering.

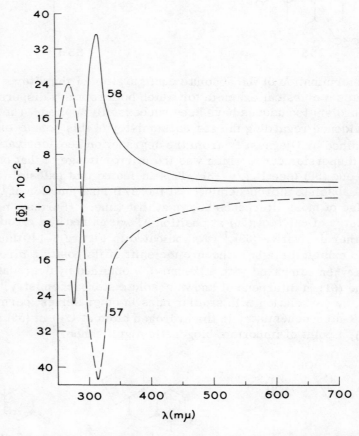

This circular dichroism observation constitutes one of the various conclusions reached by Scott and his collaborators[74] during an extensive stereochemical examination of several classes of diterpenes. Another result of their study[74] concerns the stereochemistry of gibberellic acid (62). Although the structure and stereochemistry of this diterpenic acid (62) has been the subject of investigation by various groups,[76] the configuration of the hydrogen atom at C-9 has remained unsettled until recently. Fortunately, the circular dichroism

Fig. 6-13. RD curves of the diterpenic ketone (57), derived from cafestol (56), and of 4α-ethyl-5α-cholestan-3-one (58) [modified from C. Djerassi, <u>Proc. Chem. Soc.</u>, 314 (1964)].

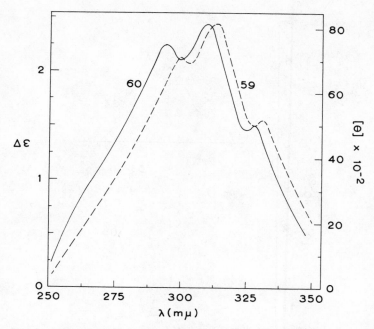

Fig. 6-14. CD curves of ketone (59), obtained from cafestol (56), and of the diterpenic ketone (60), derived from phyllocladene (61) [adapted from A. I. Scott, G. A. Sim, G. Ferguson, D. W. Young, and F. McCapra, <u>J. Am. Chem. Soc.</u>, **84**, 3197 (1962)].

curves of various keto–derivatives obtained in the gibberellic acid (62) and epigibberic acid (63) series were indicative of the stereochemistry at C–9 in these compounds. This is illustrated in Figure 6–15, where the circular dichroism curves of the three keto derivatives (63), (64), and (65) are shown. The position of maximal wavelength of each circular dichroism maximum showed that where the C–9 hydrogen and the two carbon bridge bearing the carbonyl group are in a <u>cis</u> relationship, the absorption occurs at longer wavelength than in compounds exhibiting the <u>trans</u> relationship. This small but significant difference permitted the assigment of the 9β-configuration to the hydrogen atom of the keto derivative (64) and hence for gibberellic acid (62).[74]

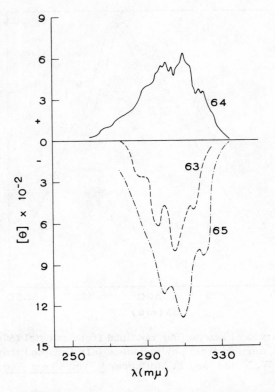

Fig. 6-15. CD curves of the diterpenic ketones (63), (64) and (65) belonging to the gibberellic acid series (62) [modified from A. I. Scott, F. McCapra, F. Comer, S. A. Sutherland, D. W. Young, G. A. Sim, and G. Ferguson, Tetrahedron, **20**, 1339 (1964)].

6-5. TETRACYCLIC AND PENTACYCLIC KETONES

A. Application of the Octant Rule to 3-Keto and 7-Keto-Steroids

Many of the first rotatory dispersion studies[6] were performed with tetra- and pentacyclic ketonic substances, since in such compounds the conformation of the ring system is essentially fixed. This is the reason why most of the available rotatory dispersion and circular dichroism data have been obtained from the steroid and triterpene series.

The rotatory dispersion Cotton effect associated with a carbonyl group located at the different positions of the steroid molecule was mentioned in Section 4-3. The sign and amplitude of the observed Cotton effects are in agreement with the predictions deduced from the octant rule.[5] Numerous interpretations of the Cotton effect associated with steroidal and triterpenic ketones by rotatory dispersion[5-7,9,14,16,19,45,50,77] and circular dichroism[72,78 - 80] have already appeared in the chemical literature. While only few of these results will be discussed here, attention will be focused on more recent applications, especially steroids and terpenoids of abnormal stereochemistry and compounds in which unexpected conformational distortions have been observed.

5α-Cholestan-3-one (66) (see Fig. 4-4) exhibits a positive Cotton effect (a = +55; [θ] = +4200).[†] This can be interpreted in light of the octant rule; the octant projection of this substance indicates that carbon atoms C-6, C-7, C-15, and C-16 lie in a positive octant.[5] In this compound C-15 and C-16 are remote from the carbonyl and probably play little part. Conversely, 3β-hydroxy-5α-cholestan-7-one-acetate (67) (see Fig. 4-5) shows a weak negative Cotton effect, attributed to carbon atoms C-2, C-3, C-15, and C-16 falling into negative octants.[5] The 5β-isomer of (66), namely, coprostan-3-one (68), also has a negative Cotton effect (a = -27; [θ] = -1500). This observation is in agreement with the octant diagram, which indicates that carbon atoms C-6, C-7, C-15, and C-16 make a negative contribution to the Cotton effect.[5]

| 6, 7, 15, 16 | | 2, 3 | | 6, 7, 15, 16 |

Octant Projection   Octant Projection   Octant Projection

66   67   68

B. Influence of a 5α-Substituent on the Cotton Effect Associated with the 3-Keto Chromophore in the Steroid Series

When the 5α-hydrogen atom of 5α-cholestan-3-one (66) is substituted by various groups differing in size or electronic distribution, or both, considerable changes in the amplitude of the dispersion curves are observed (Table 6-4). Although the 5α-substituent falls into a positive octant, in several compounds listed in Table 6-4[81] the positive Cotton effect associated with the 3-keto group is lower than in the parent compound (66). One is forced to conclude that in such compounds there is probably a reorientation of the carbonyl axis, caused by some ring distortion. This hypothesis is supported by examination of the dispersion curve of the thio-acetate (69) in a polar and a nonpolar solvent, as shown in Figure 6-16. Whether the dramatic decrease of the positive Cotton effect of (69) in heptane is entirely due to conformational mobility and not to partial solvation is difficult to assess. Further low-temperature rotatory

---

[†]The rotatory dispersion molecular amplitudes (a) and circular dichroism molecular ellipticities ([θ]) reported here generally constitute average values of the data mentioned in the chemical literature.

Table 6-4

ROTARY DISPERSION COTTON EFFECT OF
5α-SUBSTITUTED 3-KETO CHOLESTANE DERIVATIVES

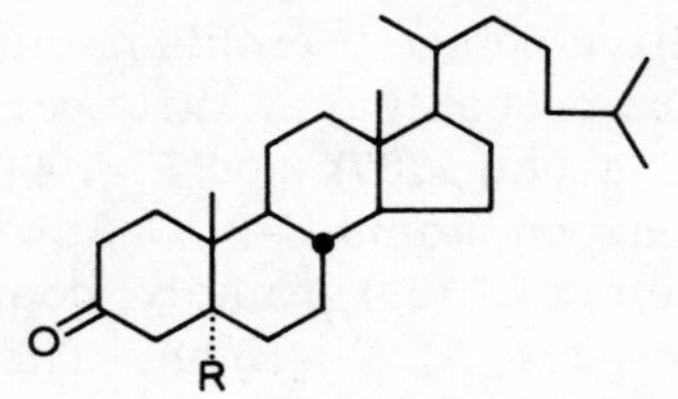

Substituent R	Rotatory dispersion molecular amplitude a
H	+55
CH$_3$	+73
C≡N	+40
CH=CH$_2$	+57
CO$_2$CH$_3$	+59
CH$_2$OAc	+39
CH$_2$—CH$_2$—O—SO$_2$—CH$_3$	+63
CH$_2$—O—SO$_2$—C$_6$H$_4$—CH$_3$	+36

dispersion or circular dichroism study of such compounds might cast more light on this intriguing problem, since a vicinal effect from 5-substituents, such as has been recognized with halogen atoms, on the 3-keto group might also influence the Cotton effect (see Chap. 7).

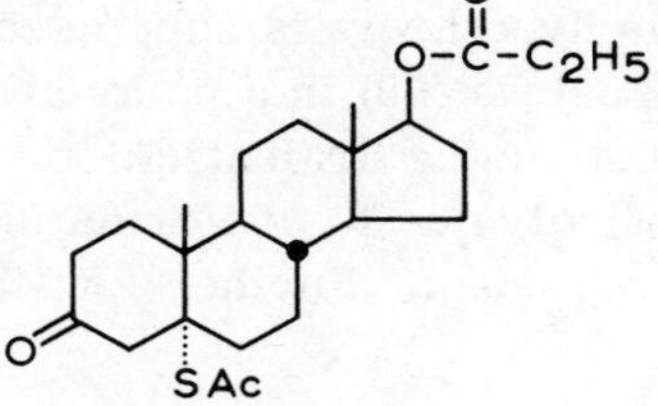

69

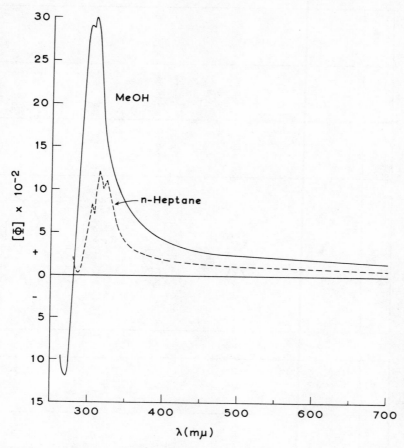

Fig. 6-16. RD curves of the 5α–thioacetate (69) in methanol and n-heptane (Courtesy of Dr. K. Kuriyama, The Shionogi Research Laboratory).

C. 16–Keto and 2–Keto A–Nor–Steroids

The very intense negative Cotton effect associated with a 16–keto grouping (14αH–configuration) has already been commented upon in Chapter 4. The sign and intensity of the Cotton effect of the 16–keto steroids and of the stereochemically related 2–keto A–nor–5α–steroids can easily be deduced by extrapolation of the principles stated above for trans–hexahydroindan–2–ones (Sec. 6–3). Optical rotatory dispersion and circular dichroism provide essentially the same information about the asymmetry surrounding the 16–keto chromophore. This is best illustrated in Table 6–5, where the amplitude and molecular ellipticity of several 16–keto– (70–73) and 2–keto–A–nor–5α–steroids (74–79) are reported. The antipodal relationship, differentiating the 16–keto from the A–nor 2–keto steroids, is clearly expressed by the opposite sign of their Cotton effect. Moreover, it is apparent that a 17β–substituent lying roughly in a nodal plane hardly influences the Cotton effect associated with the carbonyl group in these compounds.[83b] Similarly, the 19–nor steroid (77) and the 3,3–dimethyl derivative (79)

Table 6-5

OPTICAL ROTATORY DISPERSION AND CIRCULAR DICHROISM PROPERTIES OF ƒ-KETO AND A-NOR 2-KETO STEROIDS

Compound	a	$[\theta]$	Ref.
70	−264	−18700	50a, 72
71	−232†	−19000	82
72	−218†	−17900	82
73	−254	−20700†	6
74	+234	+19300†	45

Compound	a	$[\theta]$	Ref.
75	+228†	+18700	80
76	+238†	+19500	80
77	+241	+19500	80
78	+210	+18300	80
79	+221	+16500	83a

†Refers to the calculated value, applying Equation [18] of Chapter 2.

exhibit essentially the same positive Cotton effect as their parent compounds (76) or (78). These observations are in agreement with the octant rule, which predicts little (or no) influence from substituents lying in nodal or symmetry planes,[5] and in the last compound (79) the positive influence of one methyl is counterbalanced by the negative effect of the other.

D. Influence of Various Substituents on the Cotton Effect of 2- and 3-Keto Steroids

The closely related methods of optical rotatory dispersion and circular dichroism permit one to detect subtle conformational changes occurring in steroid and in polycyclic terpene molecules on introduction of a double bond or a new substituent in the ring system, or both. Some examples have already been mentioned (see Sec. 4-4), and more recent applications will be reported in this section, while the concept of conformational transmission responsible for such deformations will be discussed in Section 6-5-J.

The introduction of an acetoxy function next to the carbonyl in the cholestane molecule has led to some interesting observations.[84a] As indicated in Table 6-6, 3β-hydroxy-5α-cholestan-2-one-acetate (80c)† shows the same amplitude as 5α-cholestan-2-one(80a),[5] in agreement with the octant rule, since the equatorial acetoxy function lies in a nodal plane. The molecular amplitude of the 3α-acetoxy derivative (80b) is considerably reduced when compared with its parent unsubstituted 5α-cholestan-2-one (80a). Since a 3α-axial substituent in ring A in the chair form would be expected to enhance the Cotton effect, one would be inclined to conclude that this ring is distorted in (80b) in order to release the nonbonded interactions between the 3α-substituent and the 1α- and the 5α-axial hydrogen atoms. However, in a recent NMR study of axial and equatorial alcohols, it was indicated[84b] that the coupling constant of the 3-equatorial proton of (80b) is in perfect agreement with a normal chair conformation for ring A. This apparent contradiction between rotatory dispersion and nuclear magnetic resonance data deserves further examination. While 2α-hydroxy-5α-cholestan-3-one-acetate (81b) exhibits a similar molecular amplitude as 5α-cholestan-3-one (81a), the 2β-acetoxy derivative (81c), showing quite a different amplitude (see Table 6-6), has a modified ring A conformation in order to decrease the strong 1,3-diaxial interactions between the 2β-acetoxy and 10β-methyl groupings. A twist conformation was proposed for ring A of this compound (81c), a proposal which was supported by its nuclear magnetic resonance spectrum.[84a] The 4β-acetoxy derivative (81e) is also distorted in order to release 1,3-diaxial interactions between the 4β-acetoxy and the 10β-methyl groupings. The molecular amplitude of the 4α-isomer (81d) is somewhat decreased when compared with the unsubstituted compound (81a). This could be attributed to reorientation of the acetoxy group in (81d) in order to avoid interactions with the 6α-hydrogen atom. The acetoxy function is no longer in the nodal plane and makes a mild negative contribution to the Cotton effect. Worth noting also are the shifts observed in the wavelength at which the RD peak and the trough of these compounds occur (see Table 6-6).

---

†In formulas (80) and (81), Ac refers to the $-O-\overset{\overset{\textstyle O}{\|}}{C}-CH_3$ grouping.

Table 6-6

OPTICAL ROTATORY DISPERSION PROPERTIES OF SOME SUBSTITUTED 2- AND 3-KETO STEROIDS

Compound	OPTICAL ROTATORY DISPERSON		
	Peak	Trough	Molecular Amplitude a
5α-Cholestan-2-one (80a)	$[\Phi]_{310} + 6290°$	$[\Phi]_{267} - 5820°$	+121
3α-Hydroxy-5α-cholestan-2-one-acetate (80b)	$[\Phi]_{317} + 2540°$	$[\Phi]_{275} - 2330°$	+49
3β-Hydroxy-5α-cholestan-2-one-acetate (80c)	$[\Phi]_{305} + 6740°$	$[\Phi]_{270} - 5320°$	+120
5α-Cholestan-3-one (81a)	$[\Phi]_{307} + 3700°$	$[\Phi]_{267} - 2940°$	+55
2α-Hydroxy-5α-cholestan-3-one-acetate (81b)	$[\Phi]_{305} + 3450°$	$[\Phi]_{265} - 2790°$	+62
2β-Hydroxy-5α-cholestan-3-one-acetate (81c)	$[\Phi]_{290} + 1820°$	$[\Phi]_{250} + 620°!$	+12!
4α-Hydroxy-5α-cholestan-3-one-acetate (81d)	$[\Phi]_{300} + 1850°$	$[\Phi]_{260} - 2410°$	+43
4β-Hydroxy-5α-cholestan-3-one-acetate (81e)	$[\Phi]_{320} + 730°$	$[\Phi]_{270} - 970°$	+17

80 a, R$_1$ = R$_2$ = H
   b, R$_1$ = Ac; R$_2$ = H
   c, R$_1$ = H; R$_2$ = Ac

81 a, R$_1$ = R$_2$ = R$_3$ = R$_4$ = H
   b, R$_1$ = Ac; R$_2$ = R$_3$ = R$_4$ = H
   c, R$_1$ = R$_3$ = R$_4$ = H; R$_2$ = Ac
   d, R$_1$ = R$_2$ = R$_3$ = H; R$_4$ = Ac
   e, R$_1$ = R$_2$ = R$_4$ = H; R$_3$ = Ac

In connection with the above problem, it should be noted that while 1α-methyl A/B trans 3-keto steroids are known to exhibit a normal positive Cotton effect, 1α-substituted A/B cis compounds have been shown to present abnormal dispersion curves.[85] A boat or twist conformation has been suggested for ring A in such substances.[85]

Finally, Djerassi and Klyne[9] have called attention to the enhancement of the Cotton effect associated with the 3-keto chromophore when going from the ordinary series (with angular 10β-methyl group) to the 19-nor series (10β-hydrogen atom).

E. 19-Substituted Steroids

The new routes to 19-nor steroids have permitted access to a large number of 19-substituted compounds not readily available by former methods.[86] These compounds have proved to be of stereochemical interest, and brief mention shall now be made of some results obtained[87] with the saturated 3-keto derivatives listed in Table 6-7.

In the A/B trans-series, several compounds were obtained having various substituents at position 19. Some of them are 3,17-diketo steroids. The Cotton effect exhibited by diketo-compounds will be discussed in Chapter 7, but it may be mentioned now that in such 3,17-diketo steroids the distance separating both carbonyl groups is large enough so that the "additivity rule" can be applied (see Sec. 7-6).[6,7,88] Hence, in compounds (84) and (85) (Table 6-7), the Cotton effect associated with the 3-keto chromophore can be obtained by subtracting the value of the 17-keto grouping, ($[\theta]_{298}$ + 11440) (see Fig. 2-8). From the data reported in Table 6-7, it is apparent that the molecular ellipticity of the circular dichroism curves of these compounds is considerably reduced relative to that of 5α-cholestan-3-one (66).[87] An examination of the geometry of these 19-substituted compounds with Dreiding molecular models[89] indicates that the preferred conformation of the 10β-side chain, where the nonbonded interactions are minimized, lies between the 2β- and 11β-hydrogen atoms, i.e., in a negative octant.

Table 6-7

COTTON EFFECT ASSOCIATED WITH SOME 19-SUBSTITUTED
3-KETO 5α-STEROIDS

Compound	Substituents	Molecular Ellipticity $[\theta]$ of the 3-Keto Chromophore
66	$R_1 = CH_3$; $R_2 = C_8H_{17}$	+4200
82	$R_1 = CH_2OAc$; $R_2 = OAc$	+2125
83	$R_1 = CH_2OH$; $R_2 = OH$	+1300
84	$R_1 = CO_2CH_3$; $R_2 = $ ketone	+1750
85	$R_1 = CH_2OH$; $R_2 = $ ketone	+670

Low-temperature circular dichroism measurements performed[90] with 17β,19-dihydroxy-5α-androstan-3-one-diacetate (82) indicate a marked decrease of the Cotton effect at -192°, as well as a mild bathochromic shift of the positive maxima which also shows a fine structure not detected at room temperature (see Fig. 6-17).

As far as the 19-hydroxy-3-keto-androstanes (83) and (85) are concerned, the situation is complicated by the fact that they can exist as the free (83a) and intramolecular hemi-ketal form (83b).[91] This observation, deduced from the infrared spectrum of (83b) which shows no carbonyl absorption band for a six-membered ring ketone, was further confirmed by obtaining the rotatory dispersion curve of (83) in solvents of different polarity.[87] This situation is reminiscent of the recently described conformational equilibrium observed in six-membered ring sulfoxide derivatives.[92]

The Cotton effect associated with A/B cis-19-substituted compounds (see Table 6-8) is similar to that of coprostan-3-one (68). However, the data reported in Table 6-8 indicate that each of these 19-substituted 5β-steroids exhibits a stronger negative Cotton effect than its parent derivative (68). The molecular model[89] indicates that the preferred conformation of the 19-substituent lies between the 1β- and the 11β-hydrogen atoms. The 19-

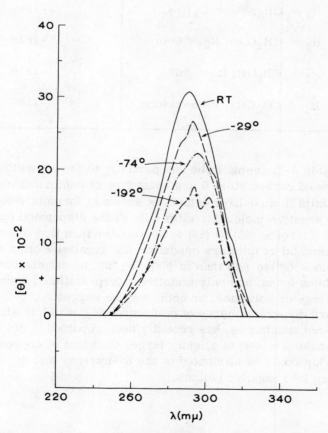

Fig. 6-17. CD curves of 17β,19–dihydroxy–5α–androstan–3–one–diacetate (82) at various temperatures (courtesy of Professor C. Djerassi, Stanford University).

Table 6-8

COTTON EFFECT ASSOCIATED WITH SOME 19-SUBSTITUTED
3-KETO 5β-STEROIDS

Compound	Substituents	Molecular Ellipticity of the 3-Keto Chromophore
68	$R_1 = CH_3$; $R_2 = C_8H_{17}$	-1500
86	$R_1 = CH_2OAc$; $R_2 = OAc$	-1820
87	$R_1 = CH_2OH$; $R_2 = OH$	-1810
88	$R_1 = CO_2CH_3$; $R_2 = ketone$	-1580

observed (see Table 6-9) seems to be due partially to the 19-methylene but mainly to the skewed carbon atom 5 in a twist type of conformation. Optical substituent then falls in a positive octant, as shown in formula (89). Thus one would expect the negative molecular ellipticity of the dispersion curves of the 19-substituted 5β-steroids (86) to (88) to be smaller than that of coprostanone (68). The experimental results are opposite: the negative Cotton effect is larger in compounds (86) to (88) than in (68). So far, no satisfactory explanation has been found, and only tentative interpretations, such as distortion of A and B rings or solvation, or both, may be suggested.

The rotatory dispersion curve of compound (90), which is structurally related to the above substances, has recently been reported.[93] Its negative molecular amplitude (a = -34) is slightly larger than that of coprostan-3-one (68) (a = -27). This could be attributed to the 5β-hydroxy and the 8,19-oxide bridge both falling into negative octants.

89

90

F. Some Pentacyclic 3-Keto Steroids

Several pentacyclic 3-keto steroids containing an extra cyclopropane, cyclobutane, or tetrahydrofuran system in ring A or B have been obtained recently.[86] The molecular ellipticity exhibited by the dichroism curves of some of these compounds is reported in Table 6-9. The comparison of the molecular ellipticity shown by 5α-cholestan-3-one (66) ($[\theta] = +4200$) with the values mentioned in Table 6-9 indicates the occurrence of substantial conformational distortion in rings A and B of such compounds. Although the examination of the molecular model[89] of (94)[94] and (95) shows that the 5α-hydroxy and 19-methylene bridge in the former and the 6,19-oxide bridge in the latter fall into positive octants, the distortion of ring B in these compounds renders the positive contribution of C-6 much more important than in the normal chair conformation. Similarly, the conformation of ring A of the cyclobutane derivative (93) is considerably modified, as shown by the large decrease of the molecular ellipticity attributed to its 3-keto chromophore. The negative ellipticity which characterizes the 3-keto group in the 5,10β-cyclopropyl derivative (91) seems to be due to a twist conformation adopted by ring A. Under such circumstances C-1 is strongly skewed into a negative octant and seems to be responsible for the negative Cotton effect observed. When the cyclopropyl group is situated between C-9 and C-19, however, as in cycloeucalenone (see Fig. 4-11), the Cotton effect is of the same sign as in the usual 10β-methyl 3-keto steroids, but slightly decreased.

Finally, although the Cotton effect of the 5,10α-cyclopropyl androstane derivative (92)[86i] is reminiscent of, but less positive than, that of a normal 3-keto 5α-steroid, the models clearly indicate that strong conformational changes occur in rings A and B. The positive Cotton effect experimentally

Table 6-9

COTTON EFFECT OBSERVED IN SOME
PENTACYCLIC STEROIDAL KETONES

Compound	Molecular Ellipticity $[\theta]$	$[\theta]$ of the 3-Keto Chromophore
91	+9360	−2080
92	+13860	+2420
93	+13120	+1680
94	+17300	+5860
95	+18100	+6660

rotatory dispersion measurements performed on these compounds fully confirm the above observations.[87] Saturated ketones with a cyclopropyl and epoxy-function next to the carbonyl group will be discussed in Chapter 7, since they involve a special extension of the octant rule.

The last compound mentioned in the preceding paragraph shows a 5,10α-"abnormal" configuration. Other steroidal and terpenic ketones having abnormal configurations will be discussed in sequence. However, before examining such substances, brief mention will be made of some other "pentacyclic" and A-homo steroidal ketones.

Somewhat related to the above-described compounds are some pentacyclic keto steroids (96) to (98) prepared at the Shionogi Research Laboratories.[81] If comparison between variations observed in the Cotton effects and slight modifications brought to these structures permits one to suggest a probable position of the groupings in a definite octant, complete interpretation of these Cotton effects seems hazardous. Indeed, not enough experimental data are available to allow reliable conclusions to be drawn.

96 a, R = H
b, R = OH

97a, R = H
b, R = Ac

Since substitution of the pentacyclic derivative (96a) (a = -147) at C-4 slightly decreases the strong negative Cotton effect, as shown by the lower value of the molecular amplitude exhibited by the 4-hydroxy compound (96b) (a = -131), the 4β-hydroxyl group in (96b) has to lie in a positive octant. Acetylation of the tertiary alcohol grouping of (97a) (a = -55) enhances the negative Cotton effect of this compound (97b) (a = -81). This indicates that in such derivatives (97a, b) the 3β-substituent falls into a negative octant. Finally, the rotatory dispersion curves of these cyclopentanone derivatives are characterized by two features: a typical fine structure of the trough and the wavelength at which this trough occurs (about 330 mμ). This is exemplified in Figure 6-18, which shows the rotatory dispersion curves of the tertiary hydroxylated steroid (97a) and its acetate (97b).

In the next compounds to be examined (98a, b, c), the ring containing the carbonyl group is a cyclohexane ring in the boat conformation. The interpretation of the Cotton effect which will be proposed should only be considered as tentative, since the octant rule has been stated mainly for the cyclohexanone in the chair conformation. If one considers the cyclohexanone ring of compound (98a) (a = -33) as formed by carbon atom 3 (carbonyl group), 2, 2', 5', 5, and

116   Saturated Carbonyl

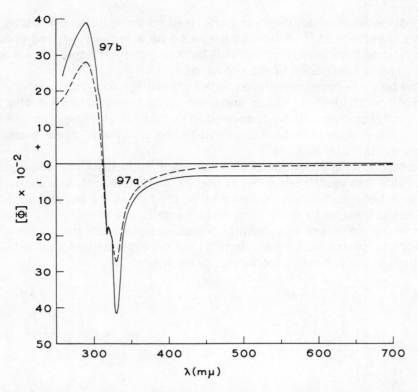

Fig. 6-18. RD curves of the pentacyclic 3β-hydroxy 5'-keto steroid (97a) and the corresponding acetate (97b) (courtesy of Dr. K. Kuriyama, The Shionogi Research Laboratory).

98a, R₁ = R₂ = H

b, R₁ = OH; R₂ = H

c, R₁ = H; R₂ = OH

4, it is apparent that carbon atom 2' is seriously skewed in a negative octant. This effect is partly counterbalanced by the positive contribution made by rings B, C, and D, as well as by carbon atoms 1 and 5'. Thus, as expected, substitution at carbon atom 2', as in (98b) (a = -39), or at position 4, as in (98c) (a = -58), enhances the negative Cotton effect, since these carbon atoms are in negative octants.

G. Tetracyclic Diterpenes

A similar situation is encountered in some recently synthesized tetra-cyclic diterpene derivatives (99a) and (99b).[95] Indeed, these compounds present a bicyclo[2.2.2] pattern similar to that encountered in the above-mentioned steroids. When considering the cyclohexanone ring formed by carbon atoms 8, 9, 11, 12, 15, and 16 in compound (99a), one sees that the observed negative Cotton effect is consistent with the octant projection [see formula (99a)]. Indeed, C-9 is severely skewed in a negative octant. Moreover, the negative contribution made by C-9 is enhanced by ring A, also in a negative octant, and only partly canceled by carbon atom 14, in a positive octant.

In the position isomer (99b), the situation is reversed, since C-11 is now skewed in a positive octant. This contribution is partly neutralized by carbon atom 13 in a negative octant.

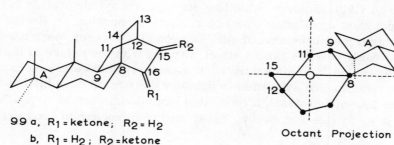

99 a, R₁ = ketone; R₂ = H₂
   b, R₁ = H₂; R₂ = ketone

Octant Projection
99 a

H. Homo-Steroids

A-Homo-5α-cholestan-3-one (100a)[96] has been shown, by rotatory dispersion, to present a negative Cotton effect (a = -60!).[97] This observation is in qualitative agreement with the negative circular dichroism maximum obtained for 19-nor-A-homo-5α-androstan-17β-ol-3-one-acetate (100b) ([θ] = -7390).[98] In such compounds, ring A is in a twist conformation and carbon atoms 1 and 10 are skewed in negative octants, while C-14 is skewed in a positive octant. Moreover, C-9, C-11, and C-12 also make negative contributions to the Cotton effect. Conversely, as expected, 17β-hydroxy-A-homo-5β-androstan-3-one (100c) exhibits a positive maximum ([θ] = +3930).[97]

Since both rings A and B are seven-membered, the situation is further complicated in the bicyclo[4.4.1]undecane steroid derivative (101),[99] exhibiting a negative Cotton effect ([θ] = -4620). On the basis of the octant rule the 5αH-configuration may very tentatively be assigned to this compound, despite the consequential 1αH-5αH interaction. With such a stereochemistry C-1 and C-10 are skewed into a negative octant, and this effect is partially compensated by C-5 in a positive octant. Furthermore, carbon atoms 6 and 7 are also in a positive octant. If the configuration at C-5 were β, a weakly positive Cotton effect would seem probable.

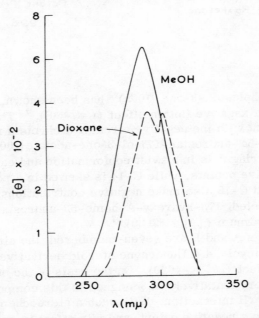

100 a, 5αH, R₁ = CH₃, R₂ = C₈H₁₇

b, 5αH, R₁ = H, R₂ = OAc

c, 5βH, R₁ = CH₃, R₂ = OH

101

I. Cotton Effects of 3-Keto Steroids and Triterpenes with Abnormal Configuration

In 1958 the striking observation was made that 19–nor–5α,10α–3–keto-steroids, such as (102), although exhibiting strong carbonyl absorption in the infrared, did not show any Cotton effect by rotatory dispersion.[100] Recent circular dichroism measurements of such compounds, however, permitted the detection of a weakly positive Cotton effect, varying with the nature of the solvent (see Fig. 6-19).[80] Some saturated 10α–methyl 3-keto steroids have also been prepared recently and submitted to rotatory dispersion examination.[101] As anticipated, 10α–dihydrotestosterone (103) exhibited a very weak positive Cotton effect (a = +7) (see Fig. 6-20). These observations are in good agree-

Fig. 6-19. CD curves of 17α–propyl–17β–hydroxy–5α,10α–estran–3–one (102) in methanol and dioxane (modified from P. Witz, Ph.D. Thesis, University of Strasbourg, May 1964).

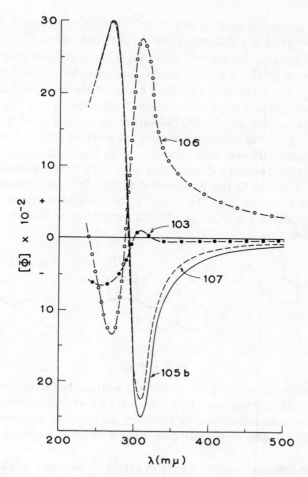

Fig. 6-20. RD curves of 10α–dihydrotestosterone (103), 5β,9β,10α–dihydrotestosterone (105b), 9β–ergost–22–en–3–one (106) and 5β,8α,10α–ergost–22–en–3–one (107) in methanol (modified from S. J. Halkes, Ph.D. Thesis, University of Leiden, February 1964).

ment with the octant rule, since the positive Cotton effect due to rings C and D in such compounds is almost quantitatively canceled by the two nearer atoms 6 and 7, lying in a negative octant.[9]

The above results emphasize that circular dichroism should be the method of choice for the detection of weak Cotton effects, which are easily masked by the background rotation of the dispersion curve.[94]

The 5α,9β,10α-steroid (104)[102] exhibits a strongly positive circular dichroism maximum ($[\theta] = +9520$), which conforms to prediction. With such a stereochemistry, the carbon atoms C-6 and C-7 lie in a positive octant and are mainly responsible for the Cotton effect. Also expected was the negative Cotton effect observed for the 5β,9β,10α-steroids (105a) ($[\theta] = -4360$)[102] and (105b) (a = -55)[101] (see Fig. 6-20), because the carbon atoms 6 and 7 now fall into a negative octant. These conclusions are in qualitative agreement with the observations made by rotatory dispersion with saturated ketones of similar stereochemistry obtained in the lumisterol series.[9,67] Incidentally, application of Equation [18] of Chapter 2 (p. 19) shows the excellent correspondence existing between the experimental Cotton effects exhibited by the steroids (105a) and (105b) (see Table 6-10).

104   105 a, R = H
            b, R = CH₃   106

Other steroids presenting an abnormal stereochemistry, such as the 9β-ergostan derivative (106) and its 5β,8α,9α,10α-stereoisomer (107), have also been prepared and submitted to rotatory dispersion measurements.[101] The Cotton effects which were observed (see Fig. 6-20) also agreed with the octant rule.[5]

Finally, the intense negative Cotton effect associated with the 3-keto chromophore in the triterpenes shionone (108)[83a,103] and friedelin (109)[6,9] (see Sec. 4-4), reminiscent of the above-reported 5β,9β,10α-steroids (105a, b), is also in agreement with the predictions deduced from the octant rule, and supports the proposed stereochemistry for the A/B ring junction.

Table 6-10 summarizes the available information about the Cotton effect associated with the 3-keto chromophore in steroids and triterpenes presenting various configurations at the A/B and B/C ring junctions.

107   108   109

Table 6-10

RELATIONSHIP BETWEEN COTTON EFFECT AND STEREOCHEMISTRY IN 3-KETO STEROIDS AND TERPENES

Compound	Configuration	Rotatory Dispersion Molecular Amplitude a	Circular Dichroism Molecular Ellipticity $[\theta]$	Ref.
5α-Cholestan-3-one (66)	5αH,8βH,9αH,10βCH$_3$	+55	+4200	9,72
17β-Hydroxy-19-nor-5α-androstan-3-one	5αH,8βH,9αH,10βH	+90	+4510	7,80
5α-Cholestan-6-en-3-one (111a)	5αH,8βH,9αH,10βCH$_3$	very weak	$\begin{cases} -130 \\ +1290\dagger \end{cases}$	105,106
Coprostan-3-one (68)	5βH,8βH,9αH,10βCH$_3$	−27	−1500$\dagger\dagger$	9,78,105
17β-Hydroxy-19-nor-5β-androstan-3-one-acetate	5βH,8βH,9αH,10βH	−30	−2460$\dagger\dagger$	9
10α-Dihydrotestosterone (103)	5αH,8βH,9αH,10αCH$_3$	+7	+570	101
5α,9β-Ergost-22-en-3-one (106)	5αH,8βH,9βH,10βCH$_3$	+41	+3360	101
17α-Propyl-17β-hydroxy 5α,10α-estran-3-one (102)	5αH,8βH,9αH,10αH	not observed	360 (dioxane) 530 (methanol)	80
17β-Hydroxy-5α,9β,10α-estran-3-one (104)	5αH,8βH,9βH,10αH	+115$\dagger\dagger$	+9520	102
17β-Hydroxy-5β,9β,10α-estran-3-one (105a)	5βH,8βH,9βH,10αH	−53$\dagger\dagger$	−4360	102
5β,9β,10α-Dihydrostestosterone (105b)	5βH,8βH,9βH,10αCH$_3$	−55	−4550$\dagger\dagger$	101
Lumistanone-A	5βH,8βH,9βH,10αCH$_3$	−52	−4250$\dagger\dagger$	9
Lumistanone-C	5αH,8βH,9βH,10αCH$_3$,14βH	+22	+1800$\dagger\dagger$	9
5β,8α,10α-Ergost-22-en-3-one (107)	5βH,8αH,9αH,10αCH$_3$	−52	−4250$\dagger\dagger$	101
Shionone (108)	4βCH$_3$,5βCH$_3$,8αH,9βCH$_3$, 10αH,13αH,14βCH$_3$	−137	−8580	79,103
Friedelin (109)	4βCH$_3$,5βCH$_3$,8αH,9βCH$_3$, 10αH,13αH,14βCH$_3$	−130	−9200	6,9,79,103

$\dagger$ Two circular dichroism values of different sign mean a double-humped curve.

$\dagger\dagger$ Refers to the calculated value, applying Equation [18] of Chapter 2.

During the course of a synthesis of homo-steroids having an extra A-ring in the molecule,[104],[105] several pentacyclic ketones were prepared showing a large array of configurations at the ring junctures. Such compounds are collected in Table 6-11, each with its respective Cotton effect,[105] which may be compared with the rotatory dispersion amplitude and circular dichroism of the parent tetracyclic steroids reported in Table 6-10.

The Cotton effect of the saturated ketone (110a) is reminiscent of that of 5α-cholestan-3-one (66) or, even more, of 17β-hydroxy-19-nor-5α-androstan-3-one (Table 6-10). The corresponding Δ^4-ketone (110b) exhibits a weak positive Cotton effect, which is similar to the low value observed for 5α-cholest-6-en-3-one (111a) (Table 6-10).[106] The Cotton effect of the A'/A cis ketone (110c) is similar to that of coprostan-3-one (68) and 17β-hydroxy-19-nor-5β-androstan-3-one-acetate, although it is weaker (Table 6-10). Circular dichroism measurement of the pentacyclic-cis-ketone (110d) did not allow detection of any maximum. This situation is reminiscent of the 5α, 10α-steroids (102) and (103) discussed previously (see Figs. 6-19 and 6-20). Examination of the molecular models[89] of ketone (110c) indicates that ring A has to adopt a boat or a twist conformation, which would explain the highly positive Cotton effect observed. The stereochemistry of the keto-compound (110f) is similar to that of 5β-lumistan-3-one (see Table 6-10), thus explaining the strongly negative Cotton effect observed. The 3α-isomer (110g) also had a Cotton effect similar to that of lumistanone C (see Table 6-10), in agreement with its stereochemistry. Finally, the all-cis-derivative (110h) exhibits a negative Cotton effect, identical to that of coprostanone (68) (see Table 6-10).

J. Conformational Transmission

In the course of the previous discussion, mention was made of the low molecular amplitude exhibited by the rotatory dispersion curves of 5α-cholest-6-en-3-one (111a) (Table 6-10) and its A'-homo analogue (110b). Sondheimer, Klyne, and their collaborators[106] also suggested that in 2β-methyl (111b) and 2,2-dimethyl-5α-cholest-6-en-3-one (111c), which show unexpected molecular amplitudes, ring A probably exists in a boat or modified boat conformation due to the double bond at position 6-7. The situation encountered in ring A of these compounds is reminiscent of the negative Cotton effect exhibited by 2α-bromo-2β-methyl-5α-cholestan-3-one (112a), in which ring A has been shown by Djerassi et al. to exist in a boat form.[107] Nonbonded 1,3-interactions occurring between the 2β-methyl and 10β-methyl in this compound (112a) are responsible for this choice of conformation. Since 2β-methyl-5α-cholestan-3-one (112b) exhibits a normal positive Cotton effect,[106] the change of conformation occurring in (112a) may be attributed to the bulky 2α-bromine.[107]

In the above reported compounds (110b, 111a) the change of conformation which takes place seems to be due, instead, to a conformational transmission in ring A by the double bond present in the ring adjacent to the carbonyl-containing one. The concept of "conformational transmission," first stated by Barton,[108] has been further developed by several groups of investigators in the case of

Table 6-11

Compound	Configuration of Hydrogen Atoms	Rotatory Dispersion Molecular Amplitude a	Circular Dichroism Molecular Ellipticity $[\theta]$
110a	2β, 3α, 5α	+95	+6370
110b	2β, 3α, Δ⁴		−400 +630
110c	2β, 3β, 5α	−20	−790
110d	2α, 3α, 5α		<300
110e	2α, 3β, 5α	−170	−14450
110f	2α, 3β, 5β	−70	−6730
110g	2α, 3α, 5β	+32	+3330
110h	2β, 3β, 5β	−26	−1580

substituted steroids and triterpenes.[109] The insertion of a double bond, as in
(111a), or of a trigonal atom such as a carbonyl (see Chap. 7), in a 3-keto
steroid stimulates a modification of the conformation of the cyclic system
(conformation transmission) explaining the unusually weak Cotton effect exhibited by such compounds (110b, 111a).

Conformational transmission seems also to be responsible for the
successive inversion of the Cotton effect observed in the progressive substitution of a 3-keto steroid into its 4,4-dimethyl homologue and into the 4,4,8β-
trimethyl 3-keto pattern exhibited by many triterpenes (see Sec. 4-4). Similarly,
sensible variations of the Cotton effect have recently been reported [108 bis] in the
methylation of ergosta-7,22-dien-3-one. These inversions observed in the
Cotton effect are attributable to conformational distortion existing in ring A.[109]
Worth noting here are the "double-humped" circular dichroism curves exhibited
by almost all the tetra- and pentacyclic 3-keto triterpenes investigated by
Ourisson and his coworkers.[79,80] This seems to indicate that in the equilibrium
mixture of conformers existing at room temperature, one form predominates
over the other (s). Only in the case of the Δ 8-4,4-dimethyl 3-keto derivatives is
an equal proportion of the various conformers apparently present.[79] Low-
temperature circular dichroism measurements of such compounds would
probably permit verification of this hypothesis (see for instance ref. 35).

111 a, $R_1 = R_2 = H$

   b, $R_1 = CH_3$; $R_2 = H$

   c, $R_1 = R_2 = CH_3$

112 a, R = Br

   b, R = H

K. 6-Keto Steroids

As already indicated in Figure 4-5, 5α-6-keto steroids exhibit a negative
Cotton effect (a = -75; [θ] = -4600).[9,72,78] Inversion of the configuration at C-5
to give the 5β-6-keto derivatives is accompanied by a considerable enhancement
of the negative Cotton effect 50a ([θ] = -9900).[72,78,85e]

An extensive circular dichroism study of 19-nor 5β-methyl keto steroids
has been reported recently.[110] It was concluded that in such compounds the
stereochemistry at C-9 and C-10 cannot be deduced easily from the dichroism
of 3-ketones but can be deduced easily from the Cotton effect exhibited by a
6-keto grouping. As indicated in Table 6-12, the molecular ellipticity shown
by the 6-keto chromophore pointed clearly to the configuration at C-9 and C-10
in such steroids (113a-d).

While there is little doubt that compound (113a) exists in the all-chair
conformation, ring B in (113b) seems to be twisted. Such a form permits a

Table 6-12

CIRCULAR DICHROISM OF 5β-METHYL 6-KETO STEROIDS WITH
DIFFERENT CONFIGURATIONS AT C-9 AND C-10

Compound	Configuration	Circular Dichroism Molecular Ellipticity $[\theta]$
113a	9β, 10α	+1720
113b	9β, 10β	-2640
113c	9α, 10α	-8580
113d	9α, 10β	-11880

better interpretation of the observed negative Cotton effect.[110] In the 9α,10α-derivative (113c), ring B seems to be in a boat form, while the all-chair conformation is again adopted by the 9α,10β-stereoisomer (113d), thus explaining the strongly negative Cotton effect due to rings C and D and to the nearer carbon atoms 3 and 4, all falling into negative octants.

L. Cotton Effect Associated with the 11-Keto Chromophore in Steroids and Triterpenes

The Cotton effect associated with the 11-keto grouping has been shown to be very sensitive to stereochemical modifications. An 11-keto steroid with the normal stereochemistry exhibits a mild positive Cotton effect (a $\cong$ + 12; [θ] $\cong$ +1200), as could be anticipated from the octant rule.[5] A dramatic effect, independent of the configuration at C-5, was observed recently when low-temperature circular dichroism measurements were performed with such 11-keto steroids.[10,72] Lowering of the temperature produces vibrational fine structure as well as inversion of the Cotton effect. This is illustrated in Figure 6-21, which reproduces the circular dichroism curves of 5α-androstan-11-one (114) at 25° and -192°.[10] This unique feature, which is not observed with

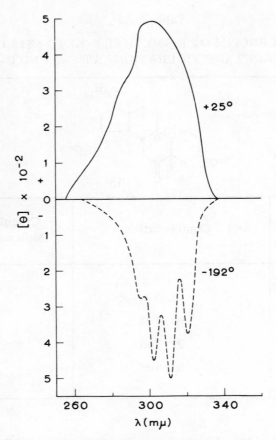

Fig. 6-21. CD curves of 5α-androstan-11-one (114) at +25° and -192° in EPA solvent (ether-isopentane- ethanol). [from K. M. Wellman, E. Bunnenberg and C. Djerassi, J. Am. Chem. Soc., **85**, 1870 (1963), reproduced by permission of the editor].

ketones at any other position of the cyclopentanoperhydrophenanthrene nucleus and which is due to an equilibrium between different conformers of ring C, makes it easy to locate the 11-keto group in the steroid molecule.[10,111] Further investigation of this low-temperature effect indicates that such a change of the sign is only found when the Cotton effect at room temperature is rather small,[111] thus making circular dichroism the appropriate method for this type of investigation.

Introduction of a double bond at C-5 enhances considerably the Cotton effect of the 11-keto function. For example, 3β,17β-dihydroxy-androst-5-en-11-one (115) exhibits a much higher molecular ellipticity ([θ] = +5300) than Δ4-isomeric compounds or 5α- and 5β-saturated 11-keto steroids.[78]

The inversion of the configuration at C-9 in an 11-keto derivative is also accompanied by a substantial increase in the positive Cotton effect, provided that no drastic change of conformation occurs in ring C.[9] Such a situation is encountered in the conversion of the 9α–derivative (116a) ([θ] = +2160) to its 9β–epimer (116b) ([θ] = +3760).[112]

Another example is provided by the inversion of the 9αH–configuration (117a) ([θ] = +8950) into the 9β–stereochemistry (117b) ([θ] = +50230) in a ring A aromatic steroid.[113] The change of stereochemistry at C–9 has been shown to be accompanied by a large increase in the positive Cotton effect in the 1–hydrogen series (117), while a less positive increment was observed during the inversion of configuration of the 9–hydrogen atom in the 1–methyl series (118a) ([θ] = +16240) into (118b) ([θ] = +26730).[94] This can be partly interpreted as reflecting the different conformations adopted by ring C in such compounds. In (117b) ring C keeps its chair form and ring A falls into a positive octant, enhancing considerably the Cotton effect. In (118b), however, in order to release strong interactions between the methyl group at C–1 and the 11–carbonyl, ring C adopts a boat conformation, hence reducing the positive contribution attributed to ring A.[94] However, these facts alone cannot be responsible for the very high molecular ellipticity exhibited by (117b). There is probably a new factor involved in the present case, namely, orbital overlap between the aromatic ring and the 11–carbonyl (see Sec. 9–7–C).

The A/B cis–diketo steroid (119)[85b] presents the 1β–methyl configuration.[85e] The rather intense positive Cotton effect exhibited by this substance seems to agree with the new assignment of configuration which has been proposed recently.[85e]

The above examples dealt with dicarbonyl-containing compounds. In such steroids the contribution of the 11-keto group can be obtained by mere subtraction of the Cotton effect attributed to the other keto-function of the molecule,

114

115

116a, 9αH
b, 9βH

117a, 9αH
b, 9βH

118a, 9αH
b, 9βH

119

provided that an absence of vicinal interactions can be assured (see Chap. 7). The same operation has been performed with success on other 11-keto steroids containing a carbonyl at different positions.[114]

In the light of the above observations, a strongly positive Cotton effect could be anticipated for the ketone (120) obtained from the triterpenic sapogenin bryogenin.[115] Indeed, this compound (120) presents both of the features that are known to increase the positive Cotton effect, i.e., a Δ^5-double bond and a 9β-configuration. Nevertheless, although the high molecular ellipticity exhibited by this triterpenic derivative (120) ($[\theta] = +19800$) is in agreement with its stereochemistry, a boat or twist conformation for ring C cannot be excluded a priori. In fact, if the molecule were to adopt such a conformation, the strong 10αH-14α-methyl interaction would be released. The same applies to gratiogenin (121), for which a strong positive Cotton effect ($[\theta] = +19140$) has been found.[111a,116]

Further insight into the conformation of ring C in these compounds might be gained from comparison of low-temperature circular dichroism measurements of these triterpenic keto-derivatives (120) and (121) with model compounds such as similar steroidal ketones.

While inversion of the configuration at C-9 and C-13 in the fusidic acid series ($8\alpha,9\beta,13\alpha,14\beta$) (vide infra), has been shown to increase considerably the negative Cotton effect, a **negative** Cotton effect has also been found to be associated with 11-keto 14β-steroids. This is attributed to an abnormal conformation of ring C in these compounds.[9,17,117]

A recently examined[118] D-homo 11-keto steroid also exhibited a weakly positive Cotton effect (a = +15), reminiscent of the molecular amplitude associated with a normal 11-keto steroid.

Some C-nor 11-keto steroids have become available.[80,119,120] The Cotton effect presented by compound (122) ($[\theta] = -5360$), for example, is in agreement with the suggestion made by Klyne[45,56] for hydrindanone systems and discussed in Section 3 of this chapter. Furthermore, it has been shown[120] that the circular dichroism of 11-keto C-nor steroids is independent on the configuration at C-5. A change of configuration at C-9, however, is expected to have a mild influence on the Cotton effect associated with such 11-keto chromophore.[120]

In the course of the synthesis of modified tetra- and pentacyclic triterpenes some seven-membered ring C ketonic derivatives have been obtained.[121] Although the circular dichroism curves of these compounds were measured, no definite conclusions could be drawn because of the conformational mobility inherent in such systems.

120   121   122

M. 15- and 17-Keto Steroids

The configuration at C-14 is known to play a direct role on the Cotton effect of a 15-keto steroid, since a 14α,15-ketone exhibits a positive dispersion curve and a 14β,15-ketone shows a negative curve.[6,117a,122] These Cotton effects are also in agreement with the suggestion of Klyne[45,56] for cis- and trans-hydrindanones. Recent circular dichroism measurements performed on 14α- and 14β-15-ketones[72,80] and on 15,20-diketo-pregnane derivatives[123] have confirmed these views.

Such differences observed in the Cotton effects of 15-keto steroids have allowed assignment of the correct stereochemistry at C-14 in compounds (123a) and (123b), obtained during a recent synthesis of 14β-hydroxyl cardenolides.[124] The 14α-derivative (123a) exhibited a strongly positive rotatory dispersion curve, which was the mirror image of the curve shown by its stereoisomer (123b).

In connection with 14-hydroxylated compounds it is worthwhile to mention that 14α-hydroxy 17-keto steroids exhibit a lower Cotton effect than their parent 14-unsubstituted compounds. Thus, while a normal 17-keto steroid such as 3β-hydroxy-5α-androstan-17-one (124) (see Figs. 2-6 and 2-8) shows a high optical rotatory dispersion molecular amplitude (a = +138)[125] and a pronounced circular dichroism molecular ellipticity ([θ] = +11440), the 14α-hydroxy androstane derivative (125)[126] presents a substantial decrease of the positive Cotton effect ([θ] = +5740). This property has also been found in derivatives of triterpenes such as (126) (a = +65).[109a,127] Such observations are unexpected, for the octant rule indicates[5,45] that the 14α-substituent is in a positive octant. A possible explanation could be that substitution at C-14 may induce a modification of ring D conformation in these compounds.

Conversely, however, as expected, removal of the 13β-methyl (which is in a negative octant) and substitution at C-14 considerably enhance the positive Cotton effect associated with the 17-keto group. This is clearly shown in compound (127), whose rotatory dispersion molecular amplitude (a = +240) is exceptionally high.[127] In conclusion, the intensity of the Cotton effect associated with the 17-keto chromophore can be used as a diagnosis of 14α-substitution in the triterpene and steroid series. Finally, worthy of mention also is the fact that 14β-17-keto steroids have been shown[127bis] to display a weak positive Cotton effect (a $\cong$ +45).

123a, 14 α H
   b, 14 β H

124

125

The 17a-keto D-homo steroids have been shown to exhibit a very weak Cotton effect.[50a] This observation was subsequently rationalized in terms of the octant rule.[5] It was pointed out that the apparent plain rotatory dispersion curve shown by the D-homo androstane derivative (128) (see Fig. 6-22), for example, resulted from the balance of contributions by the angular 13-methyl group (negative) and the many atoms in rings A, B, and C (positive).[9] More recent measurements, extended to other substituted and unsubstituted D-homo steroids, have confirmed this interpretation.[9,71,80,128] Moreover, as illustrated in Figure 6-22,[80] the weakly negative Cotton effect is much better observed by circular dichroism than by rotatory dispersion, where it is partially masked by the background curve. Finally, comparison of Figure 6-22 with Figures 4-4 and 4-7, showing the Cotton effect of 5α-cholestan-1-one, clearly indicates the relationship characterizing the stereochemical surrounding of the carbonyl chromophore in these compounds.

The Cotton effect associated with 17-keto D-homo steroids could also be interpreted in the light of the octant rule.[9,128]

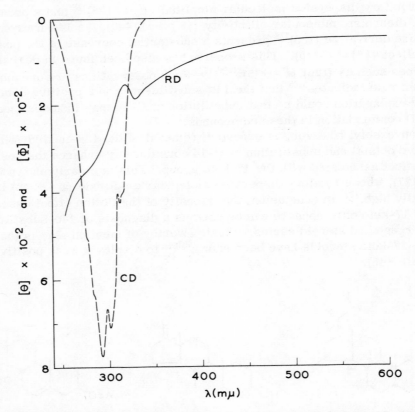

Fig. 6-22. RD and CD curves of 3β-hydroxy D-homo-5α-androstan-17a-one (128) (adapted from P. Witz, Ph.D. Thesis, University of Strasbourg, May 1964).

126   127   128

N. The Stereochemistry of Fusidic Acid

The structure and stereochemistry of fusidic acid (129)[129,130] and its related companions helvolic acid[131] and cephalosporin P$_1$[132] have for long constituted intriguing problems for the investigators interested in natural products
chemistry. The study of the stereochemistry of fusidic acid emphasizes the
caution which should be used in the interpretation of rotatory dispersion and,
more specifically in this case, circular dichroism data. Wrong conclusions
have been drawn from the circular dichroism curves[130] for three of the six
asymmetric centers whose configurations remained unknown after Godtfredsen's
investigation.[129b] This incorrect interpretation of the circular dichroism
curves seems to be due mainly to deductions drawn from the Cotton effect of
di- and triketonic derivatives. Apart from the fact that the additivity rule is
not always valid in such cases (see Chap. 7), it is unsafe to deduce the stereochemistry surrounding the various chromophores of a new polyketonic substance
without disposing of appropriate model compounds.

Now that the absolute stereochemistry of fusidic acid (129) is known,[129]
comments on some of the circular dichroism results may be warranted.

A 3-keto derivative of fusidic acid (129) was shown to have a positive
dichroism maximum ([θ] = +3960)[79,80] indicative of a trans-stereochemistry for
the A/B ring junction. It also showed position 4 to be devoid of the gem-
dimethyl group common to most triterpenes, since the circular dichroism was
positive and did not present the typical double-humped curve exhibited by most
4,4,8-trimethyl triterpenes (see Sec. 6-5J).

The 11-keto derivative (130) exhibits a negative Cotton effect ([θ] = -1320),
in agreement with the proposed stereochemistry, since in the adopted conformation ring A lies in a negative octant, and the positive contribution of the
8α-methyl is canceled by the negative contribution of carbon atoms 16 and 17.

Further insight into the stereochemistry at the B/C ring juncture of this
tetracyclic triterpene is gained from the dichroism curve of the des-A
derivative (131). This tricyclic ketone exhibits a positive Cotton effect ([θ] =
+2970). It can be attributed to carbon atoms 11, 12, 13, and 17, as well as to
the 11α-methoxy group falling into a positive octant and only partially compensated by the remote carbon atoms 15 and 16 in a negative octant. More
simply, the situation presented in (131) is reminiscent of that of a 2-keto-19-
nor-steroid, and thus the 10-methyl very probably has the equatorial β-
configuration in this compound (131).

129   130   131

Inversion of the configuration at position 9 and 13 considerably enhances the negative Cotton effect associated with the 11-keto chromophore. This is exemplified by the 11-keto diol (132) exhibiting a strongly negative dichroism maximum ($[\theta] = -12210$), in agreement with the octant projection. However, it is quite probable that in many derivatives of this triterpene (129), ring B (and perhaps even ring C) exists in a boat conformation in order to release the strong $6\beta H$-14β-methyl interactions which the all-chair form would present.

Finally, inversion of the $13\alpha H$ to the $13\beta H$-configuration of 17-keto derivatives of fusidic acid is always accompanied by a change in sign of the Cotton effect. Hence, while the keto diol (133a) exhibits a strong negative maximum ($[\theta] = -15180$), its 13β-isomer (133b) shows a positive Cotton effect ($[\theta] = +7430$). This result is also compatible with similar inversions observed in other series[80,133] and with Klyne's generalizations for hexahydrohydrindanones (vide supra).

Through recent examples from the chemical literature, this discussion has tried to demonstrate and emphasize the fundamental contribution that the octant rule has made to organic stereochemistry. Other applications of this rule to aliphatic carbonyl-containing compounds will be reported in Section 6-6.

132

133a, $13\alpha H$
b, $13\beta H$

6-6. ALIPHATIC CARBONYL COMPOUNDS

A. Carbonyl Group in Aliphatic Compounds

The carbonyl group is a strong optically active chromophore only if situated in close proximity to an asymmetric center. This has been shown by the first systematic study in the area, performed by Levene and Rothen,[134] who measured the rotatory dispersion curves of a series of aldehydes of the general formula (134), in which n = 0 to 3 and R = H.

Recently, Djerassi[6,135] repeated such measurements and also investigated a homologous series of methyl ketones (134; n = 0 to 4, R = CH_3). He emphasized[6] that free rotation of aliphatic carbonyl compounds often prevents one from making proper correlations between the observed Cotton effect and the exact conformation of the compound under investigation. Nevertheless, in a recent study on the Cotton effects and conformational equilibria in aliphatic aldehydes and ketones, Robinson[136] made an estimate of the relative stabilities and, therefore, populations of the conformations of (+)-2-methylbutanal (134; n = 0, R = H) and (−)-3-methylpentanal (134; n = 1, R = H). Generally, the rotational strengths of such aliphatic carbonyl compounds are considerably smaller than those of the corresponding cyclic analogues. Some generalizations deduced from the sign and the shape of the Cotton effect have, however, been made,[6,136] and such conclusions will be mentioned below.

The rotatory dispersion curves of aliphatic carbonyl compounds assume a progressively more plain character as the distance between the carbonyl chromophore and the asymmetric center is increased. Hence, when n is larger than 2 in the general formula (134), the dispersion curve is substantially plain within the experimental limits of the earlier spectropolarimeters.[135]

Furthermore, an inversion in sign of the Cotton effect is observed between a compound whose carbonyl chromophore is adjacent to the asymmetric center (134; n = 0, R = H, a ≅ +10) and its next higher homologue (134; n = 1, R = H, a ≅ −6).[135,136]

This observation has been used to establish the absolute configuration of the diterpene alcohol phytol (135) at position 7.[137] While S-2-methylbutanal[42] (134; n = 0, R = H), related to L-glyceraldehyde[138], exhibits a positive Cotton effect, its higher homologue (134; n = 1, R = H) shows a negative dispersion curve. Since the aldehyde (136a), obtained by degradation of phytol, exhibits a positive Cotton effect and its lower analogue (136b), a negative curve, it was concluded that carbon atom 7 of phytol (135) had the R configuration,[42] a conclusion confirmed by synthetic studies.[139]

Similarly, the absolute configuration of natural phylloquinone (vitamine K_1) (137) has recently been deduced from the rotatory dispersion curve of its derivative 6R,10R-6,10,14-trimethyl-2-pentadecanone.[140]

134

135

136 a, n = 1
   b, n = 0

137

Another example is provided by the antibiotic actidione (naramycin-A) (138), which has been degraded to (+)-4-methyl-6-oxoheptanoic acid (139).[141] Since this acid shows a positive Cotton effect and (+)-4-methyl hexanone-2 (140), which is of known absolute configuration, exhibits a negative rotatory dispersion curve, it was concluded that the two substances belong to enantiomeric series.[141]

Optically active keto derivatives of phenylalkylacetic,[142] α-phenylpropionic and α-phenylbutyric acids[143] have been prepared recently. It was shown that the absolute stereochemistry of such ketones could be deduced from their optical rotatory dispersion curves.

138

139

140

B. The 17β-Acetyl Side Chain in Tetracyclic Triterpenes and Steroids

Of particular interest are the 17-acetyl derivatives of tetracyclic triter-penes and steroids. The strongly positive Cotton effect usually associated with the 20-keto chromophore of a 17β-acetyl side chain is expressed in rotatory dispersion[6] by a large value of the molecular amplitude (a ≅ +190)[144] and in circular dichroism[78,145] by an intense molecular ellipticity ([θ] ≅ +11200).

However, substitution of the 17α-hydrogen atom of, say, 3β-hydroxy-5α-pregnan-20-one-acetate (141a) by bromine or chlorine results in an inversion of the Cotton effect.[23] Hence the 17α-bromo-derivative (141b) has a negative rotatory dispersion curve. Application of the octant rule (or the axial haloketone rule) to such compounds indicates that the preferred orientation of the 17β-acetyl side chain is as illustrated in formula (142). This conclusion has been extended to the 17αH-derivatives of structure type (141a).[23]

141a, R = H

b, R = Br

The stereochemistry of the acetyl side chain, represented in (142), has found some support from chemical reduction experiments,[146] dipole moment measurements,[147] conformational analysis,[148] and nuclear magnetic resonance studies.[149]

The absence of the 18-methyl grouping, such as in the triterpene derivative (143), obtained from dammarenediol,[150] permits free rotation around the 17-20 carbon-carbon bond, decreasing substantially the Cotton effect associated with the 20-keto chromophore. This is illustrated in Figure 6-23, where the rotatory dispersion and circular dichroism curves of ketones (143) are reported.[31,80] While the background rotations of the dispersion curve barely allows one to detect the weak Cotton effect, that effect is clearly shown by circular dichroism. Furthermore, by comparison of Figure 6-23 with Figure 6-24, which reproduces the rotatory dispersion and circular dichroism curves of 3α-acetyl-A-nor-5α-cholestane (144),[80] the antipodal relationship between these ketones (143) and (144) can easily be deduced.

142

143 a, R = H
   b, R = Ac

143 c

144

Introduction of a 12β-substituent in the dammarane molecule diminishes the free rotation of the 17β-acetyl side chain and enhances the Cotton effect. This is exemplified by the 12β-acetoxy derivative (145), obtained from betulafolienetriol,[151] whose molecular ellipticity ($[\theta]$ = -1820) is considerably higher than that of the methyl ketone (143b) ($[\theta]$ = -560).[80]

The above results indicate, first, that in the absence of the 18-methyl group, the nonbonded interactions are diminished and the possibility of free rotation augmented, with concomitant decrease of the Cotton effect. Second, the preferred conformation of the 17β-acetyl side chain is also different in such cases from the normal stereochemistry (142), since an inversion in sign of the Cotton effect is observed. Finally, circular dichroism is more appropriate than optical rotatory dispersion for examination of such weak Cotton effects. These

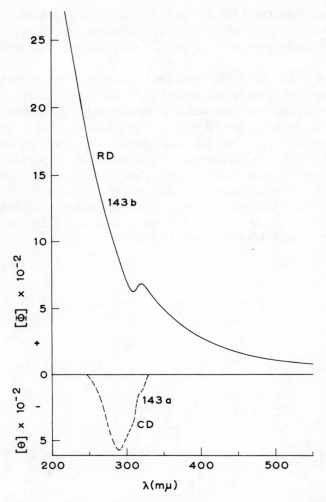

Fig. 6-23. RD curve of 3β-acetoxy-hexanordammar-20-one (143b) and CD curve of 3β-hydroxy-hexanordammar-20-one (143a) (modified from P. Witz, Ph.D. Thesis, University of Strasbourg, May 1964).

conclusions have recently been confirmed by Wellman and Djerassi,[152] who, because of the large negative Cotton effect exhibited by (143b) at low temperature, suggest the conformation represented in formula (143c) to be preponderant.

Several studies of the Cotton effect associated with 16-substituted 20-keto pregnanes have appeared recently.[123,144,152-156] It was concluded that introduction of an α-substituent at position 16 has very little or no influence on the Cotton effect associated with the 20-keto chromophore.[144,156] However, the situation is completely different in the 16,17-cis compounds (146-148). Most 16β-substituted 20-keto pregnanes show a substantial decrease in the positive Cotton effect of the 17β-acetyl side chain. Furthermore, while a 16β-carbomethoxy function, as in (146b), and a 16β-hydroxy grouping[144,154b] have little influence, some other

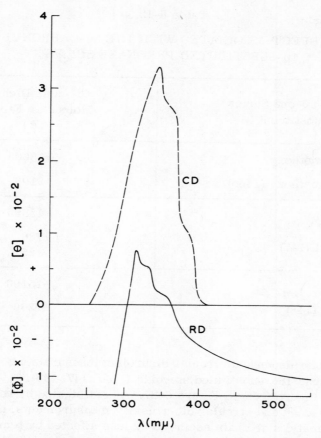

Fig. 6-24. RD and CD curves of 3α–acetyl–A–nor–5α–cholestane (144) (adapted from P. Witz, Ph.D. Thesis, University of Strasbourg, May 1964).

16β-substituents, such as 16β-carboxy (146a), 16β-methyl (147), and 16β-cyano (148), dramatically change the positive Cotton effect.[156] This is clearly shown in Table 6-13, which indicates that the 16β-methyl (147) and the 16β-cyano derivative (148) give the most profound modifications of the Cotton effect associated with the 17β-acetyl function.

Table 6–13

COTTON EFFECT ASSOCIATED WITH THE 20–CARBONYL IN THE
16–SUBSTITUTED PREGNANE SERIES

Pregnan–20–one Series 16–Substituent	Circular Dichroism Molecular Ellipticity $[\theta]$
16α–carbomethoxy	+13600
16β–carbomethoxy (146b)	+9100
16α–methyl	+15800
16β–methyl (147)	$\begin{cases} +726 \\ -825 \end{cases}$
16α–cyano	+15100
16β–cyano (148)	+7360

Temperature-dependent circular dichroism measurements have been performed on these 16β-substituted steroids (146b, 147, 148).[152] The results are reported in Figure 6-25 to Figure 6-27. As anticipated by room-temperature rotatory dispersion[153] and circular dichroism[156] measurements, the conformation of the 17β-acetyl side chain seems to be less affected by temperature changes in the 16β-carbomethoxy derivative (146b) than in the other 16,17-cis compounds, e.g., (147) and (148). This can be interpreted in terms of conformational mobility of the acetyl side chain, which seems to be more restricted in the ester (146b) than in the other examples (147) and (148) which were examined. Figures 6-26 and 6-27 indicate pronounced changes in the circular dichroism curves of (147) and (148) with temperature. This situation is reminiscent of the variations observed in the circular dichroism curves of (-)-menthone (4) with temperature (see Fig. 6-8). In the present cases, the double maxima (Fig. 6-26 and 6-27) are due to conformational changes.[152] The positive and negative maxima observed for (147) and (148) are attributed to two oppositely signed Cotton effects separated by 1-5 mμ and associated with conformations (142) and (149a), respectively, for the 17β-acetyl side chain. The fact that the molecular ellipticities of the positive and negative maxima of the double-humped curves shown in Figures 6-26 and 6-27 are very weak is also compatible with conformational changes.[152] The increase in the negative Cotton effect band at low temperature (see Figs. 6-26 and 6-27) indicates that conformers (149a, b) are the more stable ones. Conversely, the high-temperature curves show an augmentation of the Cotton effect due to the unstable rotamer,

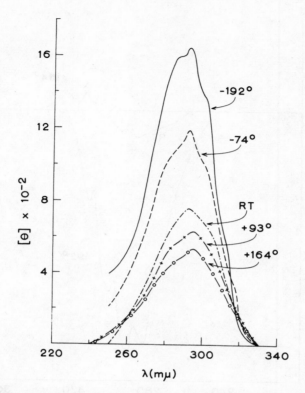

Fig. 6-25. CD curves of 3β-hydroxy-16β-carbomethoxy-pregn-5-en-20-one (146b) at various temperatures (courtesy of Professor C. Djerassi, Stanford University).

so that the positive Cotton effect completely dominates the spectra (see Figs. 6-26 and 6-27).[152]

  This conclusion is correct only if a change of the conformation of ring D[44] did not occur in these compounds, a possibility which cannot be rejected a priori. Moreover, also worthy of mention is the fact that, at room temperature, the circular dichroism curves of the cis-compounds (147) and (148) are not superimposable but are of mirror image type, probably indicative of a different proportion of conformers (142) and (149) in these compounds.

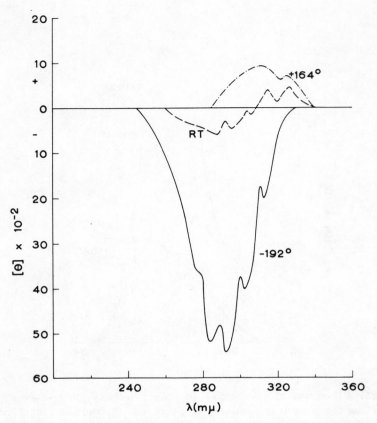

Fig. 6-26. Temperature-dependent CD curves of 3β-hydroxy-16β-methyl-pregn-5-en-20-one-acetate (147) (from K. M. Wellman and C. Djerassi, <u>J. Am. Chem. Soc.</u>, **87**, 60 (1965).

Finally, inversion of the configuration at C-14 also leads to a marked decrease in the positive Cotton effect associated with the 17β-acetyl side chain in steroids.[6,117 b,158] The much lower rotatory dispersion molecular amplitude exhibited by the 14βH-17β-acetyl steroids (a ≅ +60), compared with the normal value (a ≅ +190), may serve as an indication of the abnormal configuration (14βH) at this center.

C. The 17α-Side Chain in Steroids

The 17α-acetyl side chain is known to exhibit a strong negative Cotton effect. This has been amply verified by rotatory dispersion (a ≅ -102),[6,144,153-157] and circular dichroism studies ([θ] ≅ -8100).[123,145,152,156]

A recent application of this observation is shown by the assignment of configuration of the 14-hydroxy and 17-acetyl side chain in the steroid aglycone digipurpurogenin or isoramanone (150).[158] Optical rotatory dispersion and

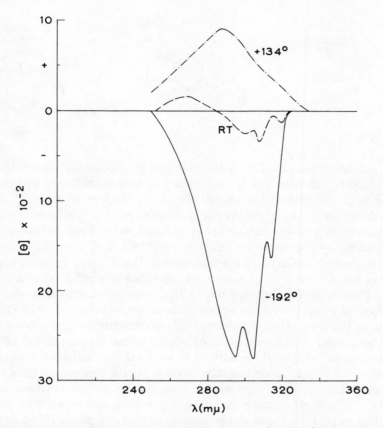

Fig. 6-27. Temperature-dependent CD curves of 3β-hydroxy-16β-cyano-pregn-5-en-20-one-acetate (148) (from K. M. Wellman, and C. Djerassi, <u>J. Am. Chem. Soc.</u>, **87**, 60 (1965).

circular dichroism measurements[158] indicated the 17-acetyl side chain to have the β-configuration, since this compound (150) exhibits a positive Cotton effect. However, the molecular amplitude of the dispersion curve (a = +55) and the molecular ellipticity of the circular dichroism curve ([θ] = +6370) seemed to indicate a 14β-configuration for the hydroxyl and/or hydrogen bonding, since this Cotton effect is substantially weaker than in a common 14α-17β-acetyl steroid (vide supra). The 14β-configuration of the tertiary hydroxyl group was confirmed when it was found that base treatment of (150) afforded isodigipurpurogenin (ramanone) (151), exhibiting a strong negative Cotton effect. Since the molecular amplitude of the dispersion curve (a = -89) and the molecular ellipticity (for the diacetate) ([θ] = -9000) of the isoderivative (151) are reminiscent of the value reported by Reichstein and his coworkers[159] for lineolone diacetate (152) (a = -112!), which has the 14β-hydroxy 17α-acetyl stereochemistry, the correct configuration could be assigned at C-14 and C-17 to the isocompound (151) and hence to the aglycone (150).

150   151   152

While introduction of a 16β-substituent in a 17α-acetyl steroid does not appreciably modify the negative Cotton effect, a 16α-substituent generally much enhances the negative molecular amplitude of the dispersion curve[153] and the molecular ellipticity of the circular dichroism curve.[156] This observation seems to indicate that such 16α-<u>cis</u> substitution induces some reorientation of the acetyl side chain, leading to an increased contribution of the ring system to the negative Cotton effect. Although the question of the 17α-acetyl side chain conformation has not yet been fully answered, the above results offer a reasonable conjecture. Thus a conformation such as that represented in formula (153a) would correspond in terms of the octant rule to the strong negative Cotton effect associated with the 20-carbonyl group in 16-unsubstituted (and perhaps 16β-substituted) steroids. In 16α-substituted steroids the conformation of the acetyl side chain seems to be slightly modified to give (153b), in which almost all of the ring system now falls into a negative octant. While this hypothesis is supported by recent observations,[152] further work is necessary before reliable conclusions can be drawn. Low-temperature circular dichroism measurements of 16-substituted 17α-acetyl steroids might also cast some light on this intriguing problem.

153 a   153 b

The ketone (155), obtained by Wagner-Meerwein rearrangement of the 16, 17α-epoxy-20-keto-pregnane (154), is known to present the 17α-acetyl configuration.[160] However, this substance exhibits a strong **positive** Cotton effect by rotatory dispersion. This seems to indicate that the conformation of the acetyl side chain is as represented in (156). While it is worth noting that in this compound (155) ring D is almost planar, much more important is the fact that (155) is a β,γ-unsaturated ketone, and the strong positive Cotton effect can be attributed to orbital overlap between the ethylenic bond and carbonyl function (see Chap. 9).

154   155   156

The subtle changes in conformation of the acetyl side chain observed in both 16,17-cis series emphasize the caution that should be taken before drawing any conclusion from the Cotton effect, since molecular models indicate that slight rotations of the acetyl side chain strongly modify the octant projection. Furthermore, no evidence is yet available about the conformation of ring D in such compounds. If the cyclopentane ring system does not maintain a "frozen" conformation but exists in an equilibrium of various conformers,[44,57] then conclusions from the Cotton effects will be even more difficult to draw.

Before further evidence is available, it may be suggested that when the observed Cotton effect of the 17-acetyl side chain is large, as in compounds (141) and (151), one rotamer predominates. Conversely, when the experimental Cotton effect is weak, as in the substituted steroids (147) and (148), the free rotation probably gives rise to a mixture of rotamers.

D. Acetyl and Aldehydo Groups in Terpenes and Steroids at Positions Other than C-17

The 4β-acetyl derivative (158) has been obtained by treatment of the corresponding acid with methyl lithium during a stereochemical study of isoagathic acid (157).[71] This compound (158) exhibits a weak positive Cotton effect (a = +25; [θ] = +1990),[161] which could serve as an indication of the stereochemistry of a 4β-carboxy group in the terpene series.

A brief mention was made in the previous subsection (see Fig. 6-24) of the weakly positive Cotton effect associated with the 3α-acetyl side chain of an A-nor cholestane derivative (144). More information on similar systems has been obtained recently in the terpene and steroid series. Table 6-14 summarizes these results.[80]

While the 3β-acetyl derivative (159) exhibits a strong positive Cotton effect, the circular dichroism curve of its 3α-isomer (160) shows a weak positive molecular ellipticity, indicating free rotation around the C-3/C-4 axis.

157   158

Table 6-14

COTTON EFFECT SHOWN BY AN ACETYL GROUPING SITUATED
IN THE STEROID MOLECULE AT POSITIONS DIFFERENT FROM C-17

Compound	Cotton Effect
159	$[\theta] = +4290$
160	$[\theta] = +360$
161	$[\theta] = -460$
162	$[\theta] = +590$
163	$a = +74$
164	$a = -69$
165	$[\theta] = +6400$
166	$[\theta] = -7720$
167	$[\theta] = +12700$
168	$[\theta] = +260$
169	$[\theta] = +4620$

Inversion of the stereochemistry at C-2 of the acetyl side chain of compound
(161) is accompanied by a change in the sign of the weak Cotton effect, as shown
by its isomer (162).[80] This situation is reminiscent of the Cotton effect exhibited
by the 16-acetyl side chain in compounds (163) and (164).[153] In these steroids the

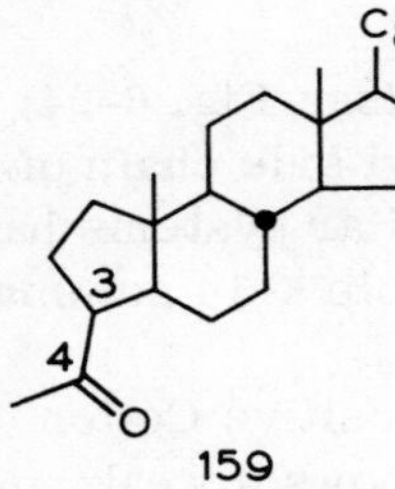

159 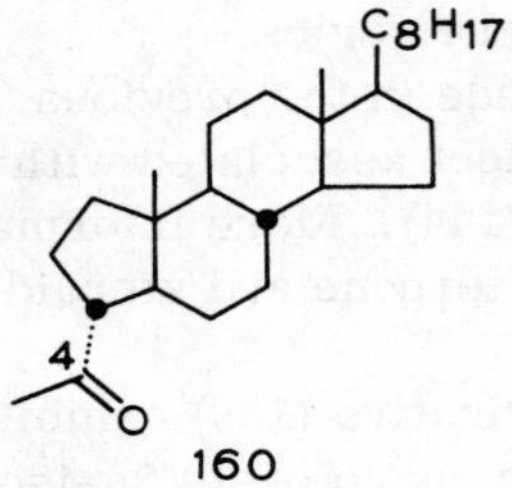   160 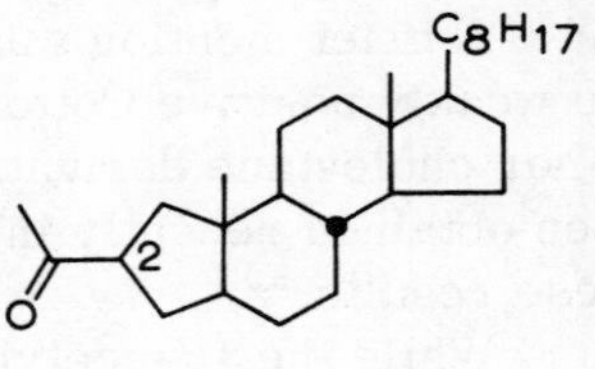   161

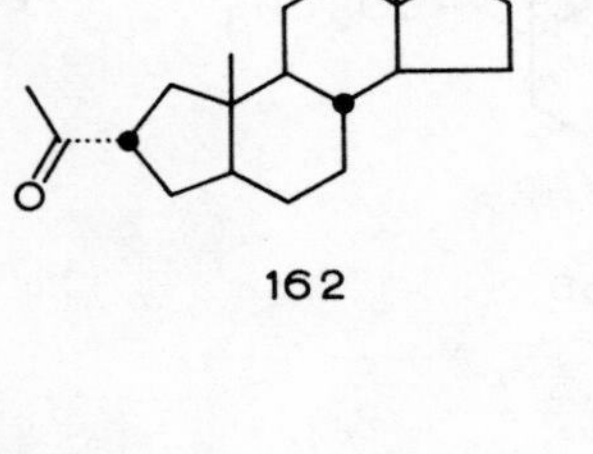

162 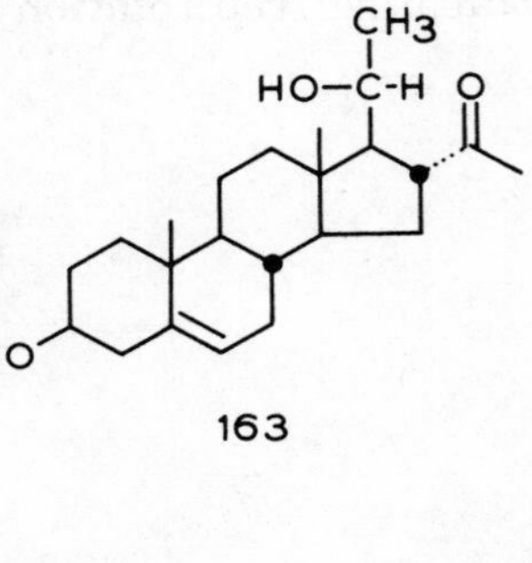   163 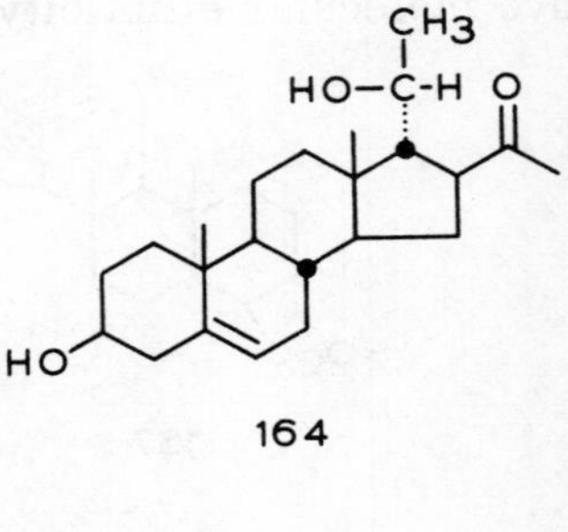   164

inversion of the configuration of the 16-acetyl side chain is also accompanied by an inversion of the Cotton effect. Furthermore, in the latter compounds, the 17-side chain somewhat inhibits free rotation of the 16-acetyl group, thus leading to a higher molecular amplitude of their dispersion curves. The same applies to the 3,3-dimethyl derivatives (165) and (166), obtained from the pentacyclic triterpene allobetulin.[162] Interestingly enough, a gem-dimethyl moiety at C-3 also inverts the Cotton effect associated with the 2-acetyl side chain. This inversion of the Cotton effect, is reminiscent of the situation encountered in 4,4-dimethyl steroids (see Chap. 4 and Sec. 6-5-J of this chapter). Introduction of a tertiary hydroxyl group on the carbon containing the acetyl side chain, as in (167), not only inverts the Cotton effect again, but also dramatically enhances its intensity, hence demonstrating the frozen stereochemistry adopted by the acetyl group. Finally, the very weak Cotton effect associated with the acetyl group in adiantone (168)[80,163] is reminiscent of the weak Cotton effect exhibited by the 20-carbonyl in methyl ketones (143a,b) obtained from dammarenediol. In these compounds (143a,b) and (168), the absence of a substituent on the adjacent angular carbon atom allows free rotation of the acetyl side chain. The free rotation is somewhat hindered in isoadiantone (169)[80,163] since the Cotton effect of the acetyl group, which is not inverted, is considerably enhanced.

Several groups have reported recently the synthesis of D-nor steroids.[164] Such compounds possessing an acetyl side chain at position 16 have been examined by circular dichroism.[164d] It was found that the Cotton effect associated with the 16-acetyl side chain has the same sign as in the normal 17-acetyl steroid derivatives. Thus D-nor-pregnenolone (170) exhibits strongly positive circular dichroism maximum ($[\theta] = +14850$), while its 17α-isomer (171) shows a negative Cotton effect ($[\theta] = -7590$). The keto-steroid (172), belonging to the 13-lumi-series, presents a strong negative maximum ($[\theta] = -13200$), which allowed the assignment of its 16α-stereochemistry.[164d]

165

166

167

168

169

170

The Cotton effect associated with an aldehyde group situated in an angular position of the steroid molecule has also been measured in some cases. Table 6–15 gives the sign of the experimental Cotton effect as well as the appropriate reference for each compound.

Table 6–15

COTTON EFFECT ASSOCIATED WITH AN ALDEHYDE FUNCTION SITUATED
IN ANGULAR POSITIONS OF THE STEROID NUCLEUS

Compound	Cotton Effect	Reference
173	Weak positive	117a
174	Weak negative	117a,165
175	Strong negative [†]	86b
176	Negative	81
177	Negative	81
178	Positive	117a

† The strong Cotton effect is due to the β, γ-unsaturated nature of the carbonyl chromophore (see Chap. 9).

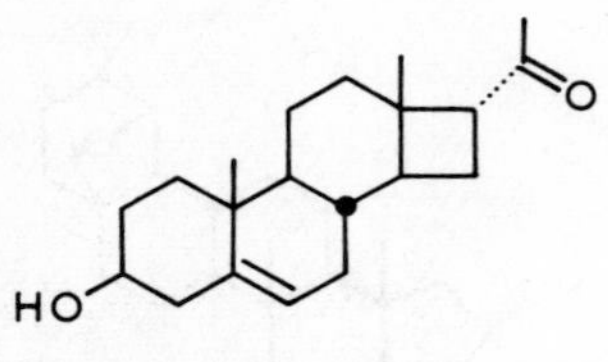

171 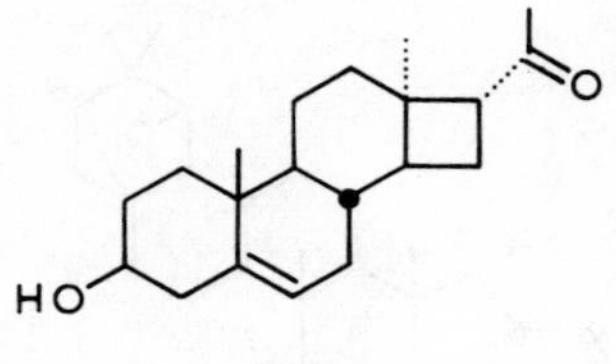   172 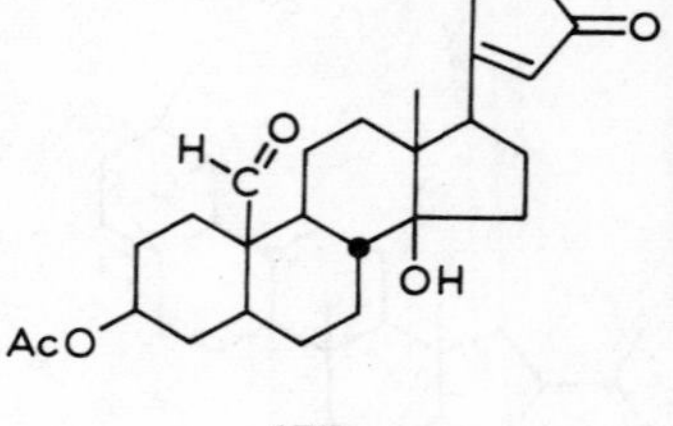   173

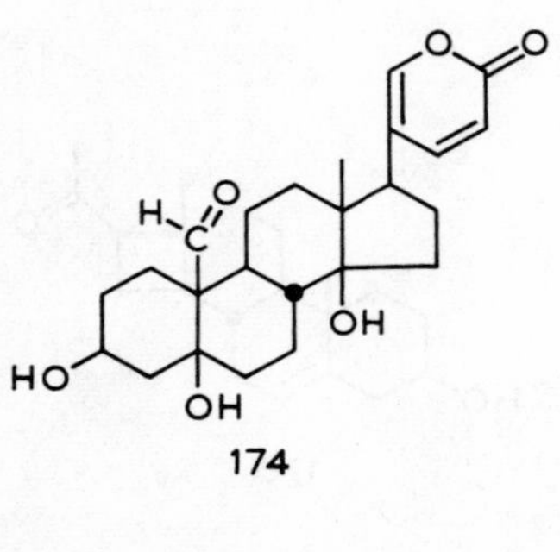

174 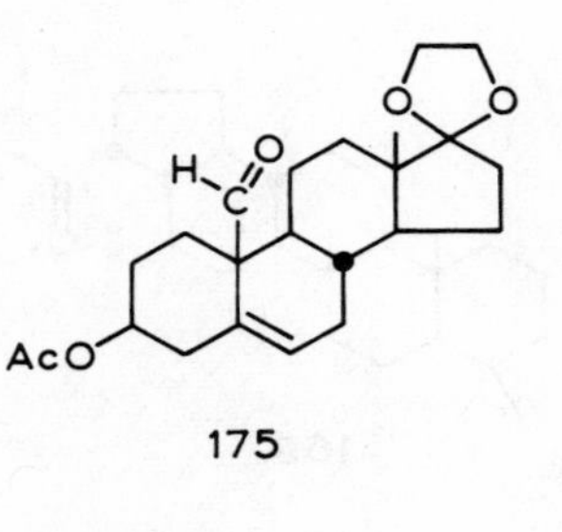   175 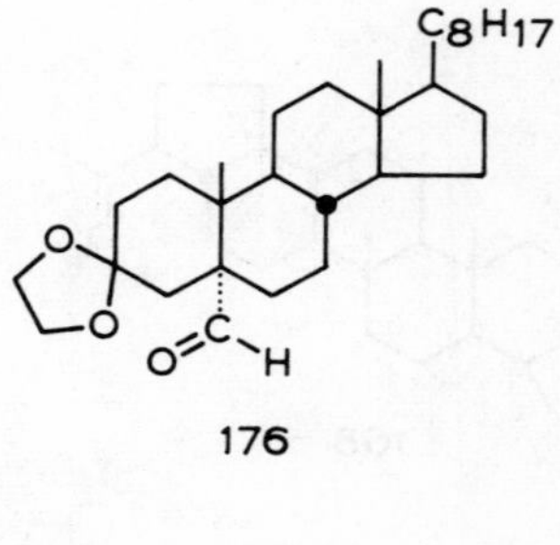   176

In a recent stereochemical study by Mazur and co-workers,[166] the configuration and rotameric conformation of a number of β, γ-unsaturated acetyl steroids were established by circular dichroism.

177   178

While the sign of the Cotton effect may be of considerable use in structural work, it should be emphasized that the molecular amplitude of the dispersion curve and the molecular ellipticity of the circular dichroism curve of such compounds should be interpreted with caution. Indeed, the nature of the carbonyl group as well as the nature and configuration of the other functions of the molecule, such as the 11β-hydroxyl group in (177), may lead to intramolecular interactions (e.g., chelation), thus modifying the intensity of the Cotton effect. It is the intent of the next chapter to draw the reader's attention to these interactions which may occur, changing the intensity and sometimes the sign of the rotatory dispersion and circular dichroism curves.

REFERENCES

1.   (a) A. E. Gillam and E. S. Stern, An Introduction to Electronic Absorption Spectroscopy in Organic Chemistry, E. Arnold, London 1958; (b) A. I. Scott, Interpretation of the Ultraviolet Spectra of Natural Products, Pergamon Press, London, 1963.

2.   (a) H. L. McMurry and R. S. Mulliken, Proc. Nat. Acad. Sci. U.S., 26, 312 (1940); (b) H. L. McMurry, J. Chem. Phys., 9, 231 (1951).

3.   A. Moscowitz, Tetrahedron, 13, 48 (1961).

4.   A. Moscowitz in Advances in Chemical Physics (I. Prigogine, ed.), vol. IV, p. 67, Interscience, New York, 1962.

5.   W. Moffitt, R. B. Woodward, A. Moscowitz, W. Klyne, and C. Djerassi, J. Am. Chem. Soc., 83, 4013 (1961).

6.   C. Djerassi, Optical Rotatory Dispersion: Applications to Organic Chemistry, McGraw-Hill, New York, 1960.

7. . W. Klyne in Advances in Organic Chemistry (R. A. Raphael, E. C. Taylor, and H. Wynberg, eds), vol VI, p. 239, Interscience, New York, 1960.

8. C. Djerassi and G. W. Krakower, J. Am. Chem. Soc., 81, 237 (1959).

9. C. Djerassi and W. Klyne, J. Chem. Soc., 4929 (1962) and 2390 (1963).

10. K. M. Wellman, E. Bunnenberg, and C. Djerassi, J. Am. Chem. Soc., 85, 1870 (1963).

11. J. M. Bijvoet, Endeavour, 14, 71 (1955).

12. E. J. Eisenbraun and S. M. McElvain, J. Am. Chem. Soc., 77, 3383 (1955), and references therein.

13. T. M. Lowry and R. E. Lishmund, J. Chem. Soc., 709 (1935).

14. C. Djerassi, Tetrahedron, 13, 13 (1961).

15. W. Klyne, Experientia, 12, 119 (1956).

16. C. Djerassi, P. A. Hart, and C. Beard, J. Am. Chem. Soc., 86, 85 (1964).

17. C. Djerassi and W. Klyne, Proc. Nat. Acad. Sci. U.S., 48, 1093 (1962).

18. C. Beard, C. Djerassi, J. Sicher, F. Šipoš, and M. Tichý, Tetrahedron, 19, 919 (1963).

19. C. Djerassi, P. A. Hart, and E. J. Warawa, J. Am. Chem. Soc., 86, 78 (1964).

20. G. Ohloff, J. Osiecki, and C. Djerassi, Chem. Ber., 95, 1400 (1962).

21. C. Djerassi and W. Klyne, J. Am. Chem. Soc., 79, 1506 (1957).

22. C. Djerassi, J. Osiecki, R. Riniker, and B. Riniker, J. Am. Chem. Soc., 80, 1216 (1958).

23. C. Djerassi, I. Fornaguera, and O. Mancera, J. Am. Chem. Soc., 81, 2383 (1959)

24. C. Djerassi, L. E. Geller, and E. J. Eisenbraun, J. Org. Chem., 25, 1 (1960).

25. N. L. Allinger, J. Allinger, L. E. Geller, and C. Djerassi, J. Org. Chem., 25, 6 (1960).

26. C. Djerassi, E. J. Warawa, R. E. Wolff, and E. J. Eisenbraun, J. Org. Chem., 25, 917 (1960).

27. C. Djerassi, N. Finch, R. C. Cookson, and C. W. Bird, J. Am. Chem. Soc., 82, 5488 (1960).

28. R. Villotti, H. J. Ringold, and C. Djerassi, J. Am. Chem. Soc., 82, 5693 (1960).

29. C. Djerassi and J. Staunton, J. Am. Chem. Soc., 83, 736 (1961).

30. (a) C. Djerassi and L. E. Geller, Tetrahedron, 3, 319 (1958); (b) A. Moscowitz, K. Wellman, and C. Djerassi, J. Am. Chem. Soc., 85, 3515 (1963); (c) ref. 35.

31. C. Djerassi, Proc. Chem. Soc., 314 (1964).

32. (a) K. M. Wellman, P. A. Laur, W. S. Briggs, A. Moscowitz, and C. Djerassi, J. Am. Chem. Soc., 87, 66 (1965); (b) K. M. Wellman, W. S. Briggs, and C. Djerassi, J. Am. Chem. Soc., 87, 73 (1965).

33. H. P. Gervais and A. Rassat, Bull. Soc. Chim. France, 743 (1961).

34. C. Coulombeau and A. Rassat, Bull. Soc. Chim. France, 2673 (1963).

35. A. Moscowitz, K. M. Wellman, and C. Djerassi, Proc. Nat. Acad. Sci. U.S., 50, 799 (1963).

36. P. Witz and G. Ourisson, Bull. Soc. Chim. France, 627 (1964).

37. J. C. Pariaud, Bull. Soc. Chim. France, 103 (1950).

38. L. J. Bellamy and R. L. Williams, Trans. Faraday Soc., 55, 14 (1959).

39. J. V. Hatton and R. E. Richards, Mol. Phys., 5, 153 (1962).

40. (a) J. Goré, Bull. Soc. Chim. France, Résumé des communications. p. 18, May 1964; (b) C. Faget, J. M. Conia, and E. Eschinazi, Comptes rendus, 258, 600 (1964); (c) J. Goré, Ph.D. Thesis, University of Caen, July 1964; (d) J. M. Conia and J. Goré, Bull. Soc. Chim. France, 1968 (1964).

41. A. J. Birch, Ann. Reports on Progr. Chem. (Chem. Soc. London), 47, 191 (1950), and references therein.

42. R. S. Cahn, C. K. Ingold, and V. Prelog, Experientia, 12, 81 (1956).

43. (a) C. Ouannès, C. Ouannès, and J. Jacques, Comptes rendus, 257, 2118 (1963); (b) C. Ouannès, D. Varech, and J. Jacques, Abstracts of Papers, International Symposium on the Chemistry of Natural Products, p. 243, Kyoto, April 1964; (c) C. Ouannès, Ph.D. Thesis, University of Paris, June 1964.

44. (a) F. V. Brutcher, T. Roberts, S. J. Barr, and N. Pearson, J. Am. Chem. Soc., 81, 4915 (1959); (b) F. V. Brutcher and W. Bauer, J. Am. Chem. Soc., 84, 2233, 2236 (1962).

45. (a) W. Klyne, Tetrahedron, 13, 29 (1961); (b) W. Klyne, Bull. Soc. Chim. France, 1396 (1960).

46. C. C. Costain and B. P. Stoicheff, J. Chem. Phys., 30, 777 (1959).

47. L. C. Krisher and E. B. Wilson, Jr., J. Chem. Phys., 31, 882 (1959).

48.   E. J. Corey, see footnote 10 in ref. 5.

49.   See also J. D. Swalen and C. C. Costain, J. Chem. Phys., 31, 1562 (1959).

50.   (a) C. Djerassi, R. Riniker, and B. Riniker, J. Am. Chem. Soc., 78, 6362 (1956);
      (b) C. Djerassi and D. Marshall, J. Am. Chem. Soc., 80, 3986 (1958); (c)
      C. Djerassi, J. Burakevich, J. W. Chamberlin, D. Elad, T. Toda, and G. Stork,
      J. Am. Chem. Soc., 86, 465 (1964).

51.   (a) W. Klyne, Experientia, 20, 349 (1964); (b) W. Klyne and W. Robertson,
      Experientia, 18, 413 (1962); (c) A. K. Bose, Tetrahedron Letters, No. 14, 461
      (1961).

52.   J. S. Birtwistle, D. E. Case, P. C. Dutta, T. G. Halsall, G. Mathews, H. D. Sabel,
      and V. Thaller, Proc. Chem. Soc., 329 (1962).

53.   J. M. Robertson, Proc. Chem. Soc., 229 (1963).

54.   D. E. Case, T. G. Halsall, and A. W. Oxford, Abstracts of Papers, International
      Symposium on the Chemistry of Natural Products, p. 54, Kyoto, April 1964.

55.   C. Djerassi, R. Mauli, and L. H. Zalkow, J. Am. Chem. Soc., 81, 3424 (1959).

56.   P. M. Bourn and W. Klyne, J. Chem. Soc., 2044 (1960).

57.   (a) C. G. Le Fèvre and R. J. W. Le Fèvre, J. Chem. Soc., 3549 (1956); (b)
      K. S. Pitzer and W. E. Donath, J. Am. Chem. Soc., 81, 3213 (1959); (c) C. W.
      Shoppee, R. H. Jenkins, and G. H. R. Summers, J. Chem. Soc., 3048 (1958);
      (d) J. Fishman and C. Djerassi, Experientia, 16, 138 (1960).

58.   C. Djerassi and J. E. Gurst, J. Am. Chem. Soc., 86, 1755 (1964).

59.   S. F. Mason, K. Schofield, and R. J. Wells, Proc. Chem. Soc., 337 (1963).

60.   (a) T. Nozoe and S. Ita, in Progress in the Chemistry of Organic Natural
      Products (L. Zechmeister, ed.), vol. XIX, p. 32, Springer, Vienna; 1961, (b)
      J. B. Hendrickson, Tetrahedron, 19, 1387 (1963); (c) P. de Mayo, Mono- and
      Sesquiterpenoids (K. W. Bentley, ed.), Interscience, New York, 1959.

61.   C. Djerassi, J. Osiecki, and W. Herz, J. Org. Chem., 22, 1361 (1957).

62.   (a) A. Romo de Vivar and J. Romo, J. Am. Chem. Soc., 82, 2326 (1961);
      (b) W. Herz, W. A. Rohde, K. Rabindran, P. Jayaraman, and N. Viswanathan,
      J. Am. Chem. Soc., 84, 3857 (1962); (c) W. Herz, A. Romo de Vivar, J. Romo,
      and N. Viswanathan, J. Am. Chem. Soc., 85, 19 (1963), and references therein;
      (d) F. Sánchez-Viesca and J. Romo, Tetrahedron, 19, 1285 (1963); (e) W. Herz,
      A. Romo de Vivar, J. Romo, and N. Viswanathan, Tetrahedron, 19, 1359 (1963);
      (f) E. Domínguez and J. Romo, Tetrahedron, 19, 1415 (1963); (g) J. Romo, A. Romo
      de Vivar, and W. Herz, Tetrahedron, 19, 2317 (1963); (h) J. Romo, P. Joseph-
      Nathan, and F. Díaz, Chem. and Ind., 1839 (1963); (i) J. Romo, P. Joseph-Nathan,
      and F. Díaz, Tetrahedron, 20, 79 (1964); (j) W. Herz, Y. Kishida, and
      M. V. Lakshmikantham, Tetrahedron, 20, 979 (1964), and references therein.

63. D. H. R. Barton, J. E. D. Levisalles, and J. T. Pinhey, J. Chem. Soc., 3472 (1962).

64. W. Acklin and V. Prelog, Helv. Chim. Acta, 42, 1239 (1959).

65. C. Djerassi and W. Klyne, Chem. and Ind., 988 (1956).

66. J. W. Cornforth and R. Robinson, J. Chem. Soc., 1855 (1949).

67. (a) J. Castells, E. R. H. Jones, G. D. Meakins, and R. W. J. Williams, J. Chem. Soc., 1159 (1959); (b) J. Castells, G. A. Fletcher, E. R. H. Jones, G. D. Meakins, and R. Swindells, J. Chem. Soc., 2627 (1960); (c) J. Castells, G. A. Fletcher, E. R. H. Jones, G. D. Meakins, and R. Swindells, J. Chem. Soc., 2785 (1960); (d) P. A. Mayor and G. D. Meakins, J. Chem. Soc., 2792 (1960); (e) P. A. Mayor and G. D. Meakins, J. Chem. Soc., 2800 (1960).

68. M. Legrand and R. Viennet, Bull. Soc. Chim. France, 713 (1964).

69. L. Velluz, G. Nominé, and J. Mathieu, Angew. Chem., 72, 725 (1960).

70. R. H. Bible and R. R. Burtner, J. Org. Chem., 26, 1174 (1961).

71. S. Bory, M. Fétizon, and P. Laszlo, Bull. Soc. Chim. France, 2310 (1963).

72. K. M. Wellman, R. Records, E. Bunnenberg, and C. Djerassi, J. Am. Chem. Soc., 86, 492 (1964).

73. (a) C. Djerassi, M. Cais, and L. A. Mitscher, J. Am. Chem. Soc., 80, 247 (1958), J. Am. Chem. Soc., 81, 2386 (1959); (b) R. A. Finnegan and C. Djerassi, J. Am. Chem. Soc., 82, 4342 (1960).

74. (a) A. I. Scott, G. A. Sim, G. Ferguson, D. W. Young, and F. McCapra, J. Am. Chem. Soc., 84, 3197 (1962); (b) A. I. Scott, F. McCapra, F. Comer, S. A. Sutherland, D. W. Young, G. A. Sim, and G. Ferguson, Tetrahedron, 20, 1339 (1964),

75. P. K. Grant and R. Hodges, Tetrahedron, 8, 261 (1960).

76. Inter alia: (a) G. Stork and H. Newman, J. Am. Chem. Soc., 81, 5518 (1959); (b) B. E. Cross, J. F. Grove, P. McCloskey, and T. P. C. Mulholland, Chem. and Ind., 1345 (1959); (c) B. E. Cross, J. Chem. Soc., 3022 (1960); (d) D. C. Aldridge, J. F. Grove, R. N. Speake, B. K. Tidd, and W. Klyne, J. Chem. Soc., 143, (1963); (e) P. M. Bourn, J. F. Grove, T. P. C. Mulholland, B. K. Tidd, and W. Klyne, J. Chem. Soc., 154 (1963), and related papers.

77. (a) C. Djerassi, J. Osiecki, and W. Closson, J. Am. Chem. Soc., 81, 4587 (1959); (b) C. Djerassi, H. Wolf, and E. Bunnenberg, J. Am. Chem. Soc., 85, 324 (1963); (c) R. Hanna, J. Levisalles, and G. Ourisson, Bull. Soc. Chim. France, 1938 (1960); (d) See also ref. 31 and references cited therein; (e) A. Lablache-Combier, J. Levisalles, J. P. Pete, and H. Rudler, Bull. Soc. Chim. France, 1689 (1963); (f) A. Lablache-Combier and J. Levisalles, Bull. Soc. Chim. France, 2236 (1964); B. Lacoume and J. Levisalles, Bull. Soc. Chim. France, 2245 (1964); and references therein.

78.   (a) L. Velluz and M. Legrand, Angew. Chem., 73, 603 (1961); (b) L. Velluz, Comptes rendus, 254, 969 (1962).

79.   P. Witz, H. Herrmann, J. M. Lehn, and G. Ourisson, Bull. Soc. Chim. France, 1101 (1963).

80.   P. Witz, Ph.D. Thesis, University of Strasbourg, May 1964.

81.   The rotatory dispersion curves of these compounds, prepared at the Shionogi Research Laboratory, Osaka, were obtained through the courtesy of Dr. Karu Kuriyama. See also W. Nagata, S. Hirai, H. Itazaki, and K. Takeda, J. Org. Chem., 26, 2413 (1961), Ann. Chem., 641, 184 (1961); Ann. Chem., 641, 196 (1961); S. Hirai, Chem. Pharm. Bull. Japan, 9, 854 (1961); and related papers in this series.

82.   Unpublished results from the Syntex Research Laboratories.

83.   (a) Private communication from Professor G. Ourisson, University of Strasbourg; (b) See also Table I in C. Beard, J. M. Wilson, H. Budzikiewicz, and C. Djerassi, J. Am. Chem. Soc., 86, 269 (1964).

84.   (a) K. L. Williamson and W. S. Johnson, J. Am. Chem. Soc., 83, 4623 (1961); (b) D. H. Williams and N. S. Bhacca, J. Am. Chem. Soc., 86, 2742 (1964).

85.   (a) H. Mori, Chem. Pharm. Bull. Japan, 10, 386 (1962); (b) W. J. Wechter, J. Org. Chem., 29, 163 (1964); (c) C. Djerassi and W. Klyne, Proc. Nat. Acad. Sci. U.S., 48, 1093 (1962); (d) C. Djerassi, E. Lund, and A. A. Akhrem, J. Am. Chem. Soc., 84, 1249 (1962); (e) H. Mori, Chem. Pharm. Bull. Japan, 12, 1224 (1964); for the stereochemistry of compound (119) see footnote 16, as well as: D. Bertin and J. Perronnet, Bull. Soc. Chim. France, 2782 (1964).

86.   (a) A. Bowers, R. Villotti, J. A. Edwards, E. Denot, and O. Halpern, J. Am. Chem. Soc., 84, 3204 (1962); (b) O. Halpern, R. Villotti, and A. Bowers, Chem. and Ind., 116 (1963); (c) B. Berkoz, E. Denot, and A. Bowers, Steroids, 1, 251 (1963); (d) O. Halpern, P. Crabbé, A. D. Cross, I. Delfín, L. Cervantes, and A. Bowers, Steroids, 4, 1 (1964); (e) K. Heusler, J. Kalvoda, C. Meystre, H. Ueberwasser, P. Wieland, G. Anner, and A. Wettstein, Experientia, 18, 464 (1962); (f) J. Kalvoda, K. Heusler, H. Ueberwasser, G. Anner, and A. Wettstein, Helv. Chim. Acta, 46, 1361 (1963); (g) J. J. Bonet, H. Wehrli, and K. Schaffner, Helv. Chim. Acta, 46, 1776 (1963); (h) D. Hauser, K. Heusler, J. Kalvoda, K. Schaffner, and O. Jeger, Helv. Chim. Acta, 47, 1961 (1964); (i) Unpublished results from Drs. R. Ginsig and A. D. Cross, Syntex Research Laboratories; (j) L. H. Knox, E. Velarde, and A. D. Cross, J. Am. Chem. Soc., 85, 2533 (1963).

87.   P. Crabbé, L. H. Knox, and A. D. Cross, in preparation.

88.   C. Djerassi and W. Closson, J. Am. Chem. Soc., 78, 3761 (1956).

89.   A. Dreiding, Helv. Chim. Acta, 42, 1339 (1959).

90.   These measurements were obtained through the courtesy of Professor C. Djerassi of Stanford University.

91.   J. A. Edwards, L. H. Knox, E. Velarde, H. Carpio, E. Blossey, A. Brambila, M. P. Nava, L. Cervantes, and P. Crabbé, in preparation; see also ref. 86h.

92.   J. C. Martin and J. J. Uebel, J. Am. Chem. Soc., 86, 2936 (1964).

93.   T. Kubota and M. Ehrenstein, J. Org. Chem., 29, 357 (1964).

94.   P. Crabbé, Tetrahedron, 20, 1211 (1964).

95.   (a) L. H. Zalkow and N. N. Girotra, J. Org. Chem., 29, 1299 (1964); (b) W. A. Ayer, C. E. McDonald, and G. G. Iverach, Tetrahedron Letters, No. 17, 1095 (1963); (c) L. H. Zalkow, N. N. Girotra, and P. Crabbé, J. Org. Chem., submitted for publication.

96.   N. A. Nelson and R. N. Schut, J. Am. Chem. Soc., 81, 6486 (1959).

97.   G. Snatzke, B. Zeeh, and E. Müller, Tetrahedron Letters, No. 22, 1425 (1963).

98.   Sample provided by Dr. R. Villotti of the Syntex Research Laboratories.

99.   Sample obtained from Dr. L. H. Knox of the Syntex Research Laboratories; see L. H. Knox, E. Velarde, and A. D. Cross, J. Am. Chem. Soc., in press.

100.   R. T. Rapala and E. Farkas, J. Org. Chem., 23, 1404 (1958).

101.   S. J. Halkes, Ph.D. Thesis, University of Leiden, February 1964.

102.   J. A. Edwards, H. Carpio, and A. D. Cross, Tetrahedron Letters, No. 45, 3299 (1964).

103.   (a) Y. Tanahashi, T. Takahashi, F. Patil, and G. Ourisson, Bull. Soc. Chim. France, 584 (1964); (b) F. Patil, G. Ourisson, Y. Tanahashi, and T. Takahashi, Bull. Soc. Chim. France, 1422 (1964).

104.   J. C. Bloch, P Crabbé, F. A. Kincl, G. Ourisson, J. Pérez, and J. A. Zderic, Bull. Soc. Chim. France, 559 (1961), and references therein.

105.   (a) J. C. Bloch, Ph.D. Thesis, University of Strasbourg, May 1964; (b) J. C. Block and G. Ourisson, Bull. Soc. Chim. France, 3011 and 3018 (1964).

106.   F. Sondheimer, Y. Klibansky, Y. M. Y. Haddad, G. H. R. Summers, and W. Klyne, J. Chem. Soc., 767 (1961).

107.   (a) C. Djerassi, N. Finch, and R. Mauli, J. Am. Chem. Soc., 81, 4997 (1959); (b) R. Mauli, H. J. Ringold, and C. Djerassi, J. Am. Chem. Soc., 82, 5494 (1960).

108.   (a) D. H. R. Barton, D. A. Lewis, and J. F. McGhie, J. Chem. Soc., 2907 (1957); (b) D. H. R. Barton, F. McCapra, P. J. May, and F. Thudium, J. Chem. Soc., 1297 (1960).

108.   bis. P. J. Flanagan, R. O. Dorchai, and J. B. Thomson, Steroids, 4. 575 (1964).

154   Saturated Carbonyl

109. (a) C. Djerassi, O. Halpern, V. Halpern, and B. Riniker, J. Am. Chem. Soc., 80, 400, (1958); (b) J. S. E. Holker and W. B. Whalley, Proc. Chem. Soc., 464 (1961); (c) M. J. T. Robinson and W. B. Whalley, Tetrahedron, 19, 2123 (1963); W. D. Cotterill and M. J. T. Robinson, Tetrahedron, 20, 765 and 777 (1964); (d) J. M. Lehn, J. Levisalles, and G. Ourisson, Bull. Soc. Chim. France, 1096 (1963), and references therein; see also refs. 77c and 79; (e) N. L. Allinger and M. A. DaRooge, J. Am. Chem. Soc., 84, 4561 (1962). (f) D. Lavie, E. Glotter, and Y. Shvo, Israel J. Chem., 1, 409 (1963), and references therein.

110. G. Snatzke and H. W. Fehlhaber, Tetrahedron, 20, 1243 (1964).

111. (a) G. Snatzke and D. Becher, Tetrahedron, 20, 1921 (1964). (b) R. E. Ballard, S. F. Mason, and G. W. Vane, Disc. Faraday Soc., 43 (1963).

112. A. D. Cross, H. Carpio, P. Crabbé, E. Denot, and J. A. Edwards, manuscript in preparation.

113. J. A. Edwards, P. Crabbé, and A. Bowers, J. Am. Chem. Soc., 85, 3313 (1963).

114. A. M. Giroud, A. Rassat, and Th. Rüll, Bull. Soc. Chim. France, 2563 (1963).

115. G. Biglino, J. M. Lehn, and G. Ourisson, Tetrahedron Letters, No. 24, 1651 (1963).

116. R. Tschesche, G. Biernoth, and G. Snatzke, Ann. Chem., 674, 196 (1964).

117. (a) C. Djerassi, O. Halpern, V. Halpern, O. Schindler, and C. Tamm, Helv. Chim. Acta, 41, 250 (1958); (b) J. S. Baran, J. Org. Chem., 29, 527 (1964).

118. Private communication from Dr. N. M. Jones and Professor W. Klyne, University of London.

119. (a) M. Rajić, T. Rüll, and G. Ourisson, Bull. Soc. Chim. France, 1213 (1961); (b) R. H. van den Bosch, M. S. de Winter, S. A. Szpilfogel, H. Herrmann, P. Witz, and G. Ourisson, Bull. Soc. Chim. France, 1090 (1963); (c) O. Jeger et al., footnote 25 of ref. 111a.

120. J. Winter, J. Rajić, and G. Ourisson, Bull. Soc. Chim. France, 1363 (1964).

121. G. Snatzke and A. Nisar, Ann. Chem., in press.

122. (a) C. Djerassi, W. Closson, and A. E. Lippman, J. Am. Chem. Soc., 78, 3163 (1956); (b) G. von Mutzenbecker and C. Djerassi, Proc. Chem. Soc., 377 (1963).

123. G. Snatzke, H. Pieper, and R. Tschesche, Tetrahedron, 20, 107 (1964).

124. C. R. Engel and G. Bach, Steroids, 3, 593 (1964).

125. See Table 4-1, p. 47, of ref. 6.

126. This compound was prepared by Dr. I. T. Harrison of the Syntex Research Laboratories; see A. F. St. André, H. B. MacPhillamy, J. A. Nelson, A. C. Shabica, and C. R. Scholtz, J. Am. Chem. Soc., 74, 5506 (1952).

127. G. Ourisson, P. Crabbé, and O. R. Rodig, Tetracyclic Triterpenes, Hermann, Paris, 1964.

127. bis. H. Mitsuhashi, T. Sato, T. Nomura, and I. Takemori, Chem. Pharm. Bull. Japan, 12, 981 (1964) and references therein.

128. (a) M. Uskoković, M. Gut, E. N. Trachtenberg, W. Klyne, and R. I. Dorfman, J. Am. Chem. Soc., 82, 4965 (1960); (b) L. Velluz, G. Amiard, R. Heymès, and B. Goffinet, Bull. Soc. Chim. France, 2166 (1961).

129. (a) D. Arigoni, W. von Daehne, W. O. Godtfredsen, A. Melera, and S. Vangedal, Experientia, 20, 344 (1964); (b) W. O. Godtfredsen and S. Vangedal, Tetrahedron, 18, 1029 (1962); (c) D. Arigoni, W. von Daehne, W. O. Godtfredsen, A. Marquet, and A. Melera, Experientia, 19, 521 (1963).

130. (a) R. Bucourt, M. Legrand, M. Vignau, J. Tessier, and V. Delaroff, Comptes rendus, 257, 2679 (1963); (b) R. Bucourt and M. Legrand, Comptes rendus, 258, 3491 (1964).

131. (a) S. Okuda, S. Iwasaki, Y. Nakayama, and K. Tsuda, Abstract of Papers, International Symposium on the Chemistry of Natural Products, p. 62, Kyoto, April 1964. (b) S. Okuda, S. Iwasaki, K. Tsuda, Y. Sano, T. Hata, S. Udagawa, Y. Nakayama, and H. Yamaguchi, Chem. Pharm. Bull. Japan, 12, 121 (1964); (c) N. L. Allinger and J. L. Coke, J. Org. Chem., 26, 4522 (1961), and references therein.

132. (a) T. G. Halsall, E. R. H. Jones, and G. Lowe, Proc. Chem. Soc., 16 (1963), and references cited therein; (b) A. Melera, Experientia, 19, 565 (1963).

133. (a) J. F. Biellmann, P. Crabbé, and G. Ourisson, Tetrahedron, 3, 303 (1958); (b) N. L. Allinger, R. B. Hermann, and C. Djerassi, J. Org. Chem., 25, 922 (1960); (c) C. Djerassi, J. Fishman, and T. Nambara, Experientia, 17, 565 (1961); (d) See also ref. 50a.

134. P. A. Levene and A. Rothen, J. Chem. Phys., 4, 48 (1936).

135. C. Djerassi and L. E. Geller, J. Am. Chem. Soc., 81, 2789 (1959).

136. M. J. T. Robinson, Chem. and Ind., 932 (1964).

137. P. Crabbé, C. Djerassi, E. J. Eisenbraun, and S. Liu, Proc. Chem. Soc., 264 (1959).

138. L. Crombie and S. H. Harper, J. Chem. Soc., 2685 (1950).

139. J. W. K. Burrel, L. M. Jackman, and B. C. L. Weedon, Proc. Chem. Soc., 263 (1959).

140.   H. Mayer, U. Gloor, O. Isler, R. Rüegg, and O. Wiss, Helv. Chim. Acta, 47, 221 (1964).

141.   (a) E. J. Eisenbraun, J. Osiecki, and C. Djerassi, J. Am. Chem. Soc., 80, 1261 (1958); (b) T. Okuda, Chem. Pharm. Bull. Japan, 7, 137 (1959); (c) M. Suzuki, Y. Egawa and T. Okuda, Chem. Pharm. Bull. Japan, 11, 582 (1963); (d) T. Okuda, M. Suzuki, T. Furumai and H. Takahashi, Chem. Pharm. Bull. Japan, 11, 730 (1963).

142.   K. Mislow and C. L. Hamermesh, J. Am. Chem. Soc., 77, 1590 (1955).

143.   B. Sjöberg, Arkiv Kemi, 15, 473 (1960).

144.   J. C. Danilewicz and W. Klyne, J. Chem. Soc., in press.

145.   G. Amiard, M. Legrand, J. Mathieu, R. Heymès, and T. van Thuong, Bull. Soc. Chim. France, 2417 (1961).

146.   W. Klyne, Ciba Foundation Colloquia on Endocrinology, 7, 127 (1953).

147.   N. L. Allinger and M. A. DaRooge, J. Am. Chem. Soc., 83, 4526 (1961).

148.   S. Rakhit and C. R. Engel, Can. J. Chem., 40, 2163 (1962).

149.   (a) A. D. Cross and P. Crabbé, J. Am. Chem. Soc., 86, 1221 (1964); (b) A. D. Cross and C. Beard, J. Am. Chem. Soc., 86, 5317 (1964); (c) L. L. Smith and D. M. Teller, J. Med. Chem., 7, 531 (1964).

150.   (a) L. van Itallie, Arch. Pharm., 250, 204 (1902); (b) J. S. Mills, J. Chem. Soc., 2196 (1956); (c) P. Crabbé, G. Ourisson, and T. Takahashi, Tetrahedron, 3, 279 (1958).

151.   F. G. Fischer and N. Seiler, Ann. Chem., 626, 185 (1959); Ann. Chem., 644, 146 (1961); Ann. Chem., 644, 162 (1961).

152.   K. M. Wellman and C. Djerassi, J. Am. Chem. Soc., 87, 60 (1965).

153.   P. Crabbé, Tetrahedron, 19, 51 (1963).

154.   (a) W. A. Struck and R. L. Houtman, J. Org. Chem., 26, 3883 (1961); (b) J. C. Danilewicz, Ph.D. Thesis, University of London, June 1963; (c) See also refs. 144 and 149.

155.   (a) J. C. Danilewicz, D. C. F. Garbutt, A. Horeau, and W. Klyne, J. Chem. Soc., 2254 (1964); (b) M. B. Rubin and E. C. Blossey, J. Org. Chem., 29, 1932 (1964).

156.   P. Crabbé, F. McCapra, F. Comer, and A. I. Scott, Tetrahedron, 20, 2455 (1964), and references cited therein.

157. (a) M. B. Rubin, Steroids, 2, 561 (1963); (b) P. Crabbé, M. Pérez, and G. Vera, Can. J. Chem., 41, 156 (1963); (c) P. Crabbé and J. Romo, Bull. Soc. Chim. Belg., 72, 208 (1963); (d) J. Romo, L. Rodríguez-Hahn, P. Joseph-Nathan, M. Martínez, and P. Crabbé, Bull. Soc. Chim. France, 1276 (1964).

158. (a) R. Tschesche, G. Brügmann, and G. Snatzke, Tetrahedron Letters, No. 9, 473 (1964); (b) H. Mitsuhashi and T. Nomura, Abstract of Papers, International Symposium on the Chemistry of Natural Products, p. 261, Kyoto, April 1964; (c) H. Mitsuhashi and T. Nomura, Steroids, 3, 271 (1964); (d) H. Mitsuhashi, T. Nomura, and M. Fukuoka, Steroids, 4, 483 (1964).

159. K. A. Jaeggi, E. Weiss, and T. Reichstein, Helv. Chim. Acta, 46, 694 (1963).

160. This compound was prepared by Dr. S. Kaufmann of the Syntex Research Laboratories; see K. Heusler and A. Wettstein, Chem. Ber., 87, 1301 (1954).

161. Private communication from Professor M. Fétizon, Faculté des Sciences, Orsay (France).

162. H. Schulze and K. Pieroh, Chem. Ber., 55, 2332 (1922).

163. G. Berti, F. Bottari, A. Marsili, J. M. Lehn, P. Witz, and G. Ourisson, Tetrahedron Letters, No. 20, 1283 (1963).

164. (a) J. L. Mateos and O. Chao, Bol. Inst. Quim. Univ. Nac. Auton. México, 13, 3 (1961); J. L. Mateos, O. Chao, and H. Flores, Tetrahedron, 19, 1051 (1963); J. L. Mateos and R. Pozas, Steroids, 2, 527 (1963); (b) M. P. Cava and E. Moroz, J. Am. Chem. Soc., 84, 115 (1962); (c) J. Meinwald, G. G. Curtis, and P. G. Gassman, J. Am. Chem. Soc., 84, 116 (1962); (d) G. Muller, C. Huynh, and J. Mathieu, Bull. Soc. Chim. France, 296 (1962).

165. H. Schröter, C. Tamm, and T. Reichstein, Helv. Chim. Acta, 41, 720 (1958).

166. M. Gorodetsky, D. Amar, and Y. Mazur, J. Am. Chem. Soc., 86, 5218 (1964).

7

Vicinal Effects in Saturated Ketones

7-1. INTRODUCTION

The object of this chapter is to call attention to secondary effects, which sometimes change either the intensity or even the sign of the Cotton effect associated with a saturated carbonyl chromophore[†] in an optically active molecule.

Effects of conformational transmission due to 1,3-nonbonded interactions on introduction of sp^2 carbon atoms into a ring adjacent to the carbonyl-containing one were mentioned in the previous chapter (Sec. 6-5). While α,β- and β,γ- unsaturated ketones will be examined in Chapter 9, attention will be focused here on the influence of halogen atoms and other functions on saturated keto-derivatives. Chelation and solvent-dependent hydrogen bonding will also be mentioned briefly. Furthermore, a suggested modification of the octant rule for α,β-epoxy and α,β-cyclopropyl ketones will be reported. Finally, polycarbonyl-containing molecules will be examined, since their Cotton effects do not necessarily correspond to the arithmetic sum of the isolated chromophores.

7-2. NEIGHBORING EFFECT OF HALOGEN ATOMS ON THE 3-KETO CHROMOPHORE IN STEROIDS

The axial haloketone rule,[1] stating the influence of a halogen atom situated in axial configuration next to a carbonyl group, constituted a forerunner of the octant rule.[2] In Chapter 6, several examples of the application of this rule were reported. In this section, mention will be made of the influence of a halogen atom situated in position β or γ relative to the keto group.

Levisalles[3] and Djerassi[4] and their collaborators have investigated a series of 5α-halo and $5\alpha,6$-dihalo 3-keto steroids. The main result of these investigations is the notable decrease observed in the molecular amplitude of such compound (Table 7-1). Only the fluoro-derivatives exhibit the expected Cotton effect, and this has been interpreted as being due to the position of fluorine in the atomic

---

[†] As in the previous chapters, "saturated" refers to molecules in which there is no double bond in the immediate vicinity of the carbonyl chromophore.

refractivity and specific rotativity scale.[4] The abnormally low rotatory dispersion molecular amplitudes exhibited by the other halo-derivatives have been attributed to a conformational change occurring in ring A.[4] This seems to result from repulsive interactions occurring through space and due to the inductive effects associated with the electronegativity of the halogen atom at C-5 and the 3-carbonyl group.

The same explanation might be the reason for the abnormal Cotton effect exhibited by the thio-acetate (69) (see Fig. 6-16) mentioned in the previous chapter. However, as will be reported in Chapter 11, it should be kept in mind that some thio-compounds exhibit a Cotton effect on their own, and it is quite possible that in the present case (69) the rotatory dispersion curve (Fig. 6-16) is the resultant of two Cotton effects (i.e., the 3-ketone and 5α-thio functions).

Table 7-1

COTTON EFFECT ASSOCIATED WITH THE 3-KETO CHROMOPHORE
IN 5α-HALO AND 5,6-DIHALO-STEROIDS

Substituents		Rotatory Dispersion Molecular Amplitude a
X	Y	
H	H	$+46^4$; $+65^3$
F	H	$+30^4$
Cl	H	$+12^4$; $+13^3$
Br	H	$+3^3$; $+6^4$
F	(α)F	$+16^4$
Cl	(α)Cl	-4^4
Cl	(β)Cl	-8^4
Br	(β)Br	-30^3; -33^4
F	(β)I	$-8!^4$
Br	(β)Cl	-15^4

7-3. NEIGHBORING EFFECTS ON THE 11-KETO AND 20-KETO CHROMOPHORES

The 11-carbonyl group has been recognized as a very sensitive chromophore. Its Cotton effect has been shown to be highly dependent on structural and configurational modifications. Mention has also been made of the inversion of the positive Cotton effect occurring at low temperatures.[5] This has been interpreted as probably resulting from change of conformation in ring C.

Recent circular dichroism measurements of 11-keto steroids bearing a nitrile grouping at C-20 have indicated an inversion of the Cotton effect occurring in cis compounds such as (1).[6] Figure 7-1 reproduces the circular dichroism curves of the 11-keto 20-cyano derivatives (1) and (2). In the cis configuration (1), a change of conformation seems to be induced in ring C because this compound exhibits a **negative** Cotton effect. While the exact reason for that change is not clear, low-temperature circular dichroism measurements of a pair of isomers, such as (1) and (2), might perhaps confirm that conformational mobility exists in ring C. In any event, the present situation is reminiscent of that encountered in 11,17-diketo steroids[7] (see Sec. 7-6), and thus the change of conformation could be due to electronic interactions occurring between the 11-carbonyl and the 20-cyano grouping.

The considerable variations observed in the Cotton effect of a 17β - and a 17α-acetyl side chain, as a consequence of substitution at C-16, have been discussed previously (Sec. 6-6). This has been confirmed by Smith and Teller[8] in a recent synthesis of some pregnane 16-thioacetates. These authors have observed dramatic changes in the Cotton effects associated with the 20-keto chromophore by mere variation of the configuration of the 16-substituent. Figure 7-2 shows the optical rotatory dispersion curves of compounds (3) and (4). The drastic decrease of the positive Cotton effect, observed in the $16,17\beta$ - cis-compound (4), is again observed, emphasizing the vicinal interactions occurring in such substances.

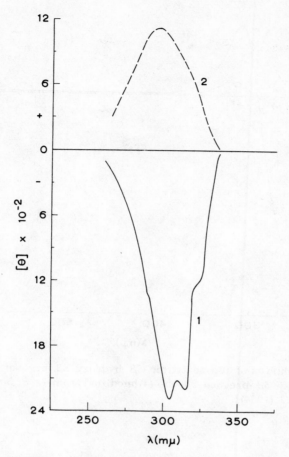

Fig. 7-1. CD curves of the geometrical isomers (1) and (2) [modified from D. Bertin and L. Nedelec, <u>Bull. Soc. Chim. France</u>, 406 (1963)].

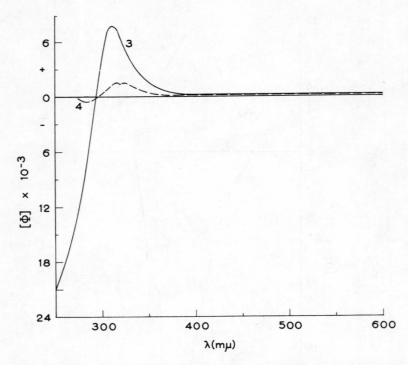

Fig. 7-2. RD curves of 16α-acetylthio-3β-hydroxy-5β-pregnan-20-one (3) and 16β-acetylthio-3β-hydroxy-5β-pregnan-20-one (4) [modified from L. L. Smith and D. M. Teller, J. Med. Chem., **7**, 531 (1964)].

7-4. HYDROGEN BONDING

The effect of axial and equatorial hydroxyl and acetoxyl substituents situated on the carbon atom adjacent to the carbonyl in a six-membered ring has already been commented upon by Djerassi.[9] The results obtained from the rotatory dispersion curves are in agreement with ultraviolet absorption spectroscopy and with the octant rule.[2] They may be summarized as follows. An **axial** hydroxyl group produces a bathochromic shift of 14 to 20 mμ, while an **equatorial** substituent induces a hypsochromic displacement. Again, an axial acetoxy group produces a bathochromic (about 10mμ), and an equatorial acetoxy function a hypsochromic shift (about 5mμ). This situation may, however, sometimes be complicated by hydrogen bonding occurring between the hydroxyl and carbonyl groupings. Some examples will now be mentioned.

The 20-keto chromophore, such as in 5α-pregnan-20-one (5), is very sensitive to the nature and configuration of the substituents situated in its vicinity. This was commented upon in Section 6-6. It was indicated that the important variations of the Cotton effect which are observed may be attributed to free or restricted rotation along the C-17-C-20 carbon-carbon axis.

In the 17β-acetyl derivatives, the Cotton effect associated with the 20-keto chromophore varies with the nature and the size of the 17α-substituent. This has been interpreted in terms of the octant rule,[2] which predicts that 17α-substituents fall into a negative octant if the conformation of the acetyl side chain is not modified.[9,1]   However, substantial changes were noted recently, when the rotatory dispersion curve of 17α-hydroxy-5α-pregnan-20-one (6) was obtained in different solvents.[11]   As indicated in Figure 7-3, the rotatory dispersion curve of (6), taken in a nonpolar solvent (hexane), where there exists an intramolecular hydrogen bond (chelate), shows a marked decrease of the Cotton effect, compared with the curve obtained in methanol,[11] where the molecular amplitude is normal. This result, confirming previous infrared observations, clearly emphasizes the important role of the solvent in the detection of hydrogen bonding.

Rotatory dispersion measurements of 16β-hydroxy-5α-pregnan-20-one (7), performed in methanol, did not allow detection of any Cotton effect, while a strong positive dispersion curve was observed in hexane solution (Fig. 7-3).[11,12] Since the positive Cotton effect of (7) (a = +134) in hexane solution is reminiscent of the molecular amplitude exhibited by its 16α-isomer (8) (a = +148) in the same solvent, one is forced to conclude that the plain curve (see Fig. 7-3), shown by (7) in methanol, is due to strong hydrogen-bonding.[11,12] The above results also

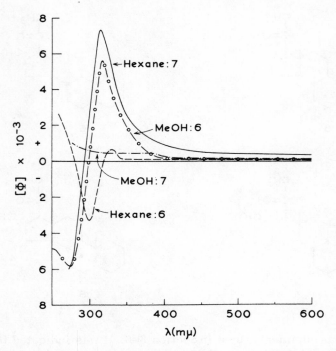

Fig. 7-3. RD curves of 17α–hydroxy-5α–pregnan-20-one (6) and of 16β –hydroxy-5α–pregnan-20-one (7) in hexane and methanol solution (adapted from J. C. Danilewicz, Ph.D. Thesis, University of London, July 1963).

indicate that the 16β –hydroxyl group, does not induce a marked change of the Cotton effect associated with the 17β –acetyl side chain, which is also true for the 16β –carbomethoxy function (see Sec. 6-6).

Also very characteristic are the changes observed in the rotatory dispersion curves of the 12-hydroxylated 20-keto pregnane derivatives (9) and (10), obtained in different solvents.[13] This is illustrated in Figure 7-4, which indicates that an inversion of the Cotton effect of the 12β –hydroxy derivative (10) occurs when passing from a polar solvent (methanol) to a nonpolar solvent (n-heptane). Also remarkable is the difference between the positive Cotton effect exhibited by the 12α–hydroxy 20-keto pregnane (9) in these two solvents.[13]

While hydrogen bonding can be detected by infrared,[14] ultraviolet,[15,16] and nuclear magnetic resonance spectroscopy,[17] optical rotatory dispersion and circular dichroism measurements not only provide structural, but may also give valuable conformational information (see also Chap. 6). Indeed, the Cotton effect associated with compound (6) in hexane solution (see Fig. 7-3), and (10) in

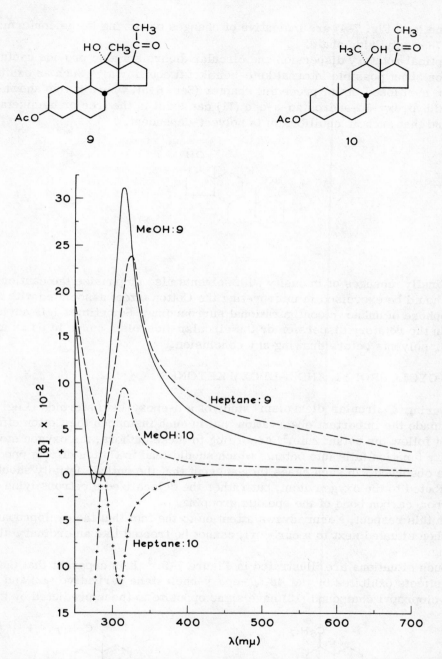

Fig. 7-4. Solvent-dependent RD curves of epimeric 12-hydroxy-12-methyl 20-keto-pregnane derivatives (9) and (10) (courtesy of Dr. K. Kuriyama, Shionogi Research Laboratory).

n-heptane (see Fig. 7-4) are indicative of changes occurring in the conformation of the 17β-acetyl side chain.

Optical rotatory dispersion and circular dichroism also provide useful information about possible internal keto-hemiketal equilibria.[18] Such an example has been mentioned in the preceding chapter (Sec. 6-5), where it was shown that 17β,19-dihydroxy-5α-androstan-3-one (11) can exist in the free or hemiketal form, and that such an equilibrium is solvent-dependent.[19]

11

Finally, changes of intensity with solvents also emphasize the caution which should be exercised in interpreting the Cotton effect associated with a new chromophore of unknown configurational surrounding. Sometimes it is advisable to obtain the rotatory dispersion or the circular dichroism curve in polar **and** nonpolar solvents before drawing any conclusion.

7-5. α-CYCLOPROPYL AND α-EPOXY KETONES

During a circular dichroism study of a α-epoxy-keto steroids, Legrand et al.[20] made the important observation that in such instances the Cotton effect does not follow the octant rule.[2] According to these authors, the oxygen atom of the epoxy function falls into octants which should lead to Cotton effects opposite to those observed. In such cases they suggest that the optical activity should not be attributed to the oxygen atom, but rather the delocalized electrons lying above the carbon-carbon bond of the epoxide grouping.

In this respect, Norin[21] draws attention to the fact that the cyclopropane ring, when situated next to a carbonyl, cannot be treated like an ordinary alkyl grouping.

Such situations are illustrated in Figure 7-5.[13] It is apparent that the Cotton effects exhibited by the 4β,5β-epoxy-cholestane derivative (12) and the 4,5α-cyclopropyl compound (13) have signs opposite to these predicted by the

12

13

octant rule.[2] Indeed, 4α-substituents should hardly affect the positive Cotton effect of a 3-keto 5α-steroid. Similarly, a 4β-substituent, in a 5β-3-keto steroid, presenting an equatorial configuration, should not modify sensibly the negative Cotton effect characterizing such stereochemistry (see Sec. 6-5). In Figure 7-5, the fine structure associated with the first extremum of the rotatory dispersion curve is also quite typical, and probably indicative of the conjugation occurring in these substances.

Recent theoretical and experimental studies suggest considering an "inverted" octant rule for α-cyclopropyl and α-epoxy ketones.[22] Moreover, worth noting also is the fact that in α-cyclopropyl and α-epoxy ketones such as

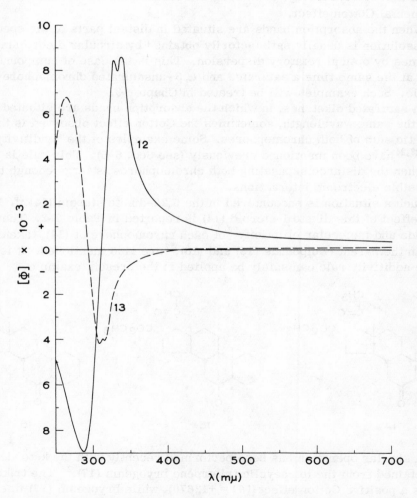

Fig. 7-5. RD curves of 4β,5β-epoxy-cholestan-3-one (12) and 4,5α-cyclopropyl-cholestan-3-one (13) (courtesy of Dr. K. Kuriyama, Shionogi Research Laboratory).

(12) and (13), molecular models indicate substantial conformational distortion to occur in ring A, and this factor might be partly responsible for the abnormal Cotton effects which are observed. Finally, when the cyclopropane ring is **adjacent** to the cyclohexanone system, as in the steroids (14) and (16), the Cotton effect associated with the carbonyl function does not seem to be affected.

7-6. POLYKETONIC COMPOUNDS

A. The Additivity Rule of Chromophores

One difficulty presented by the rotatory dispersion or circular dichroism curve of a new polycarbonyl containing molecule is the interpretation of the experimental Cotton effect.

When the absorption bands are situated in distant parts of the spectrum, their resolution is usually satisfactorily obtained by circular dichroism and sometimes by optical rotatory dispersion. This is the case of compounds presenting at the same time a saturated and α, β-unsaturated chromophore in their molecule. Such examples will be treated in Chapter 9.

In saturated diketones, in which the absorption bands are situated more or less at the same wavelength, sometimes the Cotton effect observed is the mere arithmetic sum of both chromophores. Some examples of the "additivity rule"[9,23,24] have been mentioned previously (see Sec. 6-5). This rule is applicable when the distance separating both chromophores is large enough to prevent any possible electronic interactions.

Such a situation is encountered in the 6,20-diketo steroid (14).[25] The Cotton effect of this diketo i-steroid (14) is reported in Table 7-2. The molecular amplitude and molecular ellipticity[26] of each chromophore of (14), taken separately in the parent compounds (15) and (16),[27] are also mentioned. It is apparent that the additivity rule can safely be applied in the present example.

14   15   16

A similar operation has been performed recently with the keto-derivative (18), obtained from the tetracyclic triterpene bryogenin (17).[28] The triketone (18) exhibits a positive Cotton effect ($[\theta]$ = +12670), while bryogenin (17) itself presents a stronger positive circular dichroism maximum ($[\theta]$ = +19140). The dichroic contribution of the 3-keto chromophore of (18) could then be deduced

<u>Table 7-2</u>

COTTON EFFECT OF KETONES (15) and (16)
AND THE DIKETO-STEROID (14)

Compound	Rotatory Dispersion Molecular Amplitude a	Circular Dichroism Molecular Ellipticity $[\theta]$
15	-126	-9700
16	-45 !	-3700 †
14	-113 !	-14530

† This value is obtained by applying Equation [18] of Chapter 2, and should be considered as approximation, since the exact value of the peak has not been observed in the dispersion curve.

17   18

($[\theta] \cong -6600$), and the sign and absolute value were shown to agree with the proposed structures.[28]

When both chromophores are not remotely situated one from the other, electronic interactions can occur, which makes the resulting Cotton effect substantially different from the calculated value. When the exact structure and stereochemistry of such diketo-compounds are known, the examination of their Cotton effect offers a precise means of determining the presence and amount of vicinal interactions. This is done by obtaining the Cotton effect of the two monoketones separately and comparing the calculated Cotton effect with the observed molecular amplitude or molecular ellipticity (see Table 7-2). Such an operation is of obvious theoretical interest.[29]

Conversely, when the structure or stereochemistry of the polyketone is not known, great caution should be exercised in the interpretation of the Cotton effect.

Some examples of vicinal action occurring between two absorbing functions will be mentioned in the next sections.

B. α-Diketones

The optical rotatory dispersion and circular dichroism curves of the α-diketo compound (19) are reproduced in Figure 7-6.[30] The dispersion curve of (19) is characterized by a moderate positive Cotton effect around 480 mμ. Its circular dichroism curve confirms this positive Cotton effect, but also shows a second weakly positive maximum, around 305 mμ, completely obliterated in the dispersion curve by the background rotation.

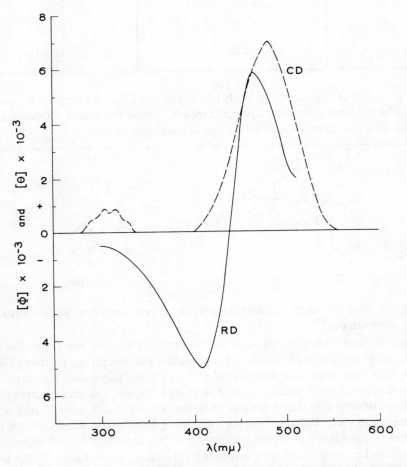

Fig. 7-6. RD and CD curves of 3,3-dimethyl-A-nor-5α-cholestane-1,2-dione (19) (modified from P. Witz, Ph.D. Thesis, University of Strasbourg, May 1964).

Introduction of a double bond at position 5,6, as in (20), leads to slightly different Cotton effect curves (see Fig. 7-7).[30] A bathochromic shift is observed in the rotatory dispersion and circular dichroism curves; moreover, a negative Cotton effect appears in the 320 mμ region (see Fig. 7-7).

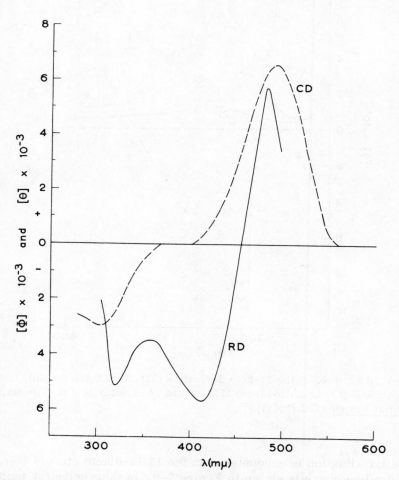

Fig. 7-7. RD and CD curves of 3,3–dimethyl–A–norcholest–5–ene–1,2–dione (20) (adapted from P. Witz, Ph.D. Thesis, University of Strasbourg, May 1964).

As expected, 11,12-diketo steroids present a chromophore which is completely new, and their Cotton effects have no relation to those of the corresponding mono-keto derivatives at C-11 and C-12.[31] This is due to enolization, and thus one is dealing here with a new chromophore, namely the 9(11)-en-11-hydroxy-12-ketone. Figure 7-8 reproduces the rotatory dispersion curves of the 11-keto (21), 12-keto (22), and 11,12-diketo (23) steroids.[31,32] The present situation [compound (23)] (see Fig. 7-8) is quite different from the above-mentioned α-diketones (19) and (20) (Figs. 7-6 and 7-7), which are **non**enolizable ketones.

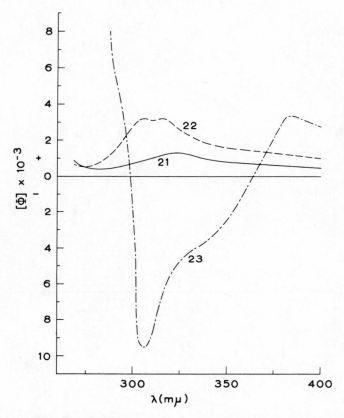

Fig. 7-8. RD curves of the 11-keto derivative (21), the 12-ketone (22), and the 11,12-diketo steroid (23) [modified from M. Legrand, A. Lacam, and R. Viennet, Bull. Soc. Chim. France, 792 (1961)].

A similar situation is encountered in the 11,12-diketo steroid (24), whose circular dichroism curve is shown in Figure 7-9. In this figure the multiple Cotton effect curves of the bridged α-diketones (25) and (26) are also reproduced.[30] These rather complicated circular dichroism curves illustrate the vicinal effects operating in such compounds.

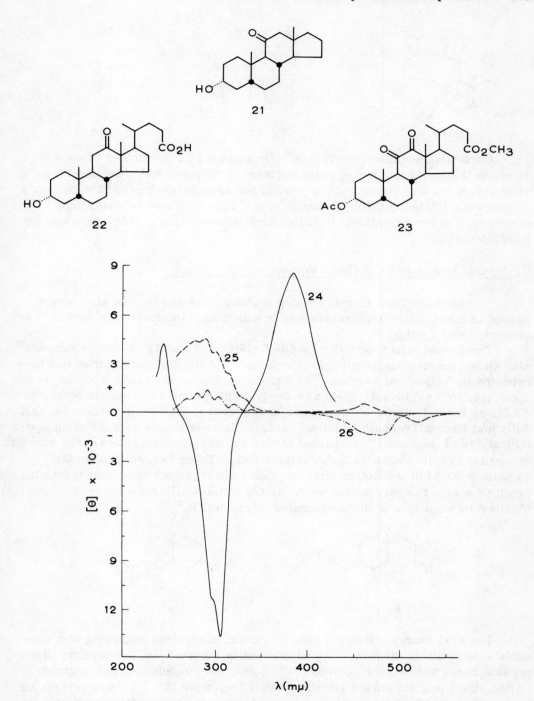

Fig. 7-9. CD curves of the nonenolizable α-diketo steroid (24), the α-diketo sesquiterpene (25), and the α-diketo monoterpene (26) (modified from P. Witz, Ph.D. Thesis, University of Strasbourg, May 1964).

24   25   26

Ourisson and his collaborators[30,33] examined a large number of such α-diketones in the monoterpene, sesquiterpene, triterpene, and steroid series. They concluded that circular dichroism is the appropriate method for the study of such complicated multiple Cotton effects. They also showed that slight structural and conformational modifications lead to considerable variations in the Cotton effect.

C. Vicinal Interactions in Other Polyketonic Compounds

The vicinal effect, characterizing α-diketo compounds, has also been observed in other polyketonic substances in which such interactions would not have been expected a priori.

The Cotton effect exhibited by 5β-2,11-diketo[34] and 11,17-diketo steroids[31] also show considerable electronic interactions. A similar observation has been reported by Velluz and Legrand,[35] who mentioned that the "additivity rule" is not applicable to 3,6-diketo,11,12-diketo, Δ^4-3,11-diketo and 11,17-diketo steroids. As far as the 3,6-diketo-chromophore is concerned, it is worth mentioning that Julia and Lavaux[36] recently obtained various diketo-steroids with different configurations of the methyl substituent at C-4 and at the ring junction. The circular dichroism results they obtained, summarized in Table 7-3, emphasize the variations noted in the Cotton effects. These observations have been used with profit to assign the correct stereochemistry to (-)-4β(H)-eudesman-3,6-dione (28), obtained by reduction of the unsaturated diketone (27).[37]

27   28

The next example shows a case of vicinal interaction occurring in a non-enolizable β-diketo steroid.[13] As illustrated in Figure 7-10, the rotatory dispersion curve of the diketo-compound (30) exhibits a much stronger **negative** Cotton effect than its parent 4-hydroxylated derivative (29). This is surprising, because 4-keto 5β-androstanes are known to show a **positive** Cotton effect.[9] Also quite characteristic of the rotatory dispersion curves of these compounds (see Fig. 7-10) is their fine structure and the difference in the wavelengths at which the extrema occur in (29) and (30).

Table 7-3

COTTON EFFECT EXHIBITED BY 3,6-DIKETO STEROIDS
PRESENTING VARIOUS CONFIGURATIONS

Compound	Circular Dichroism Molecular Ellipticity
5α-Cholestane-3,6-dione	$[\theta]_{320} = +150$ $[\theta]_{311} = -1240$ $[\theta]_{302} = -1310$ $[\theta]_{278} = +700$
4α-Methyl-5α-cholestane-3,6-dione	$[\theta]_{312} = -3750$ $[\theta]_{280} = +1530$
4β-Methyl-5α-cholestane-3,6-dione	$[\theta]_{317} = -720$ $[\theta]_{290} = -3420$
Coprostane-3,6-dione	$[\theta]_{307} = -21460$ $[\theta]_{298} = -21140$
4β-Methyl-coprostane-3,6-dione	$[\theta]_{309} = -23170$ $[\theta]_{299} = -23590$

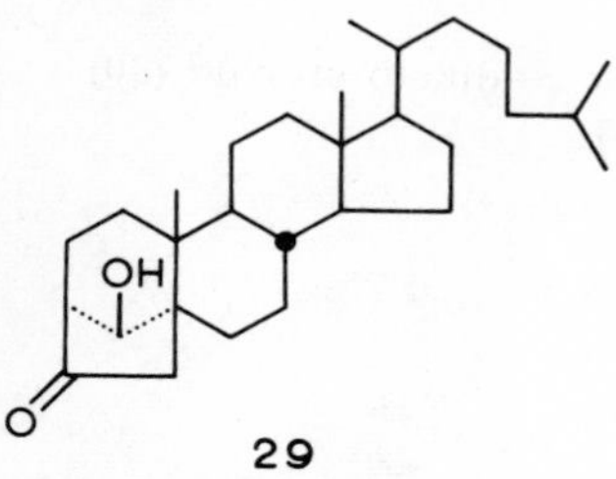

29 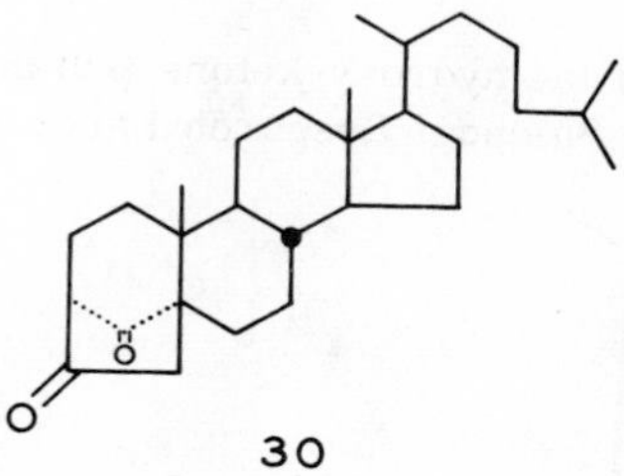   30 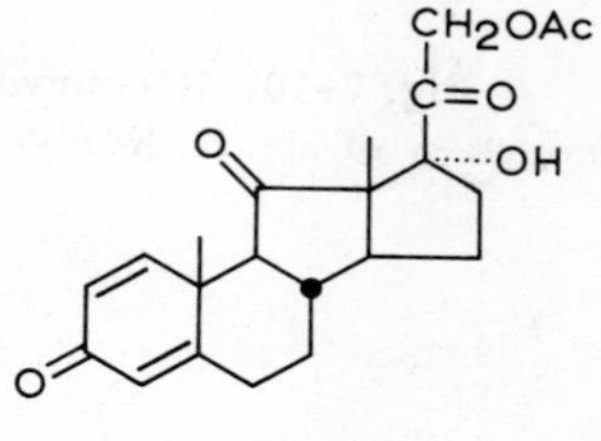   31

Furthermore, it has been shown that the dichroism curves of 3,11,17-triketo and Δ^4-3,11,17-triketo steroids are not the algebraic sum of the corresponding mono- and diketo compounds.[7] The same applies to 1β-methyl 19-nor 10αH-steroids.[38]

The circular dichroism curve of C-norprednisone acetate (31) has also been shown not to obey the additivity rule.[39]   Finally, Snatzke et al.[40] have shown that while 15,20-diketo steroids with normal stereochemistry show no vicinal effect, isomerization at C-14 and C-17 causes electronic interactions, leading to unexpected Cotton effects.

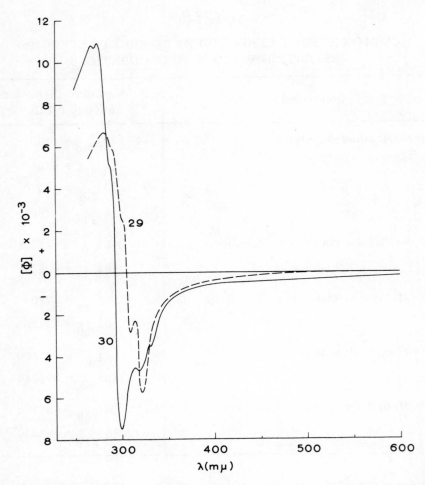

Fig. 7-10. RD curves of the hydroxy-ketone (29) and the β-diketo steroid (30) (courtesy of Dr. K. Kuriyama, Shionogi Research Laboratory).

REFERENCES

1. C. Djerassi and W. Klyne, J. Am. Chem. Soc., 79, 1506 (1957).

2. W. Moffitt, R. B. Woodward, A. Moscowitz, W. Klyne, and C. Djerassi, J. Am. Chem. Soc., 83, 4013 (1961).

3. J. C. Jacquesy and J. Levisalles, Chem. and Ind., 1310 (1961), Bull. Soc. Chim. France, 1866 (1962).

4. C. S. Barnes and C. Djerassi, Chem. and Ind., 177 (1962), J. Am. Chem. Soc., 84, 1962 (1962); See also: L. Pauling, The Nature of the Chemical Bond, 3rd. ed., Cornell University Press, Ithaca, N. Y., 1960, p. 260, for the physical properties of the fluorine atom.

5. (a) K. M. Wellman, R. Records, E. Bunnenberg, and C. Djerassi, J. Am. Chem. Soc., 86, 492 (1964); (b) R. E. Ballard, S. F. Mason, and G. W. Vane, Disc. Faraday Soc., 43 (1963); (c) G. Snatzke and D. Becher, Tetrahedron, 20, 1921 (1964).

6. D. Bertin and L. Nedelec, Bull. Soc. Chim. France, 406 (1963); see also L. Velluz, Comptes rendus, 254, 969 (1962).

7. A. M. Giroud, A. Rassat, and T. Rüll, Bull. Soc. Chim. France, 2563 (1963).

8. L. L. Smith and D. M. Teller, J. Med. Chem., 7, 531 (1964).

9. C. Djerassi, Optical Rotatory Dispersion: Applications to Organic Chemistry, McGraw-Hill, New York, 1960.

10. (a) C. Djerassi, I. Fornaguera, and O. Mancera, J. Am. Chem. Soc., 81, 2383 (1959); (b) K. M. Wellman and C. Djerassi, J. Am. Chem. Soc., in press.

11. J. C. Danilewicz, Ph.D. Thesis, University of London, July 1963.

12. J. C. Danilewicz and W. Klyne, J. Chem. Soc., in press.

13. These curves, obtained on compounds prepared at the Shionogi Research Laboratory, Osaka, are reproduced through the courtesy of Dr. Karu Kuriyama.

14. (a) L. J. Bellamy, The Infra-Red Spectra of Complex Molecules, Wiley, New York, 1958; (b) A. D. Cross, Introduction to Practical Infra-Red Spectroscopy, Butterworths, London, 1960.

15. A. E. Gillam and E. S. Stern, An Introduction to Electronic Absorption Spectroscopy in Organic Chemistry, E. Arnold, London, 1958.

16. For a relationship between ultraviolet spectra and optical rotatory dispersion, see E. C. Olson and C. D. Alway, Anal. Chem., 32, 370 (1960).

17.   L. M. Jackman, <u>Applications of Nuclear Magnetic Resonance Spectroscopy in Organic Chemistry</u>, Pergamon, London, 1959.

18.   Inter alia: (a) W. Nagata, S. Hirai, H. Itazaki, and K. Takeda, <u>J. Org. Chem.</u>, <u>26</u>, 2413 (1961); (b) S. Hirai, <u>Chem. Pharm. Bull. Japan</u>, <u>9</u>, 854 (1961), and other publications in this series; (c) T. Kubota and M. Ehrenstein, <u>J. Org. Chem.</u>, <u>29</u>, 342, 345, 351, and 357 (1964); (d) J. S. Baran, <u>J. Org. Chem.</u>, <u>29</u>, 527 (1964).

19.   P. Crabbé, L. H. Knox, and A. D. Cross, in preparation.

20.   M. Legrand, R. Viennet, and J. Caumartin, <u>Comptes Rendus</u>, <u>253</u>, 2378 (1961).

21.   T. Norin, <u>Acta Chem. Scand.</u>, <u>17</u>, 738 (1963).

22.   (a) C. Djerassi, W. Klyne, T. Norin, G. Ohloff, and E. Klein, <u>Tetrahedron</u>, <u>21</u>, 163 (1965); (b) K. Schaffner and G. Snatzke, <u>Helv. Chim. Acta,</u> in press; (c) For a discussion of the electronic distribution in the cyclopropane ring, see: M. S. Newman, <u>Steric Effects in Organic Chemistry,</u> Wiley, New York, 1956; W. Kauzmann, F. B. Clough, and I. Tobias, <u>Tetrahedron</u>, <u>13</u>, 57 (1961); M. Y. Lukina, <u>Russ. Chem. Rev.</u> (English transl.), 419 (1962).

23.   W. Klyne in <u>Advances in Organic Chemistry</u> (R. A. Raphael, E. C. Taylor, and H. Wynberg, eds.), Interscience, vol. 1, p. 239, New York, 1960.

24.   See also C. Djerassi, E. W. Foltz, and A. E. Lippman, <u>J. Am. Chem. Soc.</u>, <u>77</u>, 4354 (1955); C. Djerassi and W. Closson, <u>J. Am. Chem. Soc.</u>, <u>78</u>, 3761 (1956); see also ref. 31c.

25.   P. Crabbé, M. Pérez, and G. Vera, <u>Can. J. Chem.</u>, <u>41</u>, 156 (1963).

26.   P. Crabbé, F. McCapra, F. Comer, and A. I. Scott, <u>Tetrahedron</u>, <u>20</u>, 2455 (1964).

27.   A. E. Lippman, E. W. Foltz, and C. Djerassi, <u>J. Am. Chem. Soc.</u>, <u>77</u>, 4364 (1955).

28.   G. Biglino, J. M. Lehn, and G. Ourisson, <u>Tetrahedron Letters</u>, No. 24, 1651 (1963).

29.   W. Kuhn and K. Freudenberg, <u>Handbuch und Jahrbuch der chemischen Physik,</u> vol. 8, part 3, Akademische Verlagsgesellschaft, Leipzig, 1932.

30.   P. Witz, Ph.D. Thesis, University of Strasbourg, May 1964.

31.   (a) C. Djerassi and R. Ehrlich, <u>J. Am. Chem. Soc.</u>, <u>78</u>, 440 (1956); (b) C. Djerassi and W. Closson, <u>J. Am. Chem. Soc.</u>, <u>78</u>, 3761 (1956); (c) M. Legrand, A. Lacam, and R. Viennet, <u>Bull. Soc. Chim. France</u>, 792 (1961); see also ref. 35.

32.   P. Crabbé, <u>Tetrahedron</u>, <u>20</u>, 1211 (1964).

33.   (a) Private communication from Professor G. Ourisson, University of Strasbourg; (b) R. Hanna, C. Sandris, and G. Ourisson, Bull. Soc. Chim. France, 1454 (1959); (c) R. Hanna and G. Ourisson, Bull. Soc. Chim. France, 1945 (1961); (d) G. Jacob, G. Ourisson, and A. Rassat, Bull. Soc. Chim. France, 1374 (1959); (e) H. P. Gervais and A. Rassat, Bull. Soc. Chim. France, 743 (1961).

34.   K. Takeda and H. Minato, Steroids, 1, 345 (1963).

35.   L. Velluz and M. Legrand, Angew. Chem., 73, 603 (1961).

36.   S. Julia and J. P. Lavaux, Bull. Soc. Chim. France, 1223 (1963).

37.   D. W. Theobald, Tetrahedron, 20, 1455 (1964).

38.   A. D. Cross, E. Denot, and P. Crabbé, unpublished observations.

39.   R. H. Van den Bosch, M. S. de Winter, S. A. Szpilfogel, H. Herrmann, P. Witz, and G. Ourisson, Bull. Soc. Chim. France, 1090 (1963).

40.   G. Snatzke, H. Pieper, and R. Tschesche, Tetrahedron, 20, 107 (1964).

8

Inherently Dissymmetric Chromophores

8-1. INTRODUCTION

In Section 2-4 it was emphasized that in inherently dissymmetric chromophores the optical activity resulted from the intrinsic geometry of the chromophore. The optical isomerism—also called **atropisomerism** for skewed biaryls—existing in these compounds is due to restricted rotation about single bonds.[1] Thus atropisomerism will be observed when the energy barrier separating conformational isomers is high enough to permit their isolation and identification.[2] Such isomerism has been found in biphenyls, binaphthyls, bianthryls, and the like.[1-4]

Optical activity is associated with the inherently dissymmetric chromophore of these aromatic compounds, thus leading to Cotton effects which can be investigated either by optical rotatory dispersion or by circular dichroism. It will be recalled that these substances are characterized by very high optical activity, as a result of the nature of their chromophore; i.e., the high degree of dissymmetry of such chromophore is to be contrasted with the second-order dissymmetry of a carbonyl for which the optical activity is merely induced by its surrounding (Sec. 2-4).

Several rotatory dispersion and circular dichroism studies of optically active biaryls, biphenyls, binaphthyls, and bianthryls have appeared, illustrating the wide possibilities and important information these closely related methods can offer.[3-11]

These and related investigations of inherently dissymmetric chromophores have given a major new direction to studies of optical rotatory power.[4] Moreover, conformational and configurational correlations, as well as absolute configurations,[12] have been established in these series by mere examination of the experimental Cotton effects.

Hexahelicene (1) constitutes a classical example of an inherently dissymmetric chromophore.[3] This compound (1) consists of six benzenoid rings fused into a roughly helical form. There is no symmetry element in the molecule to prohibit optical activity, but neither is there any asymmetric carbon atom. The entire molecule acts as a single chromophore, and the asymmetry necessary for optical activity is built **into** the chromophore itself.[3] All the transitions of the chromophore, which in this case is identical with the molecule, are both electric–dipole and magnetic–dipole allowed; i.e., both μ_e^k and μ_m^k in Equation [1] of Chapter 1 are in general nonzero to the first order. Hence all the transitions have relatively large R_k values, and the optical activity exhibited is very high.[3]

1

8-2. BIPHENYLS AND BINAPHTHYLS

The transitions in the ultraviolet spectra of dissymmetric biphenyls, binaphthyls, and similar substances are optically active and give rise to Cotton effects, whose sign reflects absolute configuration and conformation.[4]

Figure 8-1 shows the circular dichroism curve and the ultraviolet spectrum of the unbridged (S)-6,6'-dinitro-2,2'-dimethylbiphenyl (2).[8] The short-wavelength positive circular dichroism maximum at 251 mμ corresponds to the $\pi - \pi*$ ultraviolet transition at 260 mμ, and the negative circular dichroism maximum at 298 mμ is related to the ultraviolet inflection at about 310 mμ. The long-wavelength **negative** dichroism maximum around 350 mμ is associated with a transition which is not apparent in the ultraviolet spectrum. These features are characteristic of the (S) configuration.[12] The rotatory dispersion curve of the (R) optical isomer of (2) (see Fig. 8-1),[6] which exhibits a positive Cotton effect near 330 mμ, confirms the above observation. In the dispersion curve of (R)-6,6'-dinitro-2,2'-dimethylbiphenyl (2) a second Cotton effect, which is negative and centered near 260 mμ, is also apparent. The different configurations characterizing these (R) and (S) isomers are then expressed by the reversed signs associated with their Cotton effects.

| 2 | 3 | 4 | 5 |

It is particularly noteworthy that the nitrobenzene transition near 340 mμ, hardly detected by ultraviolet absorption, is clearly revealed by **both** circular dichroism and optical rotatory dispersion. Moreover, the transition near 300 mμ is shown by circular dichroism to be optically active, a fact which is not observed by rotatory dispersion, since tails of neighboring Cotton effects obscure the small Cotton effect associated with this transition.[8]

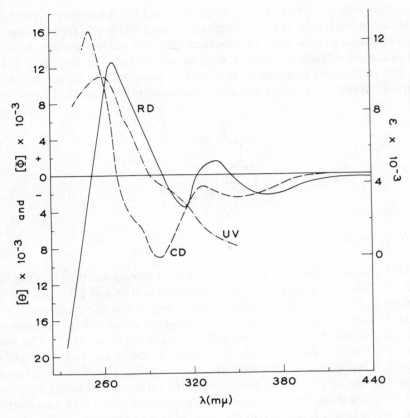

Fig. 8-1. CD and UV curves of (S)-6,6'-dinitro-2,2'-dimethylbiphenyl (2) and the RD curve of its (R)-isomer [adapted from K. Mislow, E. Bunnenberg, R. Records, K. Wellman, and C. Djerassi, J. Am. Chem. Soc., **85**, 1342 (1963)].

Sometimes the high extinctions in the absorption spectra of such compounds parallel the intensities of the circular dichroism curves as well as the high amplitude in the dispersion curves. All three phenomena are characteristic of molecules which contain inherently dissymmetric chromophores, and all three may be used simultaneously for structural and configurational assignments, since circular dichroism and rotatory dispersion phenomena are complementary manifestations of the Cotton effect associated with a particular electronic transition. On occasion (see Fig. 8-1), circular dichroism measurements have distinct advantages over rotatory dispersion, whose background rotation may hide weak Cotton effects. Conversely, the presence of high-intensity Cotton effects lying in wavelength regions which **at present** are not reached by the available instrumentation can often be easily detected by the dispersion curve at shorter wavelengths.[8]

In conclusion, a judicious use of **both** circular dichroism and rotatory dispersion is therefore indicated. On the one hand, with the instrumentation

now available, high-intensity Cotton effects lying in low-wavelength regions
("invisible giants") are best detected by rotatory dispersion measurements,
since their Cotton effects are felt as background curves and frequently even as
the dominant effect of optical rotatory power in the region under investigation.
On the other hand, circular dichroism is most useful in identifying relatively
weak optically active transitions, especially in the longer-wavelength region,
where their presence may be obscured in both ultraviolet absorption and rotatory
dispersion spectra by broad, overlapping neighboring bands.

Optical rotatory dispersion,[9] ultraviolet, and circular dichroism data[8] have
been obtained for (R)-9,10-dihydro-4,5-dimethylphenanthrene (3), and these are
reproduced in Figure 8-2. The conjugated-band Cotton effect of this compound
has its circular dichroism maximum at 262 mμ, in good correspondence with
the ultraviolet absorption maximum at 261 mμ. The molecular ellipticity of
bridged compounds such as (3) is considerably higher than in "open" biphenyls
such as (2). The rotatory dispersion curve of (3) permitted the detection only
of the long-wavelength low-intensity features. However, this curve clearly
shows that the positive long-wavelength extremum of low intensity is superimposed on a strong negative background rotation, attributed to the "invisible
giant" located at a much lower wavelength.

In Figure 8-3, the circular dichroism and ultraviolet spectra of two other
twisted bridged biphenyls (4) and (5) are reproduced.[7] The relative displacement of the biphenyl conjugation band in (4) and (5) is mirrored in the shift
observed in the position of the circular dichroism maximum. In numerous
seven-membered ring bridged biphenyls a long-wavelength Cotton effect of low
amplitude accompanies the conjugation-band Cotton effect, and both effects are
of the same sign. However, it has been pointed out that oxepin (5) does not
exhibit the long-wavelength Cotton effect.[6,7] This observation is unusual, since
most optically active biaryls present multiple Cotton effect curves. The binaphthyl
(6), also represented in Figure 8-3, shows this multiple Cotton effect pattern.
The negative long-wavelength and positive short-wavelength circular dichroism
maxima[7] are in agreement with the rotatory dispersion results.[6] The extremely
high intensity of the optical rotatory dispersion peak[6] and circular dichroism
molecular ellipticity[7] characterizing this compound (6) are in good agreement,
making both methods appropriate for such Cotton effect studies.

6   7   8a, R₁ = CH₃; R₂ = H   9
               b, R₁ = H; R₂ = CH₃

8a, $R_1 = CH_3$; $R_2 = H$
b, $R_1 = H$; $R_2 = CH_3$

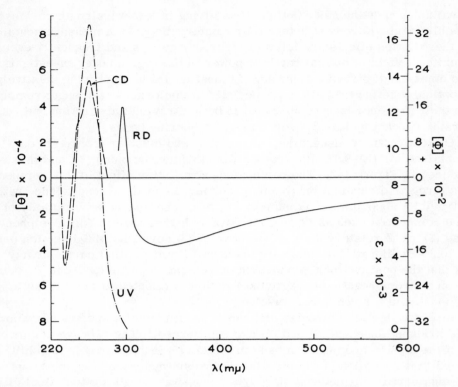

Fig. 8-2. RD, CD, and UV curves of (R)-9,10-dihydro-4,5-dimethylphenanthrene (3). [Modified from K. Mislow and H. B. Hoffs, J. Am. Chem. Soc., 84, 3018 (1962), and K. Mislow, E. Bunnenberg, R. Records, K. Wellman, and C. Djerassi, J. Am. Chem. Soc., 85, 1342 (1963)].

Mislow and his collaborators prepared a large array of inherently dissymmetric chromophores, which were then investigated by optical rotatory dispersion and circular dichroism.[4] Highly useful conclusions could be drawn, emphasizing the valuable structural, configurational, and conformational information these methods can provide.[4-9, 13-15]

8-3. HOMOCONJUGATED π-SYSTEMS

Bridged ketones, such as the R- and S-dimethylbiphenyl derivatives (7), were also investigated.[5] These compounds (7) are characterized by the extraordinary high amplitudes of their rotatory dispersion curves (a ≅ 1400) and by their fine structure, reflected in the ultraviolet spectra. To account for the fine structure, heretofore encountered only with conjugated systems, Mislow, Djerassi, and their collaborators[5] postulated homoconjugation of carbonyl and benzene π-electrons.

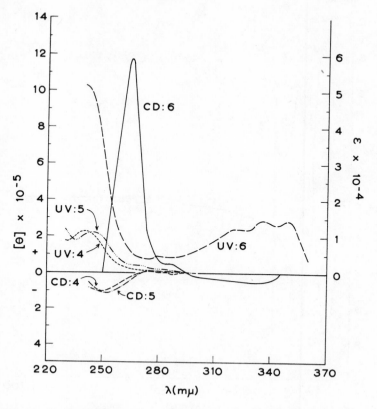

Fig. 8-3. CD and UV curves of the bridged biphenyl (4), oxepin (5), and the binaphthyl (6) [modified from E. Bunnenberg, C. Djerassi, K. Mislow, and A. Moscowitz, J. Am. Chem Soc., **84**, 2823 (1962)].

The rotatory dispersion curves of R-(7) and S-(7), reproduced in Figure 8-4, illustrate the advantage this techniques offers in the detection of nonconjugated π orbital overlaps.[5]

A direct correlation of configuration has recently been established, by optical rotatory dispersion, between the biaryls and a class of sesquiterpenes.[13] As indicated in Figure 8-5, there is a close similarity between the rotatory dispersion curve of parasantonide (8a) and that of dimethyldibenzsuberone (9). These observations led to the assignment of the R-configuration to (+)-dimethyldibenzsuberone (9),[15] since the absolute configuration of parasantonide (8a) (and also of santonide (b), both exhibiting almost superimposable dispersion curves[13]), is known.[16,17]

Inspection of the circular dichroism and rotatory dispersion curves of bridged ketones, such as the dinitroketone (10), indicates that there is a marked deviation from the pattern exhibited by other bridged 2,2'-dinitrobiphenyls. The various chromophores appear to contribute individually to the resultant Cotton effect curves.[6,8] This is exemplified in Figure 8-6, in which the algebraic

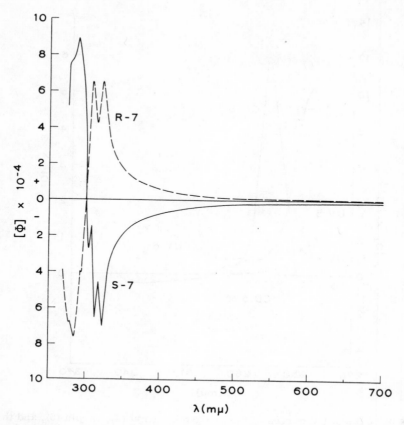

Fig. 8-4. RD curves of the (R)-and (S)-dimethylbiphenyl bridged ketone (7). [from K. Mislow, M. A. Glass, R. E. O'Brien, P. Rutkin, D. H. Steinberg, and C. Djerassi, J. Am. Chem. Soc., **82**, 4740 (1960); reproduced by permission of the editor].

summation of the circular dichroism curves (in dioxane) of bridged (S)-2,2'-dinitrobiphenyl (11) and the (S)-dimethyl bridged biphenyl ketone (7) bear a fair similarity to the experimental curve of the S–dinitro bridged biphenyl ketone (10).[8]

Another important conclusion from the above observations is the extension of the octant rule[18] proposed by Moscowitz, Mislow, Glass, and Djerassi[14,15] for dissymmetric nonconjugated chromophores. The long–wavelength carbonyl

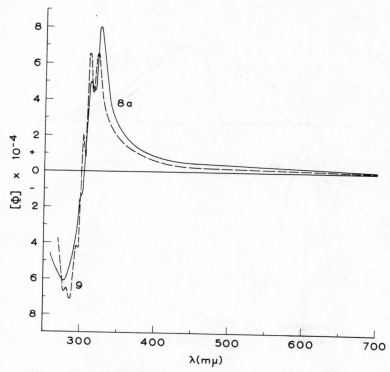

Fig. 8-5. RD curves of parasantonide (8a) and (R)-(+)-dimethyldibenzsuberone (9) [adapted from A. Moscowitz, K. Mislow, M. A. Glass, and C. Djerassi, J. Am. Chem. Soc., **84**, 1945 (1962)].

transition of an aromatic or ethylenic moiety, such as occurs in β,γ-unsaturated ketones, justifies treating the composite carbonyl-carbon-π-system as an inherently dissymmetric chromophore.[19] The Cotton effect associated with such systems is a direct reflection of the absolute conformation (i.e., sense of skew, helicity, or chirality) characterizing this combined grouping.[15] This aspect will be discussed in connection with the Cotton effect exhibited by β,γ-unsaturated ketones. Because α,β- and β,γ-unsaturated ketones exhibit Cotton effects quite distinct from saturated carbonyl-containing compounds, they deserve special attention. The purpose of the following chapter is to examine both theoretical and practical aspects associated with such Cotton effects.

During a recent rotatory dispersion study of colchicine alkaloids, examination was made of the optical properties of one such alkaloid possessing a skewed biaryl system in which one of the aryl groups is a tropolone.[20]

Finally, solvent dependence of the optical activity of such inherently dissymmetric chromophores has been examined in the case of hexahelicene.[21] This study showed that in these series too the influence of the solvent on the rotatory power has to be taken into consideration.

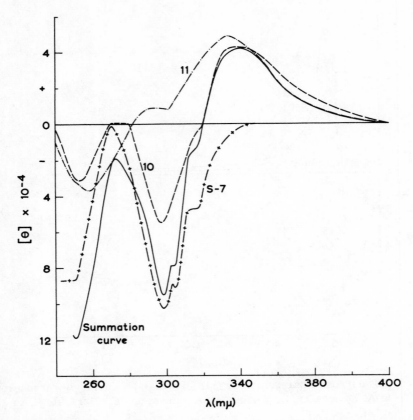

Fig. 8-6. CD curves of the S-dimethyl bridged biphenyl ketone (7), the S-dinitro bridged biphenyl ketone (10), the bridged (S)-2,2'-dinitrobiphenyl (11), and the summation curve of (7) and (11) [from K. Mislow, E. Bunneberg, R. Records, K. Wellman, and C. Djerassi, J. Am. Chem. Soc., **85**, 1342 (1964); reproduced by permission of the editor].

REFERENCES

1. E. L. Eliel, Stereochemistry of Carbon Compounds, McGraw-Hill, New York, 1962.

2. (a) K. Mislow, S. Hyden, and H. Schaefer, J. Am. Chem. Soc., 84, 1449 (1962), and references therein; (b) Y. Badar and M. M. Harris, Chem. and Ind., 1426 (1964); (c) M. S. Newman, Steric Effects in Organic Chemistry, Wiley, New York, 1956.

3. (a) A. Moscowitz, chap. 12 in Optical Rotatory Dispersion: Applications to Organic Chemistry, C. Djerassi, ed., McGraw-Hill, New York, 1960; (b) A. Moscowitz, Tetrahedron, 13, 48 (1961); (c) A. Moscowitz in Advances in Chemical Physics (I. Prigogine, ed.), vol. IV, p. 67, Interscience, New York, 1962.

4. K. Mislow, Ann. N.Y. Acad. Sci., 93, 459 (1962).

5. K. Mislow, M. A. Glass, R. E. O'Brien, P. Rutkin, D. H. Steinberg, and C. Djerassi, J. Am. Chem. Soc., 82, 4740 (1960).

6. K. Mislow, M. A. Glass, R. E. O'Brien, P. Rutkin, D. H. Steinberg, J. Weiss, and C. Djerassi, J. Am. Chem. Soc., 84, 1455 (1962).

7. E. Bunnenberg, C. Djerassi, K. Mislow, and A. Moscowitz, J. Am. Chem. Soc., 84, 2823 (1962).

8. K. Mislow, E. Bunnenberg, R. Records, K. Wellman, and C. Djerassi, J. Am. Chem. Soc., 85, 1342 (1963).

9. K. Mislow and H. B. Hopps, J. Am. Chem. Soc., 84, 3018 (1962).

10. G. M. Badger, R. J. Drewer, and G. E. Lewis, J. Chem. Soc., 4268 (1962).

11. R. Grinter and S. F. Mason, Trans. Faraday Soc., 60, 274 (1964).

12. R. S. Cahn, C. K. Ingold, and V. Prelog, Experientia, 12, 81 (1956).

13. K. Mislow and C. Djerassi, J. Am. Chem. Soc., 82, 5247 (1960).

14. K. Mislow, M. A. Glass, A. Moscowitz, and C. Djerassi, J. Am. Chem. Soc., 83, 2771 (1961).

15. A. Moscowitz, K. Mislow, M. A. Glass, and C. Djerassi, J. Am. Chem. Soc., 84, 1945 (1962).

16. (a) R. B. Woodward, F. J. Brutschy, and H. Baer, J. Am. Chem. Soc., 70, 4216 (1948); (b) R. B. Woodward and E. G. Kovach, J. Am. Chem. Soc., 72, 1009 (1950); (c) R. B. Woodward and P. Yates, Chem. and Ind., 1391 (1954).

17. R. C. Cookson and N. S. Wariyar, J. Chem. Soc., 2302 (1956).

18.   W. Moffitt, R. B. Woodward, A. Moscowitz, W. Klyne, and C. Djerassi, J. Am. Chem. Soc., 83, 4013 (1961).

19.   R. C. Cookson and J. Hudec, J. Chem. Soc., 429 (1962).

20.   J. Hrbek, J. P. Jennings, W. Klyne, and F. Šantavý, Coll. Czech. Chem. Commun., 29, 2822 (1964).

21.   N. C. Kneten, N. J. Krause, T. O. Carmichael, and O. E. Weigang, J. Am. Chem. Soc., 84, 1738 (1962).

9

Unsaturated Ketones

9-1. INTRODUCTION

In α,β-unsaturated ketones two absorption maxima have been identified.[1] The very intense maximal absorption between 220 and 260 mμ is associated with the $\pi - \pi^*$ transition of the C=C—C=O group, also called the K-band. A second, less intense absorption band, appears above 300 mμ and corresponds to the n - π^* carbonyl transition.[2] The latter band, of low intensity, has been extensively investigated by rotatory dispersion and circular dichroism chiefly because of its accessibility by conventional instrumentation.[3] Hence most of the available experimental information is related to this higher-wavelength absorption band. However, more recently developed instruments allow access to the $\pi - \pi^*$ band, whose Cotton effect can provide fundamental stereochemical information. Furthermore, in α,β-unsaturated ketones one or both orthogonal reflection planes are lost, and the octant rule[4] is in general no longer applicable in its original form.[5]

The low-intensity, long-wavelength absorption band of α,β-unsaturated ketones is highly sensitive to the polarity of the solvent (see Sec. 3-3); this has been amply commented upon by Djerassi[3,6] and Klyne.[7] Figure 9-1, which reproduces the multiple Cotton effect associated with the higher absorption band of cholest-4-en-3-one (1),[6] is self-explanatory and indicates the importance of the appropriate choice of solvent for the investigation of such compounds.

Generally, **structural alterations** in a **distant** part of the molecule do not affect the characteristic aspect of the rotatory dispersion and circular dichroism curves of a given α,β-unsaturated ketone, provided that they do not modify

1

191

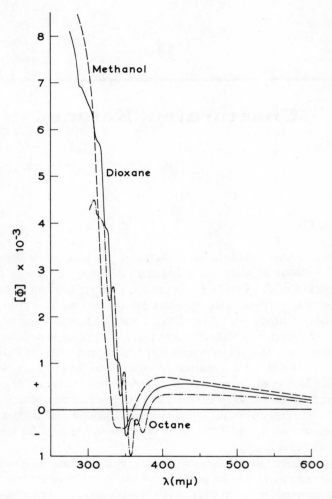

Fig. 9-1. RD curve of cholest-4-en-3-one (1) in methanol, dioxane, and octane solution [modified from C. Djerassi, R. Riniker, and B. Riniker, J. Am. Chem. Soc., **78**, 6377 (1956)].

the conformation. This is exemplified by the similar rotatory dispersion curves of (5S,10S)-5-hydroxy-10-methyl-$\Delta^{1(9)}$-2-octalone (2),[3] the sesquiter-penic derivative des-isopropylidene-petasol (3),[8] and the α,β-ethylenic steroidal ketone testosterone (4),[3] shown in Figure 9-2.

Conversely, however, the Cotton effect of the α,β-unsaturated keto-chromophore in the 340 mμ region is extremely sensitive to **conformational alterations** occurring either in the ring containing the chromophore or in adjacent rings. Moreover, electronic factors also play an important role in the Cotton effect of unsaturated carbonyl compounds.

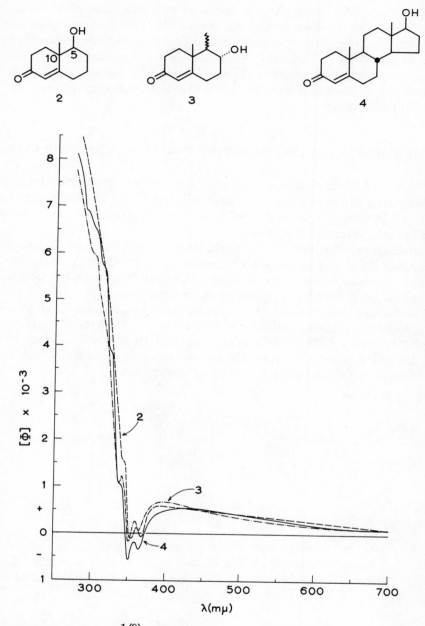

Fig. 9-2. RD curves of $\Delta^{1(9)}$-5-hydroxy-10-methyl-2-octalone (2), des-isopropylidene-petasol (3), and testosterone (4).

In the next sections the $\pi - \pi^*$ transition of the C=C—C=O system will be considered. The various factors affecting the higher $n - \pi^*$ transition will also be reviewed, since important structural and stereochemical features can be deduced from the Cotton effect associated with this absorption band. The Cotton effects of some dienone and α,β-unsaturated ketones containing another carbonyl group in the molecule will also be commented upon. Finally, the last sections of this chapter will deal with some theoretical aspects related to α,β- and β,γ-unsaturated ketones. The incidence of these concepts on the Cotton effect exhibited by optically active aromatic keto-derivatives will also be briefly examined.

9-2. THE INHERENTLY DISSYMMETRIC C=C—C=O CHROMOPHORE

The π – π^* transition of a nonplanar C=C—C=O group may be regarded as an inherently dissymmetric chromophore (see Chap. 8). Hence the helicity rule for cisoid dienes[9] can be applied to α,β-unsaturated ketones, provided that the conjugated system is nonplanar.

Calculation indicates[5] that a cisoid conformation of type (5) and transoid conformation (6) is associated with a positive Cotton effect centered at the wavelength corresponding to the K-band. Conversely, a negative Cotton effect is associated with their mirror-image representations.

The K-band of a number of α,β-unsaturated ketones has been investigated with a spectropolarimeter equipped with a Faraday effect–type analyzer built at Stanford University.[5] The Cotton effects of the K-band (240-260 mμ; ϵ : 8,000-20,000) for some of these compounds are shown in Figures 9-3 and 9-4. These Cotton effects are characterized by strong absorptions.

5

6

The cisoid α,β-unsaturated ketones jervine (7) and 3β-hydroxy-4α-methyl-5α-cholest-8(14)-en-7-one (8) show a strong negative Cotton effect. The transoid 4-methyl-cholest-4-en-3-one (9) shows a positive Cotton effect curve in the 240-260-mμ region (see Fig. 9-3).[5]

7

8

9

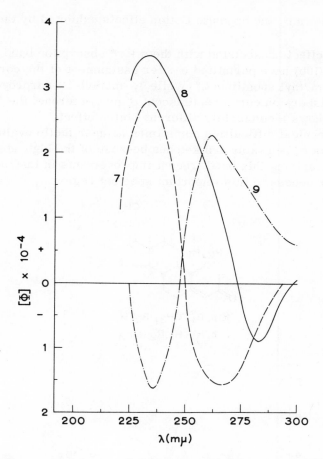

Fig. 9-3. RD curves of the $\pi - \pi^*$ transition in the cisoid α,β-unsaturated ketones jervine (7), 3β-hydroxy-4α-methyl-5α-cholest-8(14)-en-7-one (8) and 4-methyl-cholest-4-en-3-one (9) in methanol solution [modified from C. Djerassi, R. Records, E. Bunnenberg, K. Mislow, and A. Moscowitz, J. Am. Chem. Soc., **84**, 870 (1962)].

The sign of the Cotton effect of these compounds reflects the absolute conformation of the C=C—C=O group which makes the dominant contribution to the observed optical activity. The negative dispersion curves of compounds (7) and (8) indicate a conformation (5) or (6), while the positive amplitude of (9) indicates an enantiomeric conformation. Hence **the sign of the Cotton effect of the K-band permits assignment of the correct conformation to the unsaturated keto-chromophore.**[5]

The isomeric 1-methyl-19-norprogesterones (10a) and (10b) provide a further interesting example of the application of this rule. The α,β-unsaturated systems have opposite chiralities (helicity, sense of skew; see Chaps. 8 and 10) in these compounds (10a) and (10b). In the latter, ring A modifies its conformation in order to release the strong 1β-methyl 11α-hydrogen interactions.

This is clearly shown by the opposite Cotton effects exhibited by their K-band (see Fig. 9-4).[5]

The Cotton effects associated with the n - π^* absorption band in compounds (10a) and (10b) have permitted earlier assignment of the correct configuration for the 1-methyl substituent.[6] While 1α-methyl-19-norprogesterone (10a) exhibits a dispersion curve reminiscent of progesterone, the 1β-methyl derivative (10b) shows a completely different Cotton effect.[6]

Although technical difficulties sometimes hamper facile evaluation of the π - π^* transition in α,β-unsaturated ketones because of the high absorption coefficient characterizing this band, recent improvements in instrumentation now permit easier access to this important spectral region.

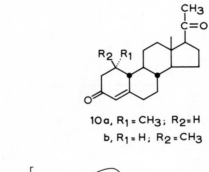

10a, R$_1$ = CH$_3$; R$_2$ = H

b, R$_1$ = H; R$_2$ = CH$_3$

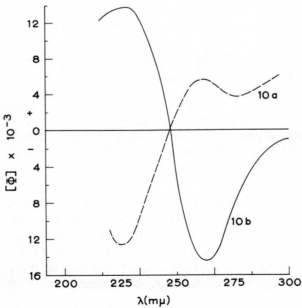

Fig. 9-4. RD curves of the π - π^* transition in the transoid α,β-unsaturated ketones 1α-methyl-19-norprogesterone (10a) and 1β-methyl-19-norprogesterone (10b) in methanol solution [modified from C. Djerassi, R. Records, E. Bunnenberg, K. Mislow, and A. Moscowitz, J. Am. Chem. Soc., **84**, 870 (1962)].

9-3. INFLUENCE OF CONFIGURATIONAL AND CONFORMATIONAL FACTORS ON THE COTTON EFFECT ASSOCIATED WITH THE n - π* BAND IN α,β-UNSATURATED KETONES.

A. Influence of Substituents in the Ring Containing the Chromophore or in the Ring Adjacent to it

Most information obtained thus far about α,β-unsaturated ketones has resulted from the examination of their n - π* absorption band, for the technical reasons cited above. The sensitivity of optical rotatory dispersion and circular dichroism to configurational and conformational alterations has already been emphasized, and further examples will be given here showing that the sign of the Cotton effect associated with the n - π* band is highly dependent on these stereochemical factors.

In Section 9-2, the conformational modification introduced in an α,β-unsaturated 3-keto steroid by substitution with a β-methyl group at C-1 has been reported.[6] A similar observation was made recently when it was found that the 1β-methyl derivative (11b) exhibits a circular dichroism curve of opposite Cotton effect to that of the corresponding unsubstituted steroid (11a).[10] Figure 9-5 illustrates this inversion of Cotton effect due to the mere introduction of a 1β-methyl substituent, which induces a change of conformation in ring A.

The conformational distortion produced by the nonbonded interaction between the axial 6β-methyl and the angular methyl group at C-10 in the substituted testosterone (13a) constitutes another classical example.[3] The rotatory dispersion curves of the equatorially substituted 6α-methyltestosterone (12a), as well as of the isomeric 6α-(12b) and 6β-(13b)-methyl-19-nortestosterones in which the angular methyl group at C-10 has been removed, are very similar to that of testosterone (4) (see Fig. 9-2). However, the conformational changes introduced in the ring system of (13a) in order to remove 1,3-diaxial interactions occurring between the 6β- and 10β-methyl groupings are reflected in its rotatory dispersion curve, which shows a completely different multiple Cotton effect (see Fig. 9-6).[3] A similar situation has been encountered recently in the case of epimeric 6α-(14a) and 6β-(14b) acetylthio-testosterone acetates (see Fig. 9-6).[11] While the Cotton effects reported in Figure 9-6 are for the n - π* carbonyl transition, these rotatory dispersion curves, indicative of conforma-

11a, R = H
   b, R = CH₃

12a, R = CH₃
   b, R = H

13a, R = CH₃
   b, R = H

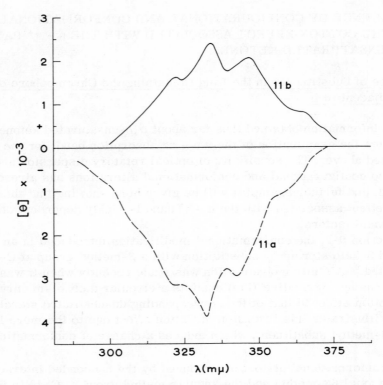

Fig. 9-5. CD curves of hydrocortisone 17,20,21-bismethylenedioxy (11a) and its 1β-methyl analogue (11b) [modified from D. Bertin and J. Perronnet, Comptes rendus, **257**, 1946 (1963)].

tional changes occurring in some of these compounds, corroborate the observations made by ultraviolet spectroscopy for the K-band and for the n - π* band of such derivatives.[12]

Substitution of the 2β-hydrogen atom in the steroid molecule by other groups also introduces conformational modifications in the ring system, due to 1,3-diaxial interactions between the 10β-methyl group and the 2β-substituent. Some conformational changes occurring in saturated 2β-substituted 3-keto steroids were reported in Section 6-4-D. In this section, distortions observed in the ring system of some Δ^4-3-keto steroids will be mentioned. While 2α-substituted Δ^4-3-keto derivatives exhibit rotatory dispersion curves similar to those of the unsubstituted compounds, 2β-substituted derivatives show a curve with substantially different features.[13,14,15] This is exemplified in Figure 9-7, in which the rotatory dispersion curve of 2α-acetoxy-testosterone-propionate (15a), its 2β-acetoxy isomer (15b), and 2β,17α-dimethyl-19-nortestosterone (16) are represented. While the first compound (15a) has a curve reminiscent of testosterone (4) (see Fig. 9-2), it is apparent from Figure 9-7 that (15b) and (16) exhibit a completely distinct multiple Cotton effect curve. Of particular impor-

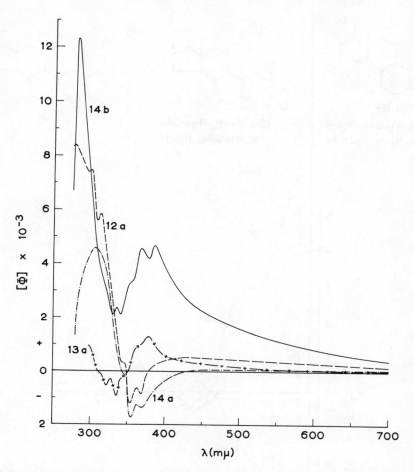

Fig. 9-6. RD curves of 6α-methyl-testosterone (12a), 6β-methyl-testosterone (13a), 6α-acetylthio-testosterone acetate (14a), and 6β-acetylthio-testosterone acetate (14b) in dioxane solution.

tance in these rotatory dispersion curves (see Fig. 9-7) is the strong background dispersion superimposed on the 330 mμ Cotton effect. In such examples the sign and magnitude of the background curve due to the $\pi - \pi^*$ absorption band may be correlated with the chirality of the α,β-unsaturated keto-chromophore.[5] For instance, the negative Cotton effect associated with the K-band of the 2β-acetoxy derivative (15b) is well observed at about 260 mμ, and indicates a helicity of the C=C—C=O system opposite to that of its parent compound (15a).[15] Finally, of interest also is the fact that the chirality of the Δ^4-3-keto chromophore seems to be the same in (15b) and (16), although the latter does not have any substituent at C-10, thus indicating that the nature of the 10β-substituent is not exclusively responsible for the change observed in the conformation in ring A in these compounds (15b) and (16).

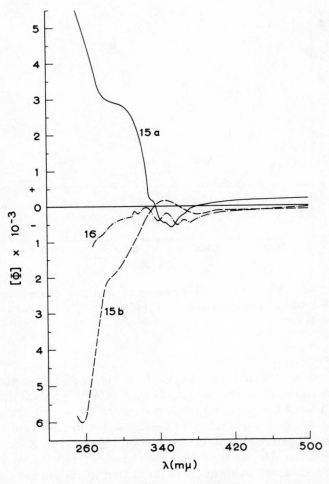

14a, R$_1$=SAc; R$_2$=H
  b, R$_1$=H; R$_2$=SAc

15a, R$_1$=H; R$_2$=OAc
  b, R$_1$=OAc; R$_2$=H

16

Fig. 9-7. RD curves of 2α-acetoxy-testosterone-propionate (15a), 2β-acetoxy-testosterone-propionate (15b), and 2β,17α-dimethyl-19-nortestosterone (16) in dioxane solution.

B. The α,β-unsaturated Keto Chromophore in Bridged Steroids

Other typical examples of the dramatic changes sometimes observed in the Cotton effect of Δ^4-3-keto chromophores, owing to conformational distortions, are suggested by 6,19-cyclo steroids.[16] The optical rotatory dispersion and circular dichroism curves of three such compounds are reproduced in Figures 9-8 to 9-10. It is apparent that the negative multiple Cotton effect associated with the Δ^4-3-keto chromophore in the 6,19-oxide bridged compound (17) (see Fig. 9-8) is of the same sign as in the usual unsubstituted Δ^4-3-keto steroids, although considerably enhanced (compare with Figs. 9-2 and 9-5). An examination of the geometry of such a system with Dreiding molecular models[17] indicates substantial distortions occurring in the conformation of rings A and B.

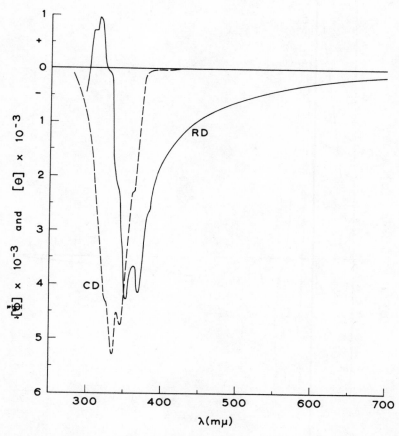

Fig. 9-8. RD and CD curves of 6β,19-oxido-testosterone (17) in dioxane solution.

The rotatory dispersion and circular dichroism curves of the diketo-lactone (18) and the cyclobutane derivative (19) are shown in Figures 9-9 and 9-10.[18] The Cotton effects of the Δ^4-3-keto and 17-keto-groups of these compounds are well resolved by both techniques, making either method appropriate for their investigation. Furthermore, in these substances a strong negative multiple Cotton effect is also associated with the α,β-unsaturated $n - \pi^*$ absorption band.

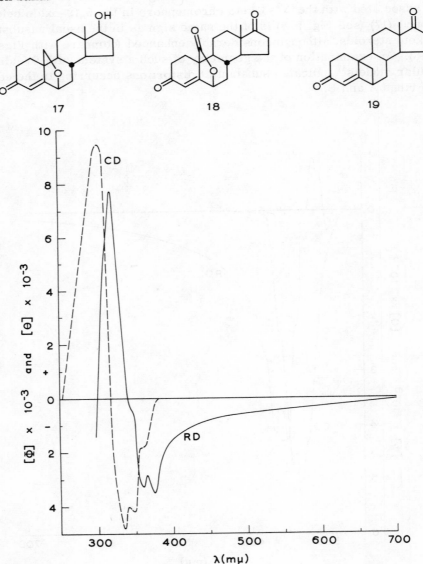

Fig. 9-9. RD and CD curves of 6β-hydroxy-19-carboxy-androst-4-ene-3,17-dione-6, 19-lactone (18) in dioxane solution.

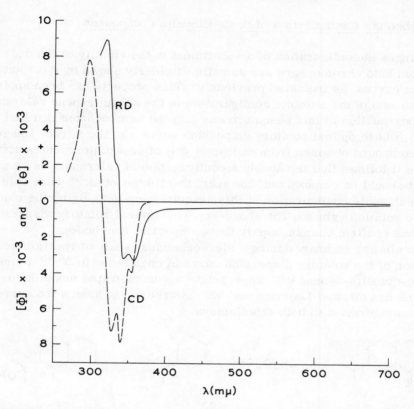

Fig. 9-10. RD and CD curves of 6β,19-cyclo-androst-4-ene-3,17-dione (19) in dioxane solution.

The rotatory dispersion curve of 17β-carbomethoxy-19-methoxy-androst-4-en-3-one-8,19-oxide (20) seems to indicate a different conformation of the C=C—C=O chromophore from that of a usual Δ^4-3-keto steroid, since a strong negative Cotton effect has been shown to be associated with its K-band.[19]

The Δ^4-3-keto 11,19-oxido-steroid (21) exhibits a positive multiple Cotton effect in the 370–320 mμ region. This also may be attributed to ring distortions introduced by the oxide bridge.[16]

C. The Absolute Configuration of Some Bicyclic Compounds

Changes in configuration of a substituent in the vicinity of the α,β-unsaturated keto chromophore are sometimes clearly shown by the rotatory dispersion curves, as indicated previously. This property has been applied recently to assign the absolute configuration to the sesquiterpene valeranone (22).[20a] Degradation of this sesquiterpene (22) led to an α,β-unsaturated keto-ester (23), whose optical rotatory dispersion curve was the mirror image of a similar compound obtained from eudesmol (24) of known stereochemistry. Therefore it follows that the absolute configuration of valeranone is as shown in (22).[20a] It should be emphasized, however, that Hikino et al.[20c] were able to settle the absolute configuration of this sesquiterpene (22), using the mono-chromatic rotation values. The above-reported optical rotatory dispersion results thus confirm unambiguously these important conclusions.

In a similar manner, during a stereochemical study of lysergic acid, comparison of the rotatory dispersion curve of enantiomeric $\Delta^{4,4a}$-N-methyl-octahydro-quinolin-3-ones with appropriate α,β-unsaturated model keto-derivatives has allowed Leemann and his coworkers[21] to assign the correct absolute configuration to both enantiomers.

22   23   24

D. The Influence of Ring Size

The influence of the size of either the ring containing the α,β-unsaturated keto-chromophore or the ring adjacent to it on the Cotton effect has been emphasized recently.[22,23] The positive sign and high intensity of the dichroism associated with A-homo-5β-androst-4(4a)-en-17β-ol-3-one (25) has been attrib-uted to strong skewing of the C=C—C=O system.[22] The chirality of the inher-ently dissymmetric chromophore of α,β-unsaturated bicyclic ketones has been shown to play a crucial role in determining the sign of its Cotton effects,[23] which are evidently subject to subtle structural and conformational alterations. This is clearly shown in Figure 9-11, where the rotatory dispersion curve of the bicyclic unsaturated ketones (26) and (27) are reproduced.[23]

25   26   27

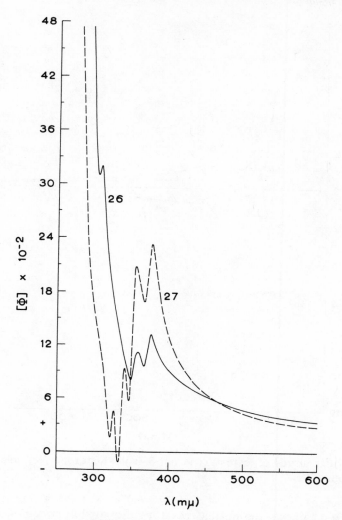

Fig. 9-11. RD curves of $\Delta^{1(9)}$-10-methyl 2-octalone (26) and Δ^7-1β-methyl-bicyclo[5.4.0]9-undecenone (27) in dioxane [from C. Djerassi and J. E. Gurst, J. Am. Chem. Soc., **86**, 1755 (1964), reproduced by permission of the editor].

E. Cotton Effects of α,β-unsaturated Keto Steroids with Abnormal Configuration

Since configurational changes occurring in rigid polycyclic molecules are often accompanied by conformational modifications, α,β-unsaturated ketones in steroids and triterpenes exhibiting an "abnormal" stereochemistry sometimes present diagnostically significant rotatory dispersion and circular dichroism curves. The next examples, chosen from the steroid series, will illustrate this concept.

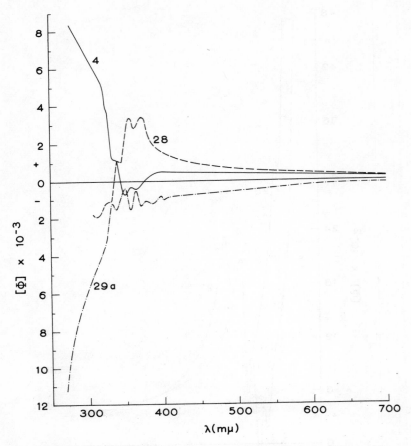

Fig. 9-12. RD curves of testosterone (4), 8-isotestosterone (28), and retrotestosterone (29a).

Figure 9-12 shows the optical rotatory dispersion curve of testosterone (4), 8-isotestosterone (28),[6] and 9β-10α-(retro)-testosterone (29a).[24] The unusual shape of the dispersion curve exhibited by 8-isotestosterone (28) may be ascribed to the fact that ring B exists in a boat conformation.[6] Moreover, in the retro-steroid (29a) ring B probably also exists in the boat form.

A similar situation is encountered in 19-nor-retrotestosterone (29b).[25] The Cotton effect exhibited by the n - π* transition in this compound is positive, as shown by the rotatory dispersion and circular dichroism curves in Figure 9-13. Since the general features of the rotatory dispersion curves of retro-testosterone (29a) and 19-nor-retrotestosterone (29b) are very similar, one can conclude that in these compounds the nature of the angular substituent at C-10 is of no particular significance for the Cotton effect. Furthermore, the dispersion curves of the retro-steroids (29a) and (29b) are the mirror images of the curve of testosterone (4) (see Fig. 9-12), thus reflecting the opposite stereochemistry at C-9 and C-10.

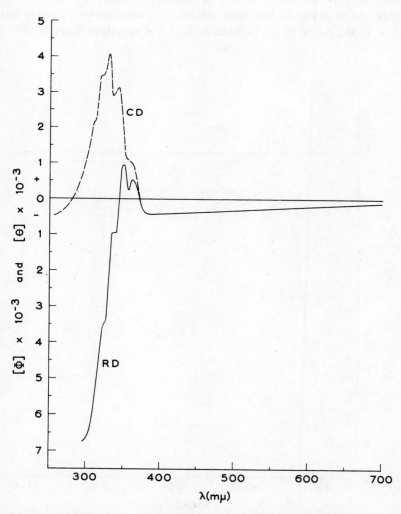

Fig. 9-13. RD and CD curves of 19-nor-retrotestosterone (29b) in dioxane.

The situation encountered in the Δ^4-3-keto derivative (30)[26] of lumisterol (31)[27] is more complicated (see Fig. 9-14). While its rotatory dispersion curve[28] is reminiscent of the above-reported retro-steroids (29a, b), the circular dichroism curve, reproduced in Figure 9-14, shows a "double-hump," which might indicate that a certain conformational mobility exists in the cyclic system. Low-temperature circular dichroism curves of this ketone, when compared with appropriate reference α,β-unsaturated keto derivatives, might help in the future in assigning the conformation of the ring system in such compounds.

The important observation has been made recently that both 10α-testosterone (32a)[29,30] and 19-hydroxy-10α-testosterone (32b)[31] exhibit negative rotatory dispersion curves. The circular dichroism curve of 19-nor-10α-androst-4-ene-3,17-dione (33),[32] which is shown in Figure 9-15, confirms this finding. While the separation between the two chromophores is quite satisfactory in Figure 9-15, there is an indication that the negative Cotton effect

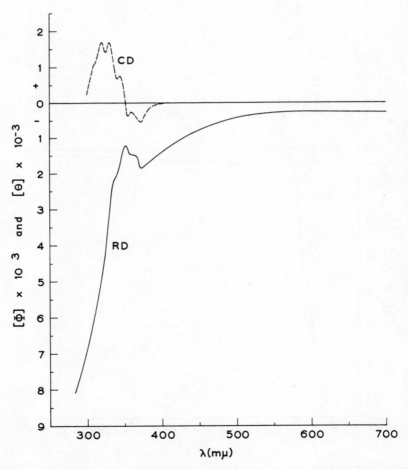

Fig. 9-14. RD and CD curves of lumista-4,22-dien-3-one (30) in dioxane solution.

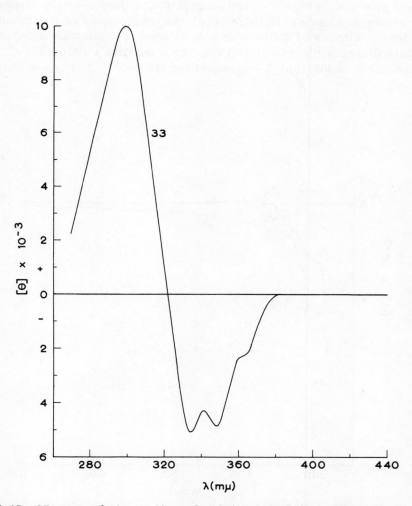

Fig. 9-15. CD curve of 19-nor-10α-androst-4-ene-3,17-dione (33) in dioxane solution.

associated with the Δ^4-3-keto system is stronger in this 10α-steroid (33) ($[\theta]_{334}$ = -5080) than in 10β-isomers. This, incidentally, is in agreement with the circular dichroism curve found for 10α-testosterone (32a) ($[\theta]_{336}$ = -5020).[30,33] If this observation about the high intensity of the Cotton effect associated with 10α-Δ^4-3-keto steroids could be generalized, it might constitute a way of differentiating between 10α- and 10β-Δ^4-3-keto (8β,9α)-isomers (see also Fig. 9-29).

The above results indicate that, while the nature of the angular substituent at C-10 sometimes is of no particular significance, slight changes in the substitution, configuration, and conformation of the ring system may have a direct bearing on the Cotton effect associated with the Δ^4-3-keto chromophore. Another example is provided by the A'-homo-steroid (34), whose rotatory dispersion curve is shown in Figure 9-16.[34] Although the environment of the α,β-unsaturated keto-system is similar to the pattern encountered in compounds (32a) and (32b), the rotatory dispersion curve of (34) exhibits a **positive** Cotton effect,[34] reminiscent of the curve of (5S,10R)-5-hydroxy-10-methyl-$\Delta^{1,9}$-2-octalone (35).[3]

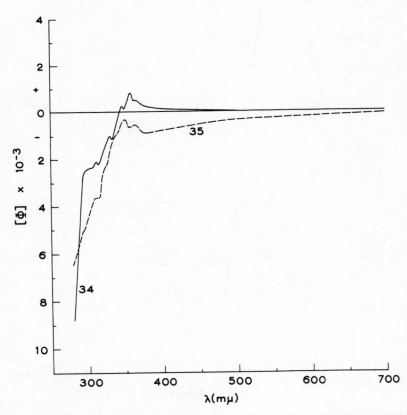

Fig. 9-16. RD curves of A'-homo-2α,5β-cholest-4'-en-3-one (34) in hexane and $\Delta^{1(9)}$-5-hydroxy-10-methyl-2-octalone (35) in dioxane.

33   34   35

F. Influence of Substitution at C-11 on the Δ^4-3-Keto Chromophore

Another example of nonbonded interactions acting on the Cotton effect associated with the Δ^4-3-keto chromophore is suggested by the changes observed by mere substitution of the steroid molecule at position 11. Introduction of an 11α-hydroxyl group in progesterone (36a) ($[\theta]_{332}$ = -4220)[30] affords 11α-hydroxy-progesterone (36b) ($[\theta]_{334}$ = -1060),[30] in which the molecular ellipticity of the n - π^* band of the Δ^4-3-keto system is considerably reduced. Conversely, however, 11β-hydroxylation leads to a Cotton effect reminiscent of the 11-unsubstituted Δ^4-3-keto chromophore. This is shown by the negative maximum exhibited by 11β-hydroxy-testosterone (36c) ($[\theta]$ = -4690).[35] Finally, introduction of an 11-keto grouping also decreases the negative Cotton effect, as shown in compound (37) ($[\theta]_{336}$ = -790).[36]

During a study of the absorption and derivative spectra of various hydroxylated progesterones, Olson and Alway[12b] have drawn attention to the variations in the intensity of the n - π^* bands observed. They also stated that an exact wavelength correlation exists between the first derivative of an ultraviolet spectrum and the fine structure of an optical rotatory dispersion curve. They further emphasized that the two techniques supplement each other as structural tools, because the absorption phenomenon is only one of the spectral properties being examined when a rotatory dispersion curve is obtained (see Chap. 2).

G. Δ^1-3-Keto Chromophore

Figure 9-17 clearly illustrates the stereochemical modifications which result from the introduction of methyl substituents at C-4 and C-8 in a Δ^1-3-keto system. The negative Cotton effect associated with the Δ^1-3-keto chromophore is progressively enhanced from compound (38) to (40).[37] Hence the molecular ellipticity increases from the steroid series (38) ($[\theta] \cong$ -3300), to the 4,4-dimethyl derivative (39) ($[\theta] \cong$ -6500), reaching a maximum intensity with the 4,4,8-trimethyl pattern, encountered in many tetra- and pentacyclic triterpenes (40) ($[\theta] \cong$ -10000).[37]

The circular dichroism data for several Δ^1-3-keto steroids are collected in Table 9-1. It is apparent that the nature of the 5- and 10-substituents in compounds (41) to (43)[38] plays an important role on the intensity of the negative Cotton effect. Furthermore, while the n - π^* band of the Δ^1-3-keto-19-nor-retrosteroid (44) shows a "double-humped" curve by circular dichroism, its rotatory dispersion curve exhibits a multiple positive Cotton effect. Finally, from the latter curve it seems that a strong negative effect is associated with the K-band of the Δ^1-3-keto chromophore (see Fig. 9-18). In this connection, Snatzke and Fehlhaber,[39] in an extensive study of saturated and unsaturated keto-steroids, mentioned that a strong positive Cotton effect is associated with the K-band of Δ^1-3-keto-5β-methyl-6β-hydroxy-19-nor steroids. They also report[39] a strongly positive Cotton effect for the n - π^* band of Δ^1-3-keto-5β-steroids such as (45).

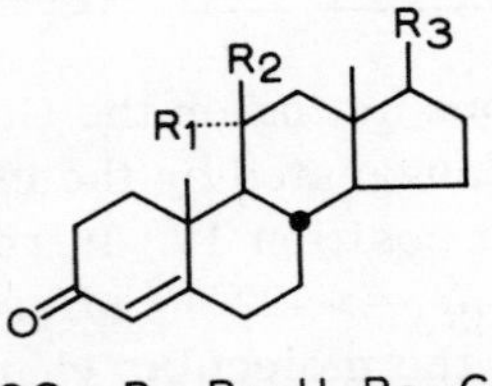

36 a, R₁ = R₂ = H; R₃ = COCH₃

b, R₁ = OH; R₂ = H; R₃ = COCH₃

c, R₁ = H; R₂ = R₃ = OH

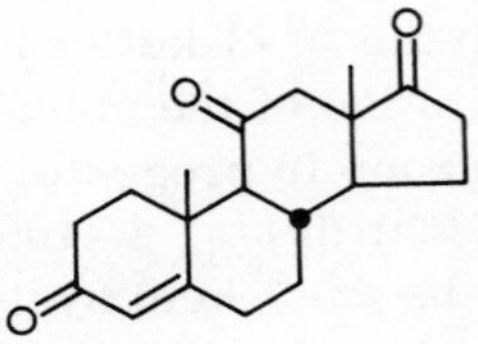

37

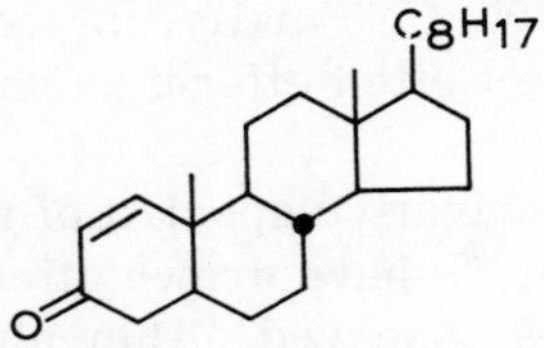

38

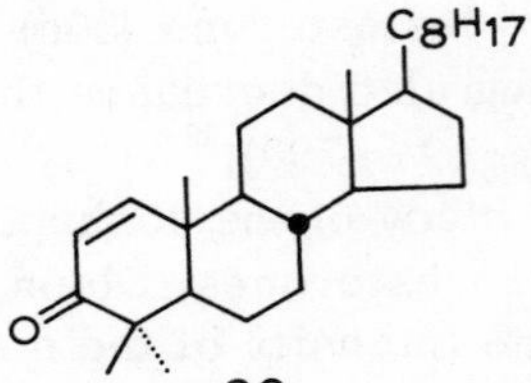

39

Table 9-1

COTTON EFFECT EXHIBITED BY VARIOUS 19-SUBSTITUTED
Δ^1-3-KETO STEROIDS

Compound	Circular Dichroism Molecular Ellipticity of the Main Maximum of the Δ^1-3-Keto Chromophore	Ref.
38	$[\theta]_{345}$ = -3500	37
41	$[\theta]_{341}$ = -2850	38
42	$[\theta]_{341}$ = -5700	38
43	$[\theta]_{338}$ = -2980	38
44	$[\theta]_{356}$ = -1730 $[\theta]_{320}$ = +600	38

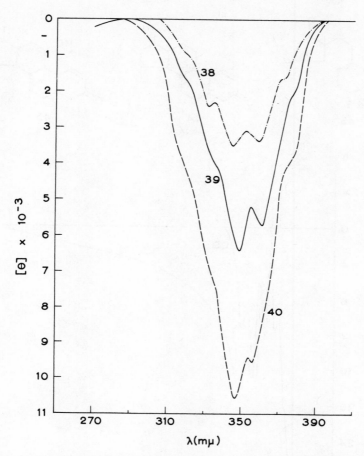

Fig. 9-17. CD curves of 5α-cholest-1-en-3-one (38), 4,4-dimethyl-5α-cholest-1-en-3-one (39), and Δ^1-allobetulen-3-one (40) in dioxane solution [modified from P. Witz, H. Herrmann, J. M. Lehn, and G. Ourisson, <u>Bull. Soc. Chim. France,</u> 1101 (1936)].

40   41   42

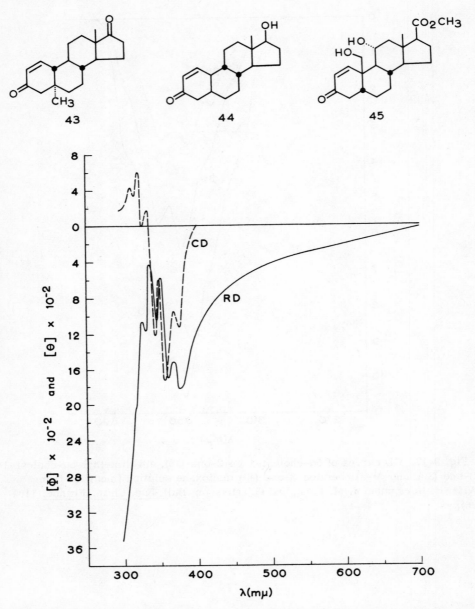

Fig. 9-18. RD and CD curves of 19-nor-9β,10α-androst-1-en-17β-ol-3-one (44) in dioxane solution.

H. Cyclopentenones

The next example, dealing with an α,β-unsaturated keto-system in ring D, shows an application of optical rotatory dispersion to both structural and stereochemical problems.

Incubation of estrone (46a) with <u>Fusarium moniliforme</u> introduced a new hydroxyl function into ring D of the molecule.[40a] Dehydration of this hydroxyl group, after protection of the 3-phenolic hydroxyl as an ether (46b), afforded an α,β-unsaturated keto-derivative (47). Since the latter compound exhibited a strong positive Cotton effect, with a characteristic fine structure at about 355 mμ reminiscent of the dispersion curve of 14β-5α-androst-15-en-3β-ol-17-one (48a)(see Fig. 9-19),[3,40b] the position of the double bond as well as the correct stereochemistry at C-14 could be assigned to this dehydration compound (47). As indicated in Figure 9-19, a 14αH-Δ^{15}-17-keto steroid (48b) is characterized by a weak negative Cotton effect.[3,40b]

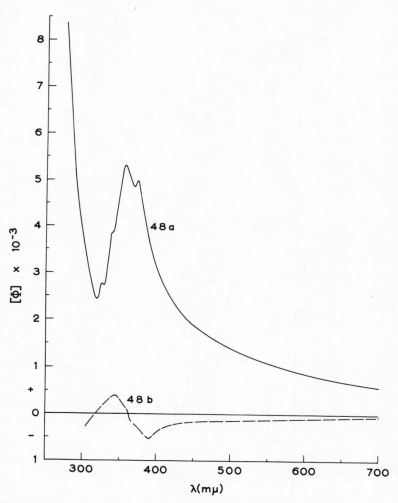

Fig. 9-19. RD curves of 3β-hydroxy-5α-androst-15-en-17-one (48b) and 3β-hydroxy-14β-5α-androst-15-en-17-one (48a) in dioxane solution [modified from C. Djerassi, <u>Optical Rotatory Dispersion</u>: <u>Application to Organic Chemistry</u>, McGraw-Hill, New York, (1960)].

The circular dichroism curves of some other α,β-unsaturated cyclo-pentenones are reproduced in Figure 9-20.[41] The A-nortestosterone (49) is characterized by a strongly negative maximum, with a fine structure at about 320-330 mμ. The A-nor 19-nor compound (50) exhibits its negative multiple Cotton effect at a higher wavelength. The 16-methylene 17-keto 19-nor steroid (51) shows a positive circular dichroism maximum which is much stronger than in the C-nor derivative (52).[42] In the latter compound no fine structure could be detected, in which respect it differs from most other cyclic α,β-unsaturated keto chromophores.

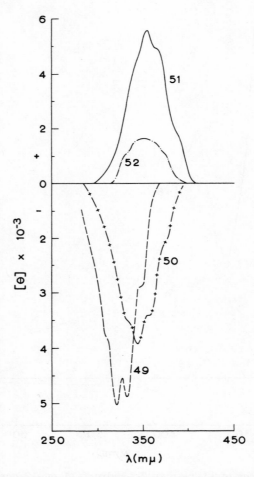

Fig. 9-20. CD curves of the α,β-unsaturated cyclopentenones (49) to (52) in dioxane solution. (Modified from P. Witz, Ph.D. Thesis, University of Strasbourg, May 1964).

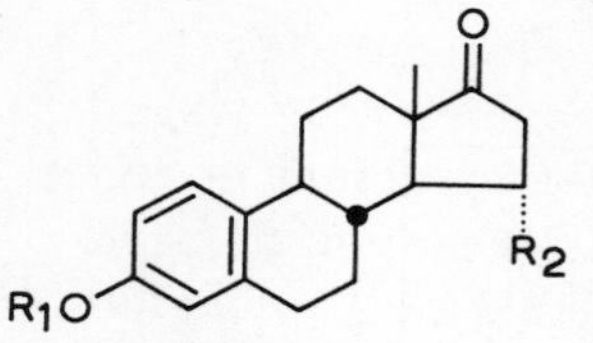

46 a, $R_1 = R_2 = H$
b, $R_1 = CH_3$; $R_2 = OH$

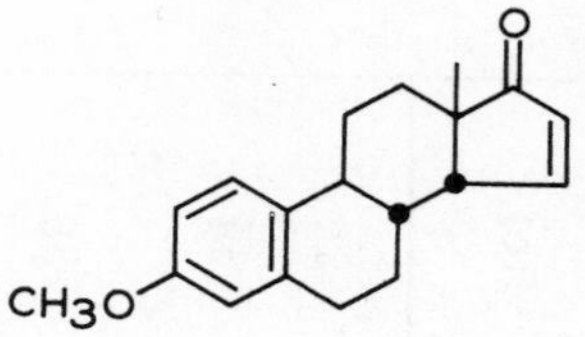

47

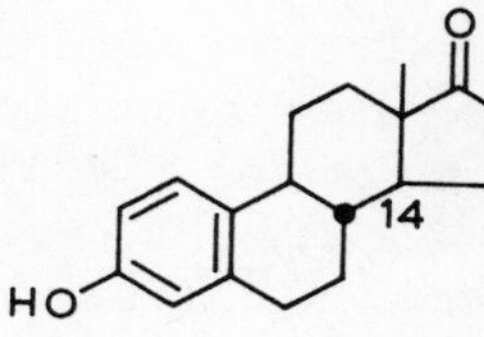

48 a, 14 β H
b, 14 α H

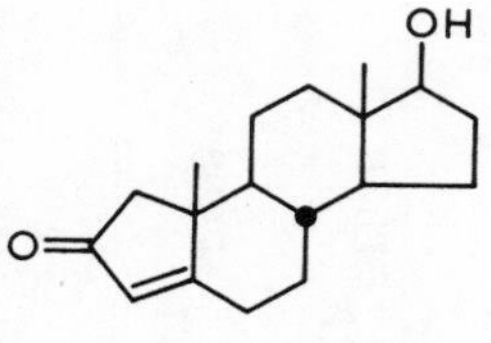

49

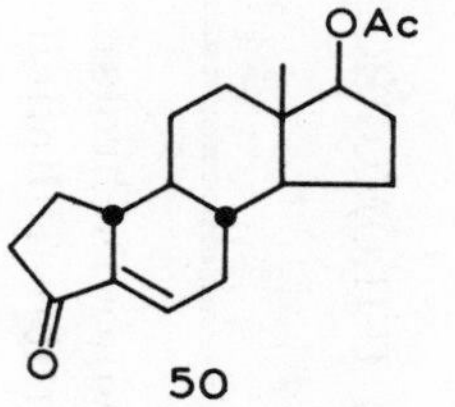

50

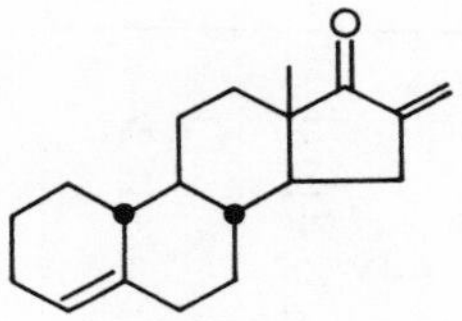

51

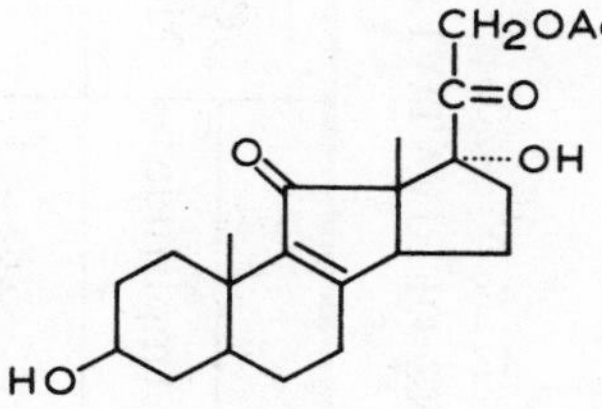

52

I. Δ^{16}-20-Keto Pregnenes

Brief mention shall now be made of the Δ^{16}-20-keto pregnene derivatives, since they are of considerable importance in steroid chemistry. The rotatory dispersion and the circular dichroism molecular ellipticity data for some such compounds are collected in Table 9-2. It is apparent from the observed results that these compounds exhibit a positive Cotton effect and that no fine structure is associated with the Δ^{16}-20-keto chromophore.[6] Moreover, introduction of a methyl-group at C-16, as in (54a), induces a considerable increase of the Cotton effect but also produces a bathochromic shift of the positive circular dichroism maximum, this shift being, of course, related to a bathochromic displacement of the ultraviolet maximum.

Worth mentioning also is the fact that although the last compound (54b) presents a negative specific rotation at the sodium D line ($[\alpha]_D$ -41°),[45] it exhibits a strong positive Cotton effect by rotatory dispersion and circular dichroism. This calls attention to the fact that caution should be used in drawing conclusions from the rotations obtained at high wavelengths.

In conclusion, the above-reported observations indicate that, in contrast to the situation encountered among saturated ketones (see Chap. 6), the Cotton effect associated with the n - π^* band of α,β-unsaturated carbonyl-containing

Table 9-2

COTTON EFFECT ASSOCIATED WITH THE Δ^{16}-20-KETO-CHROMOPHORE
IN SOME PREGNENE DERIVATIVES

Compound	Rotatory Dispersion			Circular Dichroism Molecular Ellipticity	Ref.
	Peak	Trough	Amplitude		
53a	$[\Phi]_{355}$ +3250°	$[\Phi]_{290}$ -4900°	a = +82		43
53b	$[\Phi]_{352.5}$ +3100°	$[\Phi]_{292.5}$ -5890°	a = +90		44
				$[\theta]_{335}$ +6090	35
54a	$[\Phi]_{355}$ +3330°	$[\Phi]_{300}$ -9450°!	a = +128!	$[\theta]_{329}$ +8370	43
54b	$[\Phi]_{385}$ +2740°	$[\Phi]_{293}$ -10500°	a = +132	$[\theta]_{341}$ +7990	45

compounds cannot easily be interpreted. In fact, great caution should be used in assigning absolute configuration from the n - π^* band Cotton effect.[23] Absolute stereochemical assignments can be made only in those instances in which a safe conformational relationship between a reference substance and the unknown compound can be unambiguously established.

Before such correlations are made, appropriate references should be consulted. In that respect, it may be recalled here that Djerassi[3] and Klyne[7] have reported rotatory dispersion, and Velluz and Legrand,[35] as well as Ourisson and co-workers,[34,37,41] circular dichroism of α,β-unsaturated keto-groups located in various positions in steroid and triterpene molecules.

Finally, since considerable variations (e.g., fine structure, wavelength shifts) have been observed in the Cotton effect associated with the n - π^* transition of α,β-unsaturated ketones in different solvents, this factor should also be taken into consideration in interpreting the optical properties of such new substances.

53a, 3β acetoxy; 5αH
b, 3α acetoxy; 5βH

54a, 5αH; R = CH₃
b, Δ⁵; R = C≡N

9-4. INFLUENCE OF ELECTRONIC FACTORS ON THE COTTON EFFECT OF α,β-UNSATURATED KETONES

A. 6-Halo-Δ^4-3-Keto Steroids

Substitution of Δ^4-3-keto steroids with a halogen atom at C-6 sometimes drastically changes the general nature of the Cotton effect. This is clearly exemplified in Figure 9-21,[3] which shows the rotatory dispersion curves of 6α-(55a) and 6β-fluoro-testosterone (55b) and of 6β-chloro (56a) and 6β-bromotestosterone acetate (56b).[6] It is apparent in Figure 9-21 that an equatorial substituent does not affect seriously the rotatory dispersion curve, as would be expected.[46] Hence 6α-fluoro-testosterone (55a) exhibits a rotatory dispersion curve reminiscent of that of testosterone (4) (see Fig. 9-2). A completely different situation is observed in the curves of 6β-chloro (56a) and 6β-bromo-testosterone acetate (56b) (see Fig. 9-21), because they exhibit a positive Cotton effect in the 330 mμ region. The dispersion curve of 6β-fluoro-testosterone (55b) shows a Cotton effect of the same sign as testosterone (4), but considerably shifted toward lower rotational values.

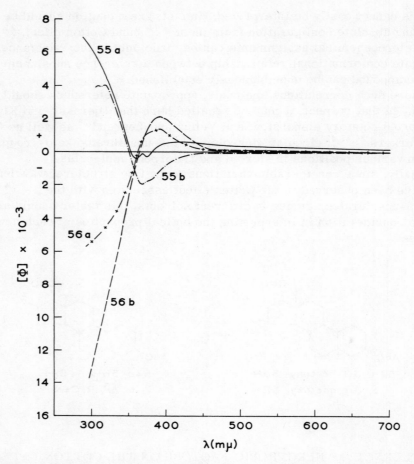

Fig. 9-21. RD curves of 6α-fluoro-testosterone (55a), 6β-fluoro-testosterone (55b), 6β-chloro-testosterone-acetate (56a) and 6β-bromo-testosterone-acetate (56b) in dioxane solution (modified from C. Djerassi, <u>Optical Rotatory Dispersion: Application to Organic Chemistry,</u> McGraw-Hill, New York, 1960).

55a, R₁ = F; R₂ = H

b, R₁ = H; R₂ = F

56a, X = Cl

b, X = Br

Figure 9-22 shows that such an effect is also detected by circular dichroism. The circular dichroism curves of the 19-chloro-Δ^4-3-keto derivative (57)[16] and of the 6β-fluoro-19-chloro-Δ^4-3-keto steroid (58),[16] represented in Figure 9-22, clearly indicate the stronger negative Cotton effect exhibited by the Δ^4-3-keto chromophore of the latter. Moreover, the position of the main negative maximum in (58) is clearly shifted toward a higher wavelength. Such a bathochromic shift is better observed by circular dichroism (see Fig. 9-22), than by rotatory dispersion (see Fig. 9-21).

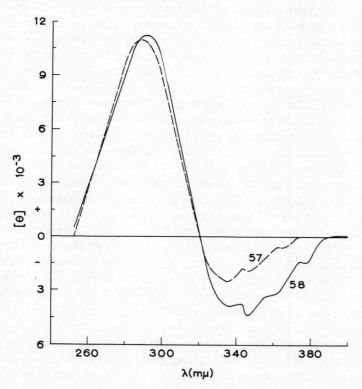

Fig. 9-22. CD curves of 19-chloro-17α-hydroxy-deoxycorticosterone (19-chloro compound S) (57) and 6β-fluoro-16α-methyl-17α-acetoxy-19-chloro-progesterone (58) in dioxane solution.

57

58

The changes induced by an axial 6β–halogen atom in the Cotton effect of these α,β–unsaturated ketones are probably largely of electronic origin. Furthermore, the different behavior of the fluorine atom when compared with the other halogen atom has been attributed[47a] to its position in the atomic refractivity and specific rotativity scale.[47b]

B. 19–Nor and 19–Substituted Δ^4-3-Keto Steroids

It has already been mentioned that testosterone (4) and 19–nortestosterone (59a) exhibit[6] similar rotatory dispersion curves. This is also true for 10β–hydroxy-19-nortestosterone (59b), indicating that in such compounds the nature of the angular substituent at C-10 has no particular bearing on the Cotton effect associated with the n - π* band of the α,β–unsaturated keto chromophore.[3] This should not, however, be regarded as a general rule. Indeed, as indicated previously in Table 9-1, the size of the 19-substituent may play some role in the intensity of the Cotton effect associated with the Δ^1-3-keto chromophore. Further examples will now be mentioned in which not only the size but also the nature of the angular substituent at C-10 has a direct influence on the sign and intensity of the Cotton effect associated with the n - π* transition of Δ^4-3-keto steroids.

Various 19-substituted Δ^4-3-keto steroids have been synthesized recently.[16] Table 19-3 reports the circular dichroism maximum associated with the n - π* transition of some of these compounds. It is apparent that most of the compounds listed in this table exhibit a negative Cotton effect at about 350-330 mμ. Furthermore, the molecular ellipticity of the very intense circular dichroism maximum associated with the Δ^4-3-keto chromophore is generally about [θ] = -2300 to -3300, which is lower than the normal value reported[35] for testosterone (4) and 19-nortestosterone (59a) (see Table 9-3). Some compounds, however, such as the 19-vinyl (64a) and the 19-caproate (62), exhibit a stronger negative circular dichroism maximum. In the case of the caproate (62), this increase in molecular ellipticity is attributed to the size of the acyl grouping, since the 19-hydroxy (60a) and 19-acetoxy (60b) derivatives show the normal value typical of most 19-substituted steroids. In the 19-vinyl compound (64a), the increase in the Cotton effect of the Δ^4-3-keto chromophore is probably due to π-orbital overlap between the 19-double bond and the α,β-unsaturated system of ring A. While the 11β-hydroxyl group in 19-methylene-hydrocortisone acetate (64b) would still have been expected to increase the negative Cotton effect (see Sec. 9-3-F), the hydrogen bonding which seems to occur between the vinyl double bond and the 11β-hydroxyl group[38] leads instead to a weak Cotton effect for the Δ^4-3-keto chromophore, similar to (63a) (see Table 9-3).[38]

59a, R=H
b, R=OH

60a, R=H
b, R=Ac

61

62   63a, R=CH₃   64a, R=H
          b, R=Cl   b, R=OH

Table 9-3

INFLUENCE OF THE 10β-SUBSTITUENT ON THE COTTON EFFECT
EXHIBITED BY THE Δ^4-3-KETO CHROMOPHORE IN THE
STEROID MOLECULE

Compound	10β-Substituent	Cotton Effect of the Δ^4-3-Keto Chromophore	
		Wavelength (mμ)	Molecular Ellipticity [θ]
59a	H	331	−4720
4	CH₃	330	−4290
60a	CH₂OH	332	−3000
60b	CH₂OAc	334	−3250
61	CH₂−O−C(=O)−CF₂Cl	335	−3810
62	CH₂−O Capr.	334	−4370
63a	CH₂−CH₃	332	−2390
63b	CH₂−Cl	334	−2600
64a	CH=CH₂	332	−4300
64b	CH=CH₂	334	−2150
65	C(=O)−OH	323	−2740
66	C(=O)−NET₂	339	+3500

Still more characteristic is the positive circular dichroism maximum
exhibited at 339 mμ by the unsaturated system of the amide (66).[38] This inversion of the Cotton effect is very probably due to electronic interactions existing
between the nitrogen atom of the amido-group and Δ^4-3-keto electrons, since
the carboxylic acid derivative (65) shows a normal negative maximum at 323 mμ.

65   66   67

9-5. POLYENES AND POLYKETONIC α,β-UNSATURATED COMPOUNDS

A. Cross-Conjugated Chromophores

In Chapter 6 mention was made of subtle conformational distortions which can occur in ring systems by conformational transmission, through long-distance effects attributed to the introduction of sp^2 carbon atoms in a ring adjacent to the carbonyl-containing cyclic system. Hence the introduction of a new double bond, a carbonyl grouping, or an epoxy function in conjugation with an α,β-unsaturated keto chromophore still complicates the interpretation of the Cotton effect, since one deals now with a new type of chromophore.

This is the case of the $\Delta^{1,4}$-3-keto chromophore, such as that in 1-dehydro-progesterone (67). This substance exhibits a weakly negative Cotton effect in the 365 mμ region.[35,48] While the fine structure associated with the $\Delta^{1,4}$-3-keto chromophore is not easily detected,[48] dramatic changes of the aspect of the circular dichroism curves have been observed in different solvents.[35] Although this may imply a certain conformational mobility, which incidentally could perhaps be confirmed by low-temperature studies, such an observation also emphasizes the importance of the choice of solvent for rotatory dispersion and circular dichroism examination of this chromophore.

Introduction of an 11α-hydroxyl group in a molecule containing the $\Delta^{1,4}$-3-keto chromophore leads to a positive multiple Cotton effect. This has been shown in the case of holadysone (68), which exhibits a weak positive circular dichroism maximum at about 360 mμ.[30] Finally, introduction of an 11β-hydroxyl group, as in (69),[35] leads to a weak negative Cotton effect reminiscent of the unsubstituted $\Delta^{1,4}$-3-keto chromophore.

Because of the weakness of these Cotton effects, circular dichroism seems to be indicated, rather than rotatory dispersion, for the examination of such

68   69   70

chromophores. This is mainly advisable when a second chromophore is present in the molecule, as in (67). Indeed, with rotatory dispersion the intense positive Cotton effect associated with the saturated 20-carbonyl masks almost completely the weak Cotton effect due to the $\Delta^{1,4}$-3-keto system in dehydro-progesterone (67). Since a better resolution of both chromophores is observed by circular dichroism, this should be the method of choice for such studies.

The last example of a $\Delta^{1,4}$-3-keto cross-conjugated system is suggested by the bridged-compound (70).[16] Figure 9-23 shows the circular dichroism associated with the ring A chromophore of this substance. While it has been mentioned that the $\Delta^{1,4}$-3-one system exhibits a weakly negative Cotton effect, it is apparent from Figure 9-23 that the distortion created in (70) by the 6,19-oxide bridge leads to a strong negative circular dichroism maximum. Thus the present situation is similar to that of a simple Δ^4-3-keto system in which the 6,19-oxide bridge is known also to enhance the negative Cotton effect (see Sec. 9-3-B). The main difference between these chromophores is, of course, the wavelengths at which their Cotton effects occur.

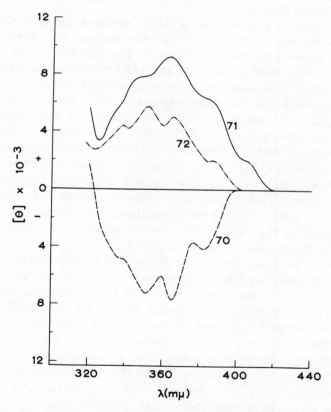

Fig. 9-23. Cotton effect associated with the unsaturated 3-keto chromophore in 6β,19-oxido-androsta-1,4-diene-3,17-dione (70), 19-hydroxy-pregna-4,6-diene-3,20-dione-acetate (71) and 19-hydroxy-6α,7α-epoxy-pregn-4-ene-3,20-dione-acetate (72) in dioxane solution.

B. Extended Conjugated Systems

The next compounds being examined present double bonds or epoxy function in conjugation with α,β-unsaturated keto-systems. The rotatory dispersion[3,6] and circular dichroism[35] of this type of chromophore have already been reported in the chemical literature. Furthermore, such a situation has been commented upon in the case of the 16-cyano-pregnene (54b) (Sec. 9-3). The introduction of the nitrile group in conjugation with the enone system has been shown to produce a bathochromic shift of the absorption maximum in (54b), enhancing at the same time the positive Cotton effect (see Table 9-2).

In Figure 9-23 the circular dichroism maxima associated with the ring A and B conjugated systems of compounds (71) and (72) are also represented. The conjugated dienone chromophore of the 19-substituted $\Delta^{4,6}$-3-keto steroid (71) exhibits a positive circular dichroism whose fine structure is centered at about 363 mμ. Epoxidation of the Δ^6-double bond in (71) affords (72), which also shows a positive Cotton effect, but at a slightly lower wavelength (about 351 mμ), as illustrated in Figure 9-23.

While the dienone (71) exhibits a strong **positive** circular dichroism maximum in the 363 mμ region (see Fig. 9-23), the dienone (73) shows an intense **negative** Cotton effect dispersion curve (a = -94), with the trough occurring at 395 mμ ([Φ] = -6600°), indicative of the antipodal relationship existing in the neighborhood of the chromophores in these substituted steroids.[43] This dependency of the Cotton effect on the stereochemistry surrounding the dienone system is best illustrated in Figure 9-24, which reproduces the rotatory dispersion curves of the four isomeric steroids (74) to (77).[24] While both 10β-methyl ergostane derivatives (74) and (76) exhibit a positive multiple Cotton effect in the 380-410 mμ region, the 10α-compounds (75) and (77) show, in the same region, negative Cotton effects of very distinct intensities. These observations demonstrate that the $\Delta^{4,6}$-3-keto chromophore is completely different from the Δ^4-3-keto system. Indeed, it has been mentioned previously that Δ^4-3-keto compounds presenting the 10β- or 10α-methyl (or hydrogen) 8β,9α-configuration exhibit negative Cotton effects (see Sec. 9-3-E).

Extension of the conjugation existing in (73) by introduction of a new double bond leads to a very intense chromophore. Thus the trienone (78)[43] exhibits an extremely intense circular dichroism negative maximum ([θ]$_{335}$ = -39270), which seems to be mainly due to the inherently dissymmetric portion of the chromophore present in the molecule (see Chaps. 8 and 10).

Besides the conjugated systems discussed above, other extended conjugated chromophores such as ene-diones have also been investigated by rotatory dispersion. For example, a negative Cotton effect has been shown to be associated with steroidal 4-ene-3,6-diones (a = -90).[49] A comparison of the Cotton effect shown by this system with the optical rotatory dispersion curve of 7β(H)-eudesm-4-ene-3,6-dione (79) (a = -32) induced Theobald[50] to suggest that the 7α-isopropyl group probably causes some conformational distortion in ring B of this sesquiterpenic derivative. Worth mention also is the very strong second Cotton effect (a = +777) presented by (79) in the wavelength range 200-300 mμ.[50]

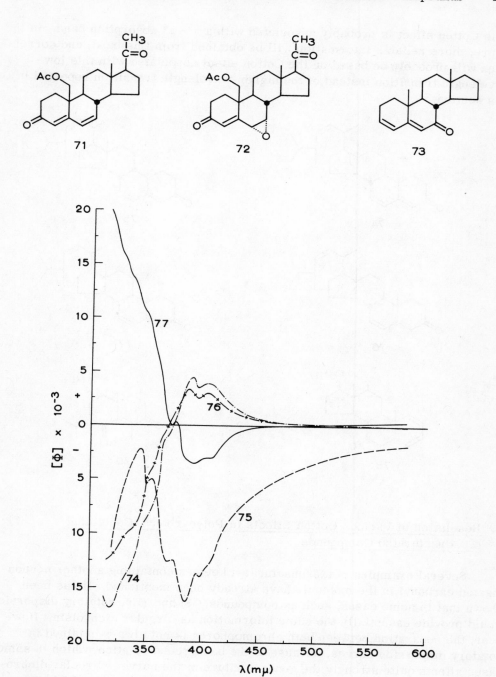

Fig. 9-24. RD curves of ergosta-4,6,22-trien-3-one (74), 9β,10α-ergosta-4,6,22-trien-3-one (75), 9β-ergosta-4,6,22-trien-3-one (76), and 10α-ergosta-4,6,22-trien-3-one (77) (modified from R. Van Moorselaar, Ph.D. Thesis, University of Leiden, February, 1962).

This Cotton effect is probably associated with a $\pi - \pi^*$ absorption band. In the future, more reliable information will be obtained from this band, and correlations will probably be based on the Cotton effect associated with this low-wavelength transition instead of the higher-wavelength transition reported in this section.

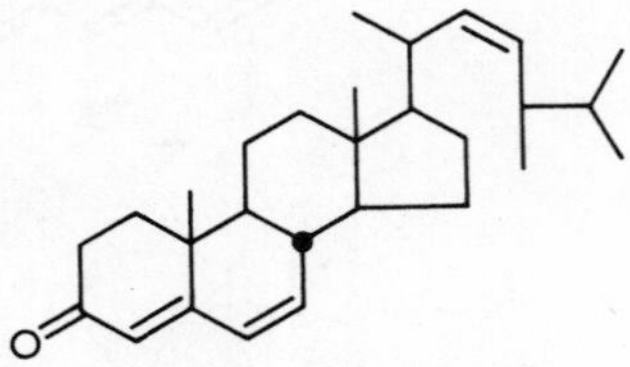

74

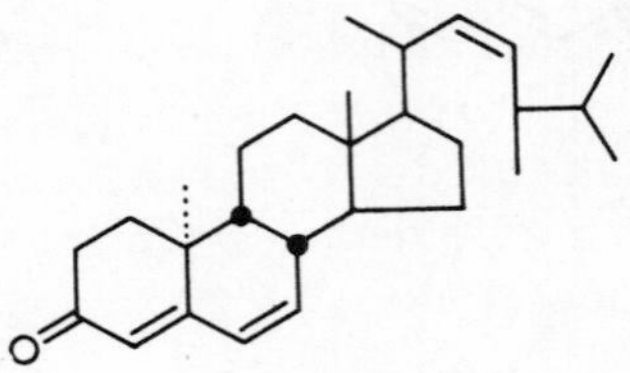

75

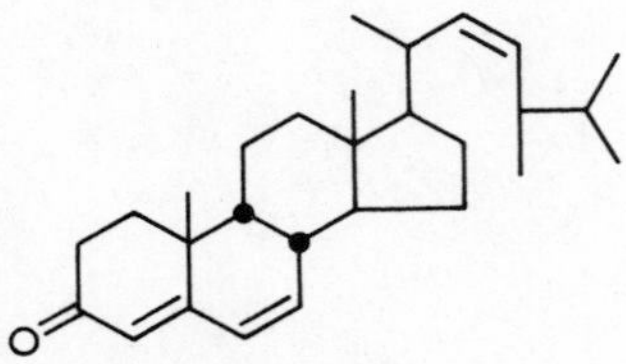

76

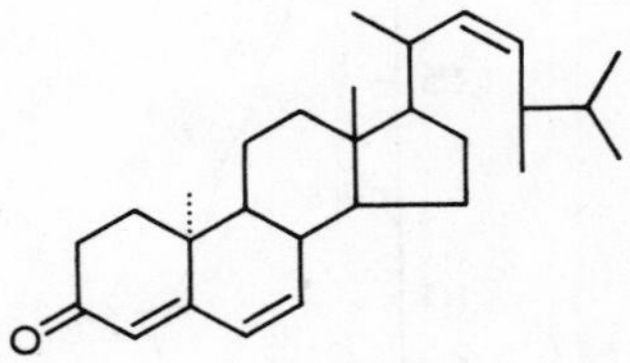

77

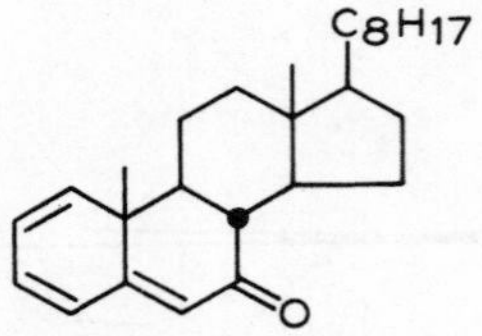

78

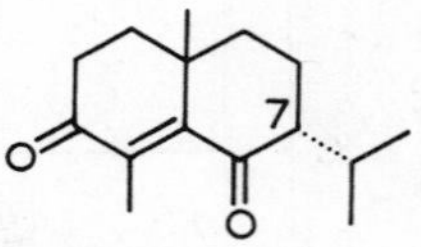

79

C. Resolution of Various Cotton Effects in Polycarbonyl-Containing α,β-Unsaturated Compounds

Several examples of α,β-unsaturated ketones containing another nonconjugated carbonyl in the molecule have already been mentioned. It has been shown that in some cases, such as compounds (18) and (19), rotatory dispersion would provide essentially the same information as circular dichroism. However, the separation between both chromophores is not always obtained in rotatory dispersion curves, because of the background rotation, which in some cases affects quite strongly the general nature of the curve. Circular dichroism should then be the method of choice, because the selectivity which characterizes this technique permits a better quantitative evaluation of both chromophores.

Since this property has already been emphasized,[18,35,51] only one example will be mentioned here.

During a recent synthesis of 16α-acetyl-progesterone (80) and 16β-acetyl-17α-progesterone (81), the problem which arose was to discover the sign of the Cotton effect associated with the newly introduced 16-acetyl side chain.[52] The rotatory dispersion curves of these compounds and of the 16-carbomethoxy derivatives (82) and (83) were obtained and are reproduced in Figure 9-25.[53] It is immediately apparent that the situation encountered in the steroids (80) and (81) is rather complicated, since each possesses three chromophores in its molecule. As indicated in Figure 9-25, the resolution of the n - π^* bands of the α,β-unsaturated grouping and the saturated carbonyls is not satisfactory enough to make a safe deduction from the dispersion curves about the contribution of the 16-acetyl side chain.

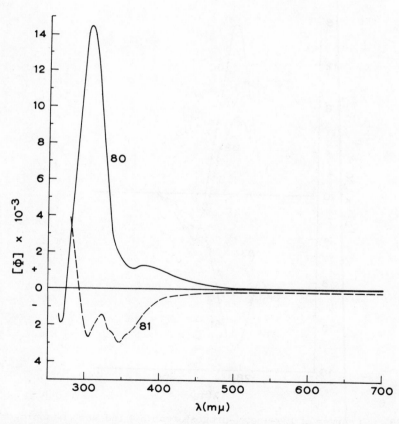

Fig. 9-25. RD curves of 16α-acetyl-progesterone (80) and 16β-acetyl-isoprogesterone (81) in dioxane solution [from P. Crabbé, Tetrahedron, **19**, 51 (1963); reproduced by permission of the editor].

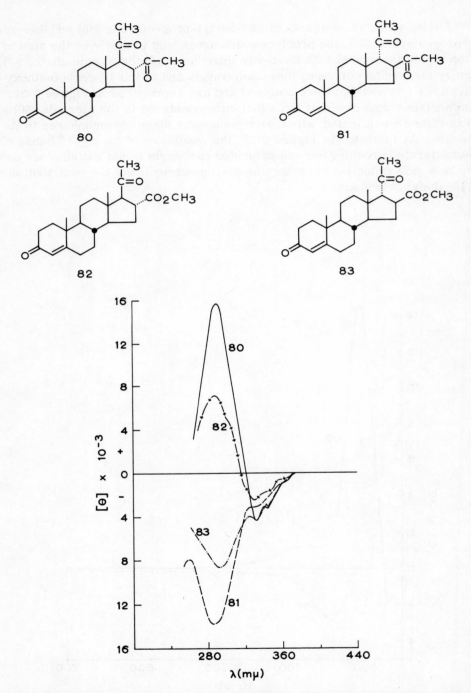

Fig. 9-26. CD curves of 16α-acetyl-progesterone (80), 16β-acetyl-isoprogesterone (81), 16α-carbomethoxy-progesterone (82), and 16β-carbomethoxy-isoprogesterone (83) in dioxane solution [modified from P. Crabbé, F. McCapra, F. Comer, and A. I. Scott, _Tetrahedron_, **20**, 2455 (1964)].

The situation is, however, much clearer in the case of the circular dichroism curves exhibited by these compounds (see Fig. 9-26).[54] In these curves the fine structure associated with the Δ^4-3-keto system is well dissociated from the other chromophores. Furthermore, from the comparison of the dichroism curves of 16α-acetyl-progesterone (80) with 16α-carbomethoxy-progesterone (82), it is apparent (see Fig. 9-26) that while the 16α-carbomethoxy group does not make any major contribution to the positive Cotton effect associated with the 17β-acetyl side chain (see Sec. 6-6), the 16α-acetyl grouping of (80) enhances it considerably. Conversely, the negative maximum of the 17α-acetyl side chain of the isoprogesterone (81) is considerably increased by the 16β-acetyl substituent, but the 16β-carbomethoxy function, as in (83), exerts little, if any, effect.

One can conclude from these observations that circular dichroism should be preferred for the detection of weak Cotton effects, or for analyzing quantitatively the Cotton effects of compounds exhibiting strong background rotations in their rotatory dispersion curve. Circular dichroism would also be indicated for a separate quantitative study of the Cotton effects associated with the various chromophores of a polyketonic compound.

9-6. A PROPOSED EXTENSION OF THE OCTANT RULE FOR THE n - π^* BAND OF α,β-UNSATURATED KETONES

It was reported in Section 9-2 that in α,β-unsaturated ketones the long-wavelength π - π^* transition centered near 240-260 mμ is optically active and that the sign of the Cotton effect reflects the chirality of the inherently dissymmetric unsaturated ketone chromophore. The helicity rule developed for 1,3-dienes[9] (see Chap. 10) has been extended to α,β-unsaturated ketones,[5] thus helping to define the conformation of such systems. The strong background rotations apparent in many rotatory dispersion curves discussed earlier are now understood to be tailings of this strong π - π^* Cotton effect. As already mentioned, there is no doubt that the new instruments becoming available will permit a closer examination of this spectral region, thus leading to safer and more concrete conclusions regarding the stereochemistry (i.e., absolute conformation) of the compounds being investigated.

As far as the higher-wavelength n - π^* transition of α,β-unsaturated carbonyls is concerned, several studies have been devoted to its Cotton effect. Modifications of the octant rule[4] have been proposed which seem to account for the experimental Cotton effects being observed.[55-57] For instance, in cyclohexenones with planar chromophores, the carbon atoms lying out of the plane of the ring are responsible for the Cotton effect.[57] In nonplanar cisoid cyclohexenones, the sign of the Cotton effect is positive when the double bond falls into a positive octant.[57] Conversely, a negative Cotton effect is observed for compounds in which the double bond lies in a negative octant.[57] The same rule, which incidentally is a development of Walley's suggestion,[55] would also apply[57] to α-aryl ketones.[58] Finally, this rule also seems to hold for cross-conjugated dienones, provided that no substituent with π or p electrons interferes with the conjugated chromophore.[57]

Should this rule indeed prove to be of general applicability, it would be a great help in interpreting the experimental Cotton effect associated with the n - π^* transition of α,β-conjugated compounds.

9-7. THE β,γ-UNSATURATED KETO CHROMOPHORE

A. Theoretical Considerations

It has been known for a long time that β,γ-unsaturated ketones often exhibit abnormally high ultraviolet extinction coefficients in the 300 mμ region. As early as 1950, in order to account for the exaltation of the 295 mμ n - π^* band in substituted phenylacetones, it was suggested[59] that interaction between carbonyl and phenyl groups takes place directly through space. This interpretation, recognized to be essentially correct, has been further developed by several investigators.[60]

According to Labhart and Wagnière,[61] in β,γ-unsaturated ketones having the appropriate molecular geometry the nonbonding n-electrons on carbonyl oxygen interact with the π-electrons of the homoconjugated ethylene-carbonyl π-system. It follows that the forbidden n - π^* transition borrows intensity from the allowed π - π^* transition. Accordingly, the extinction coefficient of the ultraviolet 300 mμ band is enhanced. Further, several authors remarked that spectroscopic interactions between a carbonyl group and a β,γ-double bond are sometimes accompanied by high optical activity.[60,62,63] Recently, Mislow, Moscowitz, and Djerassi[64] formulated the idea that the essential β,γ-unsaturated carbonyl system constitutes an inherently dissymmetric chromophore (see Chaps. 8 and 10), leading to a generalization of the octant rule[4] for this system.

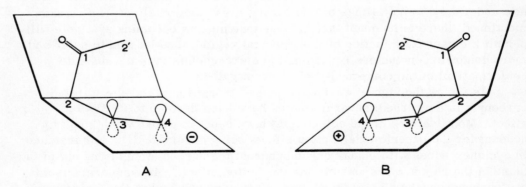

Fig. 9-27. Representation of the enantiomeric chromophores associated with dissymmetric β,γ-unsaturated ketones [from A. Moscowitz, K. Mislow, M. A. W. Glass, and C. Djerassi, J. Am. Chem. Soc., **84**, 1945 (1962), reproduced by permission of the editor].

These investigators suggested that the chirality of the β,γ-unsaturated keto chromophore may be discussed in terms of the geometric representation shown in Figure 9-27.[64] Two planes are defined by $C_2{}'-C_1{\overline{\overline{}}}O-C_2$ and $C_2-C_3-C_4$ portions of the chromophore which intersect at a dihedral angle greater than 90° (about 120° in rigid structures). As indicated in Figure 9-27, the arrangement $C_2{}'-C_1{\overline{\overline{}}}O-C_2-C_3-C_4$ assumes one of two enantiomeric conformations, one giving rise to a negative (A) and the other to a positive (B) Cotton effect.[64]

B. Applications

On the basis of the schematic representations shown in Figure 9-27, the positive Cotton effects exhibited by bicyclo[2.2.1]hept-5-en-2-one (dehydronor-camphor) (84) and bicyclo[2.2.2]oct-5-en-2-one (85) (see Fig. 9-28)[60] confirm that in these compounds the β,γ-unsaturated keto chromophore pertains to the configuration (B) (see Fig. 9-27).

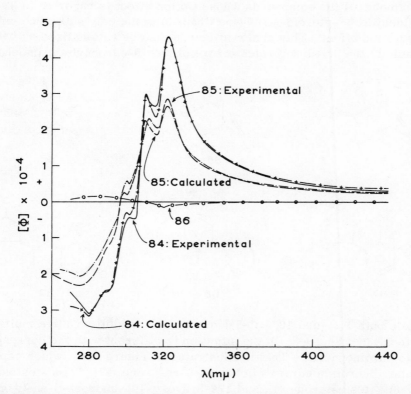

Fig. 9-28. Calculated and experimental RD curves of dehydronorcamphor (84) and bicyclo[2.2.2]oct-5-en-2-one (85); experimental RD curve of norcamphor (86) [modified from K. Mislow, Ann. N. Y. Acad. Sci., **93**, 459 (1962)].

The shape of the rotatory dispersion curves of the dissymmetric chromophore present in these bicyclic compounds [(84) and (85)] has been calculated from that of the absorption curves through use of the Kronig-Kramers' transforms (see Chap. 2).[60,64] Experimental and calculated dispersion curves of these two β,γ-unsaturated ketones [(84 and (85)] are shown in Figure 9-28. Moreover, Figure 9-28 also reproduces the rotatory dispersion curve of norcamphor (86) which, since it does not contain the dissymmetric β,γ-keto chromophore, exhibits a very weak Cotton effect.[60]

The rather intense Cotton effect associated with β,γ-unsaturated carbonyl chromophores has been reported by several investigators. Snatzke et al.[22] discussed the molecular ellipticity shown by such a chromophore in seven-membered ring compounds pertaining to the A-homo steroid series. Mason and his coworkers,[63d] Ourisson and his coworkers,[37,41] and Gorodetsky and Mazur[65] have reported and commented upon the optical rotational strength of Δ^5-3-ketones in the steroid, 4-substituted steroid, 4-substituted 19-nor steroid and triterpene series. Moreover, the strong positive Cotton effect exhibited by the β,γ-unsaturated ketone (155) mentioned in Chapter 6 is now rationalized as resulting from partial overlap between the carbonyl and ethylenic orbitals. Finally, among all the compounds whose Cotton effect is reported in Table 6-15, the 19-aldehydo Δ^5-steroid (175) (see Chap. 6) is the only substance exhibiting a strong Cotton effect. This observation can also be rationalized as being attributable to the β,γ-unsaturated nature of the 19-carbonyl chromophore.

84   85   86

87   88   89

While both 10α- and 10β-Δ^4-3-keto steroids exhibit negative multiple Cotton effects (see Sec. 9-3-E), the situation is different with the corresponding Δ^5-3-keto chromophores. This is illustrated in Figure 9-29, which reproduces the circular dichroism curves of cholest-5-en-3-one (87),[63d] 10α-testosterone acetate (88),[33] testosterone (4), and 17β-hydroxy-10α-androst-5-en-3-one (89).[33] It is immediately apparent that the Cotton effects exhibited by (87) and (89) have opposite sign, thus expressing better than their Δ^4-isomers the different configuration at C-10.

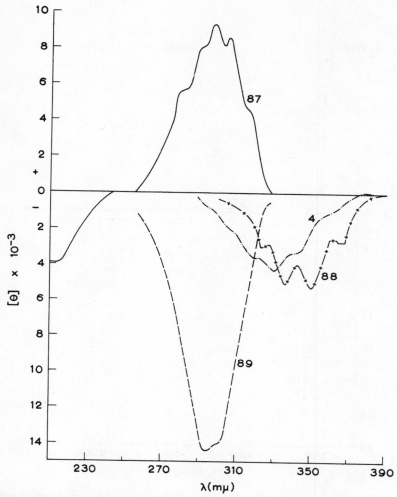

Fig. 9-29. CD curves of testosterone (4), cholest-5-en-3-one (87), 10α-testosterone-acetate (88), and 17β-hydroxy-10α-androst-5-en-3-one (89).

One further example of the strong Cotton effect exhibited by β,γ-unsaturated ketones is posed by the rotatory dispersion curve of the pentacyclic steroid (91), as illustrated in Figure 9-30. The drastic difference in molecular amplitude between the β-hydroxy-ketone (90; a = -39)[66] and the β,γ-unsaturated ketone (91; a = -500)[66] is reminiscent of the situation encountered in the case of norcamphor (86) and dehydronorcamphor (84), discussed above.

Verbenalin (92)[67] and chrysanthenone (93)[68] are other β,γ-unsaturated ketones for which an intensified carbonyl absorption band has been reported. However, the geometry of the carbonyl-double bond system in these compounds can no longer be represented by Figure 9-27.[64b] Instead, Figure 9-31 shows a reasonable representation of the geometry of the β,γ-unsaturated ketone system in verbenalin (92).[64b]

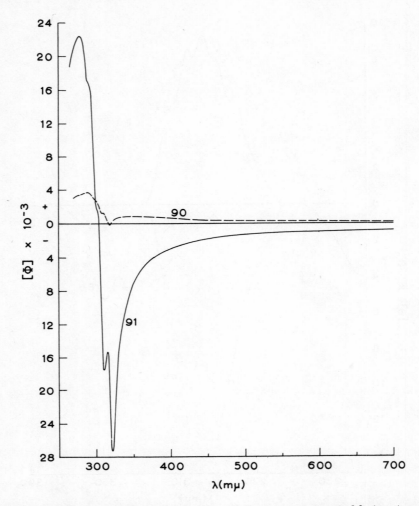

Fig. 9-30. RD curves of the β-ketol (90) and the β,γ-unsaturated keto-steroid (91) in dioxane solution (courtesy of Dr. K. Kuriyama, The Shionogi Research Laboratory).

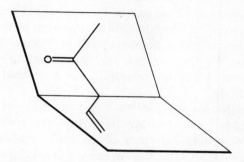

Fig. 9-31. The geometry of the β,γ-unsaturated keto chromophore in verbenalin (92) [modified from A. Moscowitz, K. Mislow, M. A. W. Glass, and C. Djerassi, J. Am. Chem. Soc., **84**, 1945 (1962)].

The weak Cotton effects shown by verbenalin (92; a = -6)[64b] and chrysanthenone (93; a = +48)[64b] are more reminiscent of saturated than of β,γ-unsaturated ketones. In fact, the positive Cotton effect of chrysanthenone (93) has been interpreted[69] in terms of the octant rule applied to cyclobutanones (see Sec. 6-2-C). Indeed, reexamination of the absorption spectra of (92) and (93) reveals that the intensity of the band at 290 mμ may be largely attributed[64b] to overlap from an intense band at 238 mμ, presumably in part the π - π^* transition described by Winstein and his collaborators[70] for related unsaturated ketones. Hence the amplitude of the Cotton effect curves of β,γ-unsaturated ketones is critically dependent on the relative disposition of carbonyl function and double bond. Moreover, conformations approximating the array in Figure 9-27 quite often lead to intense ultraviolet absorptions and strong Cotton effects.[64b]

Finally, it may be mentioned that Mason et al.[63d] have observed a bathochromic shift of the circular dichroism maxima of cholest-5-en-3-one (87) from ethanol to cyclohexane solution, thus indicating that the Cotton effect of the β,γ-unsaturated keto chromophore is also solvent-dependent.

C. Aromatic Ketones

Some bridged β,γ-benzo-ketones, characterized by homoconjugated π-systems, were mentioned in Chapter 8. The very intense Cotton effects exhibited by such systems can be interpreted in terms of homoconjugation of carbonyl and benzene π-electrons.[71]

Cookson and Hudec[63b] have come to similar conclusions on the basis of their rotatory dispersion study of epimeric 3-aryl-5α-cholestan-2-ones (94a, b) and phenyl-dehydrocamphor. They have indicated that in 3-phenyl-cholestan-2-ones the very intense positive Cotton effect of the axial 3α-isomer (94a), which is accompanied by the typically intense absorption in the carbonyl region, suggests the prevalence of conformations in which the orientation of π-electrons of the benzene ring relative to electrons of the carbonyl group is geometrically favorable to enhancement.[63b] Furthermore, the sign of the Cotton effect of (94a; a = +374) is in harmony with the geometry (B) of Figure 9-27, for the indicated absolute configuration.[64b] Conversely, the equatorial 3β-isomer (94b; a = +45), in which such orientations are not possible, has a normal absorption spectrum and molecular amplitude.

It has been mentioned earlier[18](Sec. 6-5-L) that during a synthesis of 19-nor-9β,10α-steroids[72] the circular dichroism and rotatory dispersion techniques have permitted a detailed study of the conformation of the intermediates (95b) and (96b), corresponding to the inversion of configuration of the hydrogen atom at C-9 of the diketo-steroids (95a) and (96a). The difference between the positive Cotton effects exhibited by (95b; $[\theta]$ = +50230) and (96b; $[\theta]$ = +26730) had been attributed to a ring-C boat conformation in (96b).[18] Reexamination of the molecular model[73] of compound (95b) indicates that the arrangement of the 11-carbonyl group vis-à-vis the aromatic A-ring is similar to the conformation recognized for 3α-phenyl-5α-cholestan-2-one (94a). Thus the very strong positive Cotton effect of (95b) is now interpreted in terms of homoconjugation of the carbonyl and benzene π-electrons, since the geometry is favorable to homoconjugation.

In cases in which free rotation may occur, the experimental Cotton effect sometimes permits the assignment of rotomeric conformations to β,γ-unsaturated ketones. Such a concept, which is supported by theoretical considerations, has allowed Moscowitz, Mislow, Glass, and Djerassi[64b] to extend their conclusions to conformational analysis of open-chain α-phenyl ketones. They considered

94a, R₁ = C₆H₅; R₂ = H
   b, R₁ = H; R₂ = C₆H₅

95a, 9αH
   b, 9βH

96a, 9αH
   b, 9βH

only the conformations in which the phenyl and carbonyl groups have the proper orientation for high optical activity, thus including the conformers approximating the geometry shown in Figure 9-27. For each enantiomer (R) and (S), two relevant diastereomeric conformations exist, one (97a) corresponding to a positive, the other (97b) to a negative Cotton effect. In the (S)-(97a) conformation, the smaller S-group on the asymmetric carbon is in a less favorable steric position than the larger L-group, because of steric compression against R_1 and against the phenyl **ortho**-hydrogen. Instead, in (S)-(97b) it is the larger group which occupies the unfavorable configuration; hence conformation (97a) predominates in the equilibrium. For similar reasons, (R)-(98b) predominates in the enantiomeric equilibrium. It follows that the (S)-isomer has a net positive and the (R)-isomer a net negative Cotton effect. The amplitude of the Cotton effect is a function of the relative difference in size of L and S: the larger the relative difference, the greater the deviation of (97a)/(97b) or (98a)/(98b) ratio from unity and the more pronounced the **net** Cotton effect.[64b]

These important concepts have permitted clarification of a number of previously unexplained observations which had been reported in the chemical literature.

S-97a   S-97b

S-98a   S-98b

REFERENCES

1. (a) A.E. Gillam and E. S. Stern, An Introduction to Electronic Absorption Spectroscopy in Organic Chemistry, E. Arnold, London 1958; (b) A. I. Scott, Interpretation of the Ultraviolet Spectra of Natural Products, Pergamon Press, London, 1963.

2. R. C. Cookson and S. H. Dandegaonker, J. Chem. Soc., 1651 (1955), and references cited therein.

3. C. Djerassi, Optical Rotatory Dispersion: Applications to Organic Chemistry, McGraw-Hill, New York, 1960.

4.   W. Moffitt, R. B. Woodward, A. Moscowitz, W. Klyne, and C. Djerassi, J. Am. Chem. Soc., 83, 4013 (1961).

5.   C. Djerassi, R. Records, E. Bunnenberg, K. Mislow, and A. Moscowitz, J. Am. Chem. Soc., 84, 870 (1962).

6.   C. Djerassi, R. Riniker, and B. Riniker, J. Am. Chem. Soc., 78, 6377 (1956).

7.   W. Klyne in Advances in Organic Chemistry (R. A. Raphael, E. C. Taylor, and H. Wynberg, eds.), Interscience, vol. I, p. 239, New York, 1960.

8.   A. Aebi and C. Djerassi, Helv. Chim. Acta, 42, 1785 (1959).

9.   A. Moscowitz, E. Charney, U. Weiss, and H. Ziffer, J. Am. Chem. Soc., 83, 4661 (1961).

10.   D. Bertin and J. Perronnet, Comptes rendus, 257, 1946 (1963).

11.   (a) K. Takeda, T. Komeno, and S. Ishihara, Chem. Pharm. Bull. Japan, 11, 500 (1963); (b) K. Tori and K. Kuriyama, Chem. and Ind., 1525 (1963).

12.   (a) H. J. Ringold and A. Bowers, Experientia, 17, 65 (1961); (b) E. C. Olson and C. D. Alway, Anal. Chem., 32, 370 (1960); (c) See also refs. 3 and 11.

13.   H. Kaneko, M. Hashimoto, Y. Mitta, and K. Kawase, Chem. Pharm. Bull. Japan, 11, 264 (1963).

14.   S. L. Patashnik, H. L. Kimball, and S. Burstein, Steroids, 2, 19 (1963).

15.   K. Kuriyama, E. Kondo, and K. Tori, Tetrahedron Letters, No. 22, 1485 (1963).

16.   For leading references see ref. 86 in chap. 6; for the physical properties, see also P. Crabbé, L. H. Knox, and A. D. Cross, in preparation.

17.   A. Dreiding, Helv. Chim. Acta, 42, 1339 (1959).

18.   P. Crabbé, Tetrahedron, 20, 1211 (1964).

19.   T. Kubota and M. Ehrenstein, J. Org. Chem., 29, 357 (1964).

20.   (a) W. Klyne, S. C. Battacharyya, S. K. Paknikar, C. S. Narayanan, K. S. Kulkarni, T. Křepinský, M. Romaňuk, V. Herout, and F. Šorm, Tetrahedron Letters, No. 23, 1443 (1964), and references therein; (b) K. S. Kulkarni, S. K. Paknikar and S. Bhattacharyya, Tetrahedron, 20, 1289, (1964); (c) H. Hikino, Y. Hikino, Y. Takeshita, K. Meguro, and T. Takemoto, Chem. Pharm. Bull. Japan, 11, 1207 (1963).

21.   H. G. Leemann and K. Stich, Chimia, 17, 184 (1963), and references therein.

22.   G. Snatzke, B. Zeeh, and E. Müller, Tetrahedron Letters, No. 22, 1425 (1963), Tetrahedron, 20, 2937 (1964); see also G. Snatzke and A. Niser, Ann. Chem., in press.

23.   C. Djerassi and J. E. Gurst, J. Am. Chem. Soc., 86, 1755 (1964).

24.   R. van Moorselaar, Ph.D. Thesis, University of Leiden, February 1962.

25.   (a) L. Velluz, G. Nominé, R. Bucourt, A. Pierdet, and J. Tissier, Comptes rendus, 252, 3903 (1961); (b) M. Legrand and R. Viennet, Comptes rendus, 254, 322 (1962); (c) J. A. Edwards, H. Carpio, and A. D. Cross, Tetrahedron Letters, No. 45, 3299 (1964).

26.   This sample was kindly provided by Sir Ewart Jones of Oxford University.

27.   J. Castells, E. R. H. Jones, G. D. Meakins, and R. W. J. Williams, J. Chem. Soc., 1159 (1959), and subsequent papers from Oxford University; see also ref. 67 of chap. 6.

28.   This curve has been obtained from Professor C. Djerassi of Stanford University.

29.   R. Wenger, H. Dutler, H. Wehrli, K. Schaffner, and O. Jeger, Helv. Chim. Acta, 45, 2420 (1962); Helv. Chim. Acta, 46, 1096 (1963).

30.   R. Tschesche, I. Mörner, and G. Snatzke, Ann. Chem., 670, 103 (1963).

31.   F. Sondheimer, R. Mechoulam, and M. Sprecher, Tetrahedron Letters, No. 22, 38 (1960), Tetrahedron, 20, 2473 (1964).

32.   This compound was prepared by Dr. O. Halpern of the Syntex Research Laboratories.

33.   This circular dichroism result was obtained through the courtesy of Professor G. Ourisson and Dr. W. Wojnarowski at the University of Strasbourg, on a sample prepared by Dr. R. Ginsig of the Syntex Research Laboratories.

34.   J. C. Bloch, Ph.D. Thesis, University of Strasbourg, May 1964; J. C. Bloch and G. Ourisson, Bull. Soc. Chim. France, 3011 and 3018 (1964).

35.   L. Velluz and M. Legrand, Angew. Chem., 73, 603 (1961).

36.   A. M. Giroud, A. Rassat, and T Rüll, Bull. Soc. Chim. France, 2563 (1963).

37.   P. Witz, H. Herrmann, J. M. Lehn, and G. Ourisson, Bull. Soc. Chim. France, 1101 (1963).

38.   These compounds were prepared in the Syntex Research Laboratories by Drs. E. Blossey, J. A. Edwards, R. Ginsig, O. Halpern, and R. Villotti.

39.   G. Snatzke and H. W. Fehlhaber, Tetrahedron, 20, 1243 (1964).

40.   (a) P. Crabbé and C. Casas-Campillo, J. Org. Chem., 29, 2731 (1964); (b) F. Sondheimer, S. Burstein, and R. Mechoulam, J. Am. Chem. Soc., 82, 3209 (1960).

41.   P. Witz, Ph.D. Thesis, University of Strasbourg, May 1964.

42.　R. M. van den Bosch, M. S. de Winter, S. A. Szpilfogel, H. Herrmann, P. Witz, and G. Ourisson, Bull. Soc. Chim. France, 1090 (1963).

43.　Unpublished results from the Syntex Research Laboratories.

44.　(a) J. C. Danilewicz, Ph.D. Thesis, University of London, June 1963; (b) The rotatory dispersion curves of Δ^{16}-20-keto-steroids, also presenting a keto group at C-3 and C-11 have been reported by L. Velluz, G. Amiard, R. Heymès, and B. Goffinet, Bull. Soc. Chim. France, 2166 (1961). For the circular dichroism of such compounds, see ref. 35.

45.　J. Romo, L. Rodriguez-Hahn, P. Joseph-Nathan, M. Martinez, and P. Crabbé, Bull. Soc. Chim. France, 1276 (1964).

46.　(a) C. W. Bird, R. C. Cookson, and S. H. Dandegaonker, J. Chem. Soc., 3675 (1956); (b) see also ref. 12.

47.　(a) See footnote 11 in ref. 4. (b) Pauling, The Nature of the Chemical Bond, 3d ed., p. 260, Cornell University Press, Ithaca, N. Y., 1960.

48.　(a) M. B. Rubin and E. C. Blossey, J. Org. Chem., 29, 1932 (1964); (b) C. Djerassi, Proc. Chem. Soc., 314 (1964).

49.　(a) See ref. 6; (b) P. Crabbé, E. A. Azpeitia, and C. Djerassi, Bull. Soc. Chim. Belg., 70, 168 (1961).

50.　D. W. Theobald, Tetrahedron, 20, 1455 (1964).

51.　C. Djerassi, H. Wolf, and E. Bunnenberg, J. Am. Chem. Soc., 84, 4552 (1962).

52.　P. Crabbé, L. M. Guerrero, J. Romo, and F. Sánchez-Viesca, Tetrahedron, 19, 25 (1963).

53.　P. Crabbé, Tetrahedron, 19, 51 (1963).

54.　P. Crabbé, F. McCapra, F. Comer, and A. I. Scott, Tetrahedron, 20, 2455 (1964).

55.　W. B. Whalley, Chem. and Ind., 1024 (1962).

56.　R. E. Ballard, S. F. Mason, and G. W. Vane, Disc. Faraday Soc., 35, 43 (1963).

57.　G. Snatzke, private communication; see also G. Snatzke, Tetrahedron, in press.

58.　Inter alia: (a) B. Sjöberg, Ark. Kemi, 15, 481 (1960); (b) A. K. Bose, M. S. Manhas, R. C. Cambie, and L. N. Mander, J. Am. Chem. Soc., 84, 3201 (1962); (c) R. C. Cambie, L. N. Mander, A. K. Bose, and M. S. Manhas, Tetrahedron, 20, 409 (1964).

59.　E. L. Alpen, W. D. Kumler, and L. A. Strait, J. Am. Chem. Soc., 72, 4558 (1950).

60.　K. Mislow, Ann. N. Y. Acad. Sci., 93, 459 (1962).

61.   H. Labhart and G. Wagnière, Helv. Chim. Acta, 42, 2219 (1959).

62.   (a) R. B. Woodward and E. G. Kovach, J. Am. Chem. Soc., 72, 1009 (1950);
        (b) R. B. Woodward and P. Yates, Chem. and Ind., 1391 (1954), and related
        references.

63.   (a) R. C. Cookson and N. S. Wariyar, J. Chem. Soc., 2302 (1956); (b) R. C.
        Cookson and J. Hudec, J. Chem. Soc., 429 (1962); see also R. C. Cookson
        and S. McKenzie, Proc. Chem. Soc., 423 (1961); (c) S. F. Mason, J. Chem. Soc.,
        3285 (1962), and R. E. Ballard, S. F. Mason, and G. W. Vane, Trans. Faraday
        Soc., 59, 775 (1963); (d) R. Grinter, S. F. Mason, and G. W. Vane, Trans.
        Faraday Soc., 60, 285 (1964); (e) A. Moscowitz, Proc. Chem. Soc., 60 (1964);
        (f) S. F. Mason, Proc. Chem. Soc., 61 (1964).

64.   (a) K. Mislow, M. A. W. Glass, A. Moscowitz, and C. Djerassi, J. Am. Chem.
        Soc., 83, 2771 (1961); (b) A. Moscowitz, K. Mislow, M. A. W. Glass, and
        C. Djerassi, J. Am. Chem. Soc., 84, 1945 (1962); (c) E. Bunnenberg, C. Djerassi,
        K. Mislow, and A. Moscowitz, J. Am. Chem. Soc., 84, 2823 (1962); (d) See also
        ref. 60, and K. Mislow and J. G. Berger, J. Am. Chem. Soc., 84, 1956 (1962).

65.   M. Gorodetsky and Y. Mazur, Tetrahedron Letters, No. 4, 227 (1964);
        M. Gorodetsky, D. Amar, and Y. Mazur, J. Am. Chem. Soc., 86, 5218 (1964).

66.   The rotatory dispersion curves of these compounds, prepared at the Shionogi
        Research Laboratory, Osaka, were obtained through the courtesy of Dr. Karu
        Kuriyama.

67.   G. Büchi and R. E. Manning, Tetrahedron Letters, No. 26, 5 (1960).

68.   J. J. Hurst and G. H. Whitham, J. Chem. Soc., 2864 (1960).

69.   (a) J. Goré, Ph.D. Thesis, University of Caen, July 1964; (b) J. M. Conia and
        J. Goré, Bull. Soc. Chim. France, 1968 (1964).

70.   S. Winstein, L. de Vries, and R. Orloski, J. Am. Chem. Soc., 83, 2020 (1961).

71.   (a) K. Mislow, M. A. W. Glass, R. E. O'Brien, P. Rutkin, D. H. Steinberg, and
        C. Djerassi, J. Am. Chem. Soc., 82, 4740 (1960); (b) K. Mislow, M. A. W. Glass,
        R. E. O'Brien, P. Rutkin, D. H. Steinberg, J. Weiss, and C. Djerassi, J. Am.
        Chem. Soc., 84, 1455 (1962).

72.   J. A. Edwards, P. Crabbé, and A. Bowers, J. Am. Chem. Soc., 85, 3313 (1963).

73.   A. Dreiding, Helv. Chim. Acta, 42, 1339 (1959).

10

Optically Active Dienes

10-1. INTRODUCTION

While optical rotatory dispersion and circular dichroism studies of organic compounds have thus far been performed mainly with saturated and α,β-unsaturated ketones, attention is being given now to other types of chromophores. Hence, in Chapters 8 and 9, some examples of applications of the optical rotatory dispersion and circular dichroism techniques to inherently dissymmetric chromophores were mentioned. Emphasis was placed on the important structural, configurational, and conformational information that these phenomenologically closely related methods can provide to the organic chemist.

In this chapter, optically active dienes will be discussed, while the subsequent chapters will deal with other types of chromophore with which a Cotton effect has been found to be associated.

10-2. THE HELICITY RULE OF SKEWED DIENES

A fundamental analysis of the Cotton effect associated with 1,3-cyclohexadienes has revealed that the skewness (helicity, chirality) imposed on such diene systems by structural factors constitutes the major element of asymmetry responsible for the Cotton effect. The helicity of the skewed diene makes a contribution to optical activity far outweighing that of adjacent asymmetric centers. It has been shown theoretically and confirmed experimentally[1] that **the sign of the Cotton effect of skewed cisoid dienes depends upon the sense of helicity of the diene system.** The rule of cisoid dienes can be given as follows:[1] a strong positive Cotton effect associated with the lowest frequency cisoid diene $\pi - \pi*$ absorption band (about 260–280 mμ in polycyclic compounds) indicates that the diene chromophore is twisted in the form of a right-handed helix (1). A strong negative Cotton effect is indicative of a left-handed twist (2).

The calculated and experimental optical rotatory dispersion curves of (+)-<u>trans</u>-9-methyl-1,4,9,10-tetrahydronaphthalene (3)[1,2] are shown in Figure 10-1, and the satisfactory correspondence encountered in these curves supports the above rule.

244

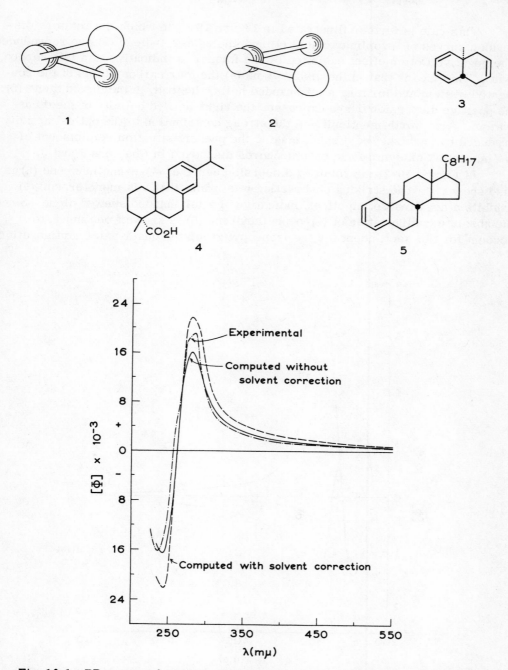

Fig. 10-1. RD curves of (+)-<u>trans</u>-9-methyl-1,4,9,10-tetrahydronaphthalene (3): experimental curve in cyclohexane, computed with correction for refractive index of solvent and computed without solvent correction [from A. Moscowitz, E. Charney, U. Weiss, and H. Ziffer, <u>J. Am. Chem. Soc.</u>, **83**, 4661 (1961); reproduced by permission of the editor].

This rule is further illustrated in Figure 10-2, in which the rotatory dispersion curves of levopimaric acid (4) and cholesta-2,4-diene (5) are reproduced.[2] The negative Cotton effect exhibited by the former is indicative of a left-handed twist. This means that in the cisoid diene (4) the four carbon atoms of the conjugated system are forming a left-handed helix. Instead, in the cisoid diene (5), the positive dispersion curve expresses the right-handed helicity of the diene system. Also worth mentioning is the strong contribution to the optical activity produced by such skewed dienes, making the present situation reminiscent of the inherently dissymmetric chromophores discussed in Chapters 8 and 9.

In Figure 10-2, the rotatory dispersion curve of (−)-α-phellandrene (6) is also shown.[3,4] The striking observation was made[3] that this monoterpene (6) exhibits a negative Cotton effect, indicative of a left-handed skewed diene. Since the absolute configuration of (−)-α-phellandrene (6) is known,[5] one must, to account for this fact, adopt for the isopropyl group the quasi-axial configuration

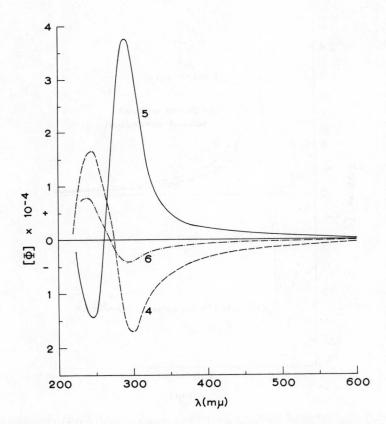

Fig. 10-2. RD curves of levopimaric acid (4), cholesta-2,4-diene (5) and (−)-α-phellandrene (6) [from A. W. Burgstahler, H. Ziffer, and U. Weiss, J. Am. Chem. Soc., **83**, 4660 (1961), and H. Ziffer, E. Charney, and U. Weiss, J. Am. Chem. Soc., **84**, 2961 (1962); reproduced by permission of the editor].

6a   6   6b

represented in (6a); while a quasi-equatorial configuration of this alkyl substituent (6b) would lead to a positive Cotton effect, as indicated by the arrow.

As a matter of fact, conformational mobility has been recognized to exist in (6).[4] Indeed, optical rotatory dispersion measurements performed at different temperatures (11° to 82°) indicate an augmentation of population of the constituent of higher energy (6a), which increases with temperature. This increase is accompanied by a substantial enhancement of the negative amplitude of the dispersion curve.[4] The negative Cotton effect observed at room temperature thus reflects a conformational equilibrium (6a) ⇌ (6b), in which the rotational strength (see Sec. 1-3) of the levorotatory conformer (6a) is higher than that of the dextrorotatory component (6b).[4]

Deen and Jacobs[6] were the first to conclude that an asymmetrically situated butadiene system will, either in itself or owing to its environment, bring about optical activity correlated with its longest-wavelength transition. Unfortunately, the optical rotatory dispersion instrument these investigators had at their disposal did not allow them to reach the region of Cotton effect exhibited by such dienes.[6] This is shown in Figure 10-3, in which the "partial" rotatory dispersion curves[7] of ergosterol (7), and its irradiation stereoisomers lumisterol (8), pyrocalciferol (9), and isopyrocalciferol (10) are reproduced. These curves have been completed, in dotted lines, by more recent measurements,[1] which permitted the location of the position of the first rotatory dispersion extremum. Further study of these Cotton effects is still desirable, since either the rotatory dispersion molecular amplitude or the circular dichroism molecular ellipticity

7   8   9

10   11

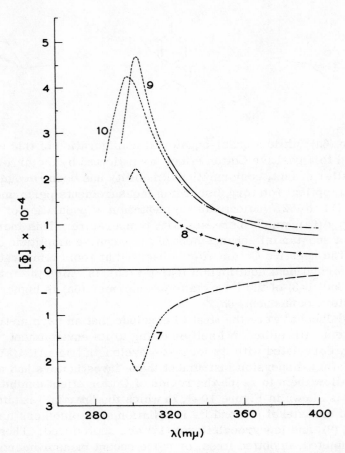

Fig. 10-3. Partial RD curves of ergosterol (7), lumisterol (8), isopyrocalciferol (9) and pyrocalciferol (10).

of such cisoid dienes might lead to a relationship between the intensity of the Cotton effect and the skewness of the diene system. This point is of definite stereochemical and theoretical interest.

Furthermore, although pyrocalciferol (9) and isopyrocalciferol (10) are enantiomeric at C-9 and C-10, both exhibit a positive Cotton effect. This observation lends weight to the assertion that the sign of the Cotton effect depends only on the helicity of the cisoid diene. However, as is apparent in Figure 10-3, the exact position of the peak in (9) is slightly shifted toward higher wavelengths, compared with the peak of the dispersion curve of (10).

Recently, $\Delta^{2,4}$-and $\Delta^{1,3}$-steroid dienes were synthesized and their optical rotatory dispersion curves obtained.[8] As expected, the $\Delta^{2,4}$-dienes corresponding to right-handed helices (cf. compound 5), all exhibited strong positive Cotton effects. By contrast, the $\Delta^{1,3}$-dienes, such as (11), presenting a left-handed helicity, showed a negative Cotton effect.

Optical rotatory dispersion has permitted the solution of the problem of the absolute stereochemistry of the sesquiterpene (+)-occidentalol (12).[9] The dispersion curve of (12) exhibits an intense positive Cotton effect (see Fig. 10-4), indicating that the diene system is skewed in the form of a right-handed helix.[10] This observation permitted exclusion of the $5\alpha,10\beta$-stereochemistry.[10,11] Furthermore, since the equatorial configuration had been proposed for the 2-hydroxy-isopropyl side chain at C-7,[9c] a 5,10-cis configuration could be deduced for the ring juncture in occidentalol (12).[11] Moreover, the comparison between the rotatory dispersion curve of the unsaturated ketone (13), derived from occidentalol (12), with the curve of unsaturated ketone (14), obtained from α-santonin (15) of known absolute configuration,[12] led to the assignment of the 10β-methyl configuration to (12). Indeed, as indicated in Figure 10-4, ketones (13) and (14) exhibit rotatory dispersion curves which are mirror images.[10] Therefore it follows that the ring junction in occidentalol (12) is cis-β, and the side chain at C-7 has the equatorial-β-configuration.

12   13   14   15

The effect of the sense of skew on the optical properties of dienes is further demonstrated in the thebainone methyl enol ether (16) and in thebaine (17), which belong to the morphine alkaloid series. The former exhibit a positive Cotton effect, the latter a strong negative Cotton effect, indicative of a left-handed skewed diene.[1] Finally, the dispersion curves of two related compounds—namely, (18) and (19)—are reproduced in Figure 10-5.[13] While the cisoid diene (18) shows a positive Cotton effect, its isomer (19) presents a negative curve. In the curve of the latter compound (19), which is **not** a homoannular diene, the Cotton effect associated with the B-band of the aromatic moiety is superimposed on the strong negative background curve, probably indicative of a negative Cotton effect due to the diene system and appearing at a lower wavelength.

The high intensity associated with the Cotton effect of skewed dienes has led Moscowitz et al.[1,14] to call them "inherently dissymmetric chromophores." It should be emphasized, however, that in all examples examined so far, **at least one asymmetric center is present in the molecule.** For this reason these cisoid dienes were not included in Chapter 8.

16   17

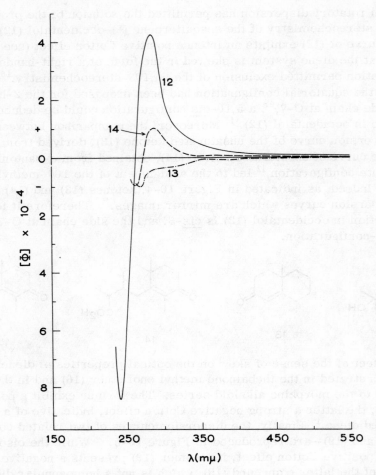

Fig. 10-4. RD curves of occidentalol (12), its α,β-unsaturated keto-derivative (13), and the unsaturated keto-sesquiterpene (14) obtained from α-santonin (15) [from H. Ziffer, T. J. Batterham, U. Weiss, and E. Von Rudloff, _Tetrahedron_, **20**, 67 (1964); reproduced by permission of the editor].

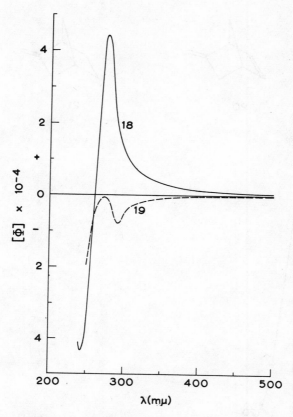

Fig. 10-5. RD curves of dienes (18) and (19) in methanol solution [courtesy of Dr. Karu Kuriyama, the Shionogi Research Laboratory].

So far, all the published information related to the Cotton effect of such dienes has been obtained by optical rotatory dispersion. It is obvious, however, that circular dichroism measurements would lead to similar conclusions. For quantitative studies, circular dichroism would probably better reflect the helicity characterizing these dienes, since the background rotation would not interfere with the Cotton effect.

10-3. HOMOCONJUGATED DIENES

Winstein and his collaborators[15] have discussed coupling between the non-conjugated ethylene moieties of norbornadiene in the photoexcited state. This has induced Mislow, Moscowitz, et al.[14] to prepare (+)-5-methylenebicyclo[2.2.1] hept-2-ene (20) and to compare its absorption properties with these of methylenenorbornane (21) (see Fig. 10-6).[16] As shown in Figure 10-6, formula (20) exhibits a marked red shift relative to (21). The two weakly coupled double bonds are rigidly disposed in (20) to form a homoconjugated dissymmetric

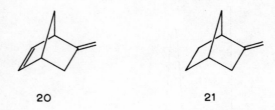

20   21

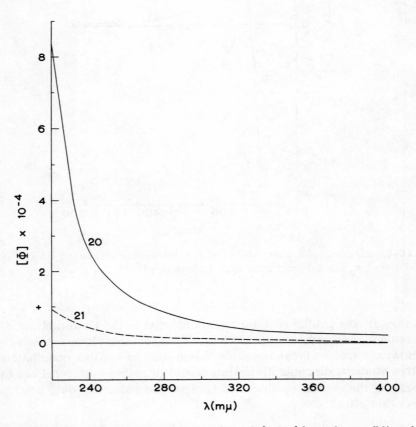

Fig. 10-6. RD curves of (+)-5-methylenebicyclo[2.2.1] hept-2-ene (20) and methylenenorbornane (21) [from K. Mislow, <u>Ann. N. Y. Acad. Sci.</u>, **93**, 459 (1962); reproduced by permission of the editor].

chromophore. The relevant $\pi - \pi^*$ Cotton effect, of which only the tail is observed in Figure 10-6, expresses the high rotations typical of extended dissymmetric π-systems. Theoretical arguments based on the coupled-oscillator theory support this view.[15,16,17]

10-4. SKEWED STYRENES

A class of aromatic compounds, somewhat related to skewed biphenyls (see Chap. 8) and optically active dienes, is the optically active styrene–like substances. Three such compounds belonging to the steroid series have been submitted recently to rotatory dispersion measurements. The rotatory dispersion curves[18] of these steroids (22), (23), and (24)[19] are reproduced in Figure 10-7.

22   23   24

Both 6–dehydro steroids (22; a = –337) and (23; a = –309), exhibit a strong **negative** Cotton effect between 240 and 270 mμ. The quantitative difference observed is probably a reflection of slight conformational changes occurring in the ring system of (23) because of 1–methyl 11–methylene interactions. Conversely, the hexahydrophenanthrene–type steroid (24; a = +187) shows a **positive** Cotton effect in the same spectral range. Examination of Dreiding molecular models[20] indicates the chirality of the conjugated system to be opposite in (24) to that of compounds (22) and (23). The Δ^6–compounds (22) and (23) present a right-handed helix type of conformation of their styrene chromophore, while the chromophore in the $\Delta^{9,11}$–styrene–type steroid (24) is left-handed. These results are in agreement with the rotatory dispersion observations reported by Leemann and Fabbri[21] for the $\Delta^{1,10b}$–N–methyl-hexahydro-benzo [f]-quinolin 2-ols (25) and (26). While the (–)-stereoisomer (26) exhibits a negative Cotton effect, the (+)-compound (25) displays a positive Cotton effect.[21] Indeed, the configuration at the B/C ring junction is the same in (24) and (25), and the Cotton effect associated with these styrene derivatives is of the same sign.

Hence in these compounds the chirality imposed on the styrene systems by structural and configurational factors, such as the stereochemistry of asymmetric atoms in direct vicinity of the chromophore, constitutes the major element of asymmetry responsible for the Cotton effect.

25

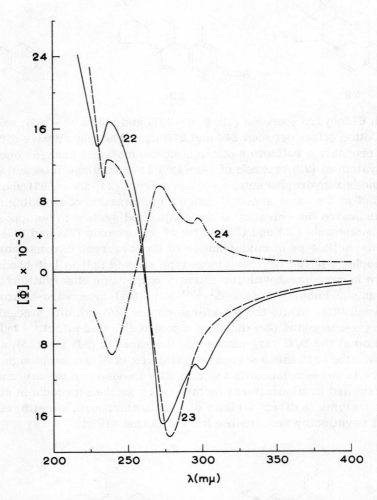

Fig. 10-7. RD curves of 3-hydroxy-estra-1,3,5(10),6-tetraen-17-one-3-acetate-17-cycloethylene-ketal (22), 1-methyl-3,17β-dihydroxy-estra-1,3,5(10),6-tetraene-diacetate (23), and 3,17β-dihydroxy-estra-1,3,5(10),9(11)-tetraene-diacetate (24) in dioxane solution.

REFERENCES

1.   A. Moscowitz, E. Charney, U. Weiss, and H. Ziffer, J. Am. Chem. Soc., 83, 4661 (1961).

2.   H. Ziffer and U. Weiss, J. Org. Chem., 27, 2694 (1961).

3.   (a) A. W. Burgstahler, H. Ziffer, and U. Weiss, J. Am. Chem. Soc., 83, 4660 (1961); (b) U. Weiss, H. Ziffer, and E. Charney, Chem. and Ind., 1286 (1962).

4.   H. Ziffer, E. Charney, and U. Weiss, J. Am. Chem. Soc., 84, 2961 (1962).

5.   K. Freudenberg and W. Lwowski, Ann. Chem., 587, 213 (1954), and references therein.

6.   R. Deen and H. J. C. Jacobs, Koninkl. Nederl. Akadem. Wetenschappen (Amsterdam), 64, 313 (1961).

7.   R. van Moorselaar, Ph.D. Thesis, University of Leiden, February 1962.

8.   B. Berkoz, A. D. Cross, M. E. Adame, H. Carpio, and A. Bowers, J. Org. Chem., 28, 1976 (1963).

9.   (a) T. Nakatsuka and Y. Hirose, Bull. Agric. Chem. Soc. Japan, 20, 215 (1956); (b) Y. Hirose and T. Nakatsuka, Bull. Agric. Chem. Soc. Japan, 23, 140 (1959); (c) E. von Rudloff and H. Erdtman, Tetrahedron, 18, 1315 (1962); (d) M. Nakazaki, Chem. and Ind., 413 (1962), Bull. Chem. Soc. Japan, 35, 1387 (1962).

10.   H. Ziffer, T. J. Batterham, U. Weiss, and E. von Rudloff, Tetrahedron, 20, 67 (1964).

11.   K. Mislow and A. Moscowitz, Tetrahedron Letters, No. 11, 699 (1963).

12.   H. Bruderer, D. Arigoni, and O. Jeger, Helv. Chim. Acta, 39, 858 (1956).

13.   These rotatory dispersion curves were obtained through the courtesy of Dr. Karu Kuriyama, The Shionogi Research Laboratory, Osaka (Japan).

14.   L. S. Forster, A. Moscowitz, J. G. Berger, and K. Mislow, J. Am. Chem. Soc., 84, 4353 (1962).

15.   C. F. Wilcox, S. Winstein, and W. G. McMillan, J. Am. Chem. Soc., 82, 5450 (1960).

16.   K. Mislow, Ann. N. Y. Acad. Sci., 93, 459 (1962).

17.   (a) D. D. Fitts and J. G. Kirkwood, Proc. Nat. Acad. Sci. U. S., 42, 33 (1956), and 43, 1046 (1957); (b) W. Moffitt, J. Chem. Phys., 25, 467 (1956); (c) W. Moffitt, D. D. Fitts, and J. G. Kirkwood, Proc. Nat. Acad. Sci. U.S., 43, 723 (1957).

18.   These rotatory dispersion tracings were obtained on a Bellingham and Stanley-Bendix-Ericsson automatic recording spectropolarimeter at the University of London through the kind cooperation of Professor W. Klyne.

19.   These compounds were prepared in the Syntex Research Laboratories.

20.   A. Dreiding, Helv. Chim. Acta, 42, 1339 (1959).

21.   H. G. Leemann and S. Fabbri, Helv. Chim. Acta, 42, 2696 (1959).

11

Asymmetrically Perturbed Symmetric Chromophores other than Ketones

11-1. INTRODUCTION

Up to this point most of the discussion related to Cotton effects has been centered on the carbonyl group (see especially Chaps. 6, 7, and 9). This is largely because the carbonyl chromophore has particularly favorable properties for rotatory dispersion and circular dichroism examination, and because ketones and aldehydes are among the most widely distributed functional groups. As in ultraviolet[1] and infrared[2] spectroscopy, there is little doubt that the carbonyl chromophore will continue to occupy a preeminent place in rotatory dispersion and circular dichroism studies of optically active substances.

It is obvious, however, that other chromophores are available which are optically active and absorb in a spectral region convenient for spectropolarimetric investigation. These compounds, usually derivatives of specific functional groups, are particularly important, since rotatory dispersion and circular dichroism now permit an easy investigation of the asymmetry surrounding the determined function, which is not readily amenable by any other method. Some of these potentially useful chromophores have already been reviewed,[3,4] and this discussion will report on recent and important developments in these fields.

The octant rule,[5] which has proved to be so valuable for the interpretation of the Cotton effect associated with carbonyl-containing compounds, has as yet no equivalent counterpart for the chromophores which will be examined here, apart from some rare exceptions. For that reason, this chapter will give only a survey, illustrated with examples, of the functional groups which can now be successfully investigated by optical rotatory dispersion and circular dichroism.

The arbitrary division of this chapter will therefore follow a sequence based on functional groupings rather than chromophoric nature. Some specific derivatives of alcohols, as well as the related sugars and amines, will be examined first. The Cotton effect associated with the acid function, along with some of its most characteristic derivatives, will then be reviewed. Aromatic optically active compounds (e.g., alkaloids, rotenones, steroids) will also be discussed.

Moreover, some specific derivatives of double bonds, as well as sulfur derivatives will be mentioned. Because of their importance, a special section will be devoted to α-hydroxy and α-amino acids. Finally, a miscellaneous section will report on some observations made with compounds which do not belong to the above groups of substances.

11-2. DERIVATIVES OF THE ALCOHOL GROUPING

It was mentioned in Section 5-2 that the plain dispersion curves associated with secondary and tertiary hydroxyl groups sometimes provide useful stereochemical information. However, since the alcohol group does not absorb in a suitable spectral range, one cannot subject it to the type of scrutiny illustrated previously for ketones unless one transforms it into derivatives with more favorable spectroscopic properties. The feasibility of this approach will be demonstrated by several examples.

Optical rotatory dispersion curves of acetates, which show Cotton effects in the region of 220 mμ, are more significant than plain curves at longer wavelengths.[6] This is illustrated in Table 11-1, where the optical rotatory dispersion curves (in hexane solution) and Cotton effects for 20-acetates of the steroid series are collected.[6,7] The inversion of the configuration of the secondary hydroxyl group at C-20 is accompanied, in these compounds, by an inversion of the Cotton effect of the corresponding acetoxy-derivative. Hence, in the pairs of compounds reported in Table 11-1, the 20α- and 20β-acetate exhibited negative and positive Cotton effects, respectively.[6,7]

Table 11-1

COTTON EFFECT ASSOCIATED WITH THE 20-ESTER GROUP IN STEROIDS

5α-Pregnane	First Extremum	Molecular Rotation at Lowest Wavelength Recorded	Molecular Amplitude a[†]
17β-series			
20α-OAc	$[\phi]_{234}$ −725°	$[\phi]_{208}$ +2750°	−35
20β-OAc	$[\phi]_{232}$ +2650°	$[\phi]_{217}$ +1160°	+15
17α-(iso)-series			
20a-OAc	$[\phi]_{234}$ −1280°	$[\phi]_{208}$ +3320°	−46
20β-OAc	$[\phi]_{234}$ +790°	$[\phi]_{208}$ −5100°	+59

† Incomplete

Another elegant method of assigning the correct stereochemistry of a secondary or a tertiary hydroxyl group is by examination of the Cotton effect associated with the readily prepared nitrite esters.[8-10] Attention had been called earlier to the fact that nitrites may represent useful "chromophoric" derivatives for alcohols,[11] but it is only recently that systematic studies[8-10] have emphasized the importance of this finding. Indeed, it has been shown that the sign of the Cotton effect of nitrite esters varies with the configuration of the parent hydroxyl grouping. Furthermore, the intensity of the Cotton effect also changes considerably from one position to the other, so that the sign and intensity of the Cotton effect can sometimes provide valuable information about the location and the configuration of a hydroxyl group in a known skeleton. Such information is summarized in Table 11-2,[8-10] which gives the Cotton effect associated with a secondary nitrite group in the steroid molecule.

Table 11-2

COTTON EFFECT EXHIBITED BY SECONDARY NITRITE FUNCTIONS SITUATED ON THE STEROID SKELETON

Position and Configuration of the Secondary Nitrite Chromophore	Circular Dichroism Molecular Ellipticity $[\theta]$
3α-ONO (5αH)	−130
3β-ONO (5αH)	+500
3α-ONO (5βH)	−400
3β-ONO (Δ^5)	+350
11α-ONO	−4300
11β-ONO	+3300
17α-ONO	+2700
17β-ONO	−4000
20α-ONO	+2400
20β-ONO	−3400

Figure 11-1 illustrates the Cotton effect associated in rotatory dispersion and circular dichroism with the nitrite chromophore situated at position 20 in the pregnane molecule (1) and presenting the 20α-configuration. The multiple Cotton effect which could be expected from the fine structure observed in the ultraviolet absorption spectrum is clearly revealed in the circular dichroism and rotatory dispersion curves.[10]

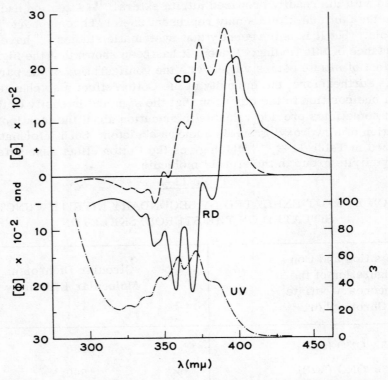

Fig. 11-1. RD, CD, and UV curves of 20α-hydroxy-5α-pregnan-nitrite (1) in dioxane-pyridine solution [from C. Djerassi, H. Wolf, and E. Bunnenberg, J. Am. Chem. Soc., **85**, 2835 (1963); reproduced by permission of the editor].

Figure 11-2 shows the ultraviolet, rotatory dispersion, and circular dichroism curves of the Δ^4-3-keto-20β-nitrite (2).[10] Not only is the sign of the Cotton effect due to the 20β-nitrite in (2) opposite to that of (1), but in the circular dichroism curve of the former (2) there is a satisfactory separation between the multiple Cotton effects of the Δ^4-3-keto chromophore around 335 mμ, and the 20β-nitrite around 380 mμ. The higher selectivity shown by circular dichroism would make it the appropriate method for the investigation of molecules which have several multiple Cotton effect chromophores.[12]

The xanthate derivatives[13] have also proved to be very useful for configurational assignments of alcohols. For example, the Cotton effect exhibited by the xanthates of the C-20 epimeric 20-hydroxypregnanes is of opposite sign, which is very helpful in deciding on the stereochemistry at that center.[14]

The rotatory dispersion curve of methyl α-D-glucopyranoside-6-(S-benzyl) xanthate (3) shows only a slight inflection in the region of the 354 mμ

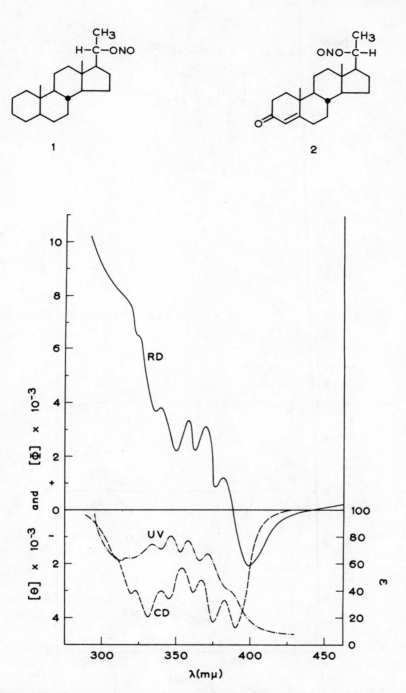

Fig. 11-2. RD, CD, and UV curves of 20β-hydroxy-pregn-4-en-3-one-nitrite (2) in dioxane-pyridine solution [from C. Djerassi, H. Wolf, and E. Bunnenberg, J. Am. Chem. Soc., **85**, 2835 (1963); reproduced by permission of the editor].

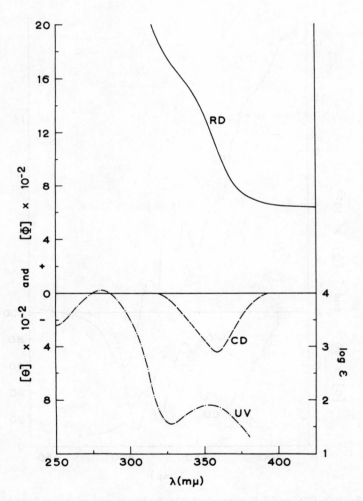

Fig. 11-3. RD, CD, and UV curves of methyl α-D-glucopyranoside 6-(S-benzyl) xanthate (3) in dioxane solution [from C. Djerassi, H. Wolf, and E. Bunnenberg, <u>J. Am.</u> <u>Chem. Soc.</u>, **84**, 4552 (1962); reproduced by permission of the editor].

ultraviolet absorption maximum, indicative of a negative Cotton effect, super-imposed on a positive background rotation.[15] This is illustrated in Figure 11-3,[14] where the circular dichroism curve of this substance (3) is also represented and shows a clearly defined negative maximum, thus demonstrating that the 354 mμ absorption band is indeed optically active.[14] The curves reported in Figure 11-3 constitute a good illustration of a situation in which the background effect of a dispersion curve is a disadvantage and in which the circular dichroism curve yields more precise and useful information.[12]

In an extensive study by Sjöberg et al.[15] it was shown that the relative con-figuration of alcohols and their corresponding amines can be deduced from the Cotton effect curves of their xanthate and dithiocarbamate derivatives. However, the xanthate derivatives suffer from the practical disadvantage that the presence of other groups in the molecule, such as a Δ^4-3-keto function, may interfere in the method of preparation.[8]

The dithiocarbamates[15] and dithiourethanes,[13] also possessing the C=S chromophore, have been suggested for the examination of Cotton effect.[14] Since the main use of such derivatives is in the α-hydroxy acid and α-amino acid series, these chromophores will also be covered in the appropriate section (Sec. 11-9). Nevertheless, a further illustration of the utility of such derivatives for rotatory dispersion stereochemical studies is shown in Figures 11-4 and 11-5, which reproduce the dispersion curves of (+)-borneol (4a) and (-)-isoborneol (5a) and several of their derivatives containing the C=S chromophore.[15]

4a, R = H

b, R = CH$_3$-S-$\overset{\text{S}}{\overset{\|}{\text{C}}}$-

c, R = (C$_6$H$_5$)$_3$-C-S-$\overset{\text{S}}{\overset{\|}{\text{C}}}$-

d, R = C$_6$H$_5$-$\overset{\|}{\underset{\text{S}}{\text{C}}}$-$\overset{|}{\underset{\text{C}_6\text{H}_5}{\text{N}}}$-Ċ=S

5a, R = H

b, R = CH$_3$-S-$\overset{\text{S}}{\overset{\|}{\text{C}}}$-

c, R = (C$_6$H$_5$)$_3$-C-S-$\overset{\text{S}}{\overset{\|}{\text{C}}}$-

d, R = C$_6$H$_5$-$\overset{\|}{\underset{\text{S}}{\text{C}}}$-$\overset{|}{\underset{\text{C}_6\text{H}_5}{\text{N}}}$-Ċ=S

The optical rotatory dispersion curves of bornyl methyl xanthate (4b), bornyl trityl xanthate (4c), and bornyl N-phenyl-N-thiobenzoyl-thiourethane (4d) are of opposite sign to those of the corresponding derivatives of the isoborneol (5a) series. Moreover, the N-phenyl-N-thiobenzoyl-thiourethane derivative (5d) exhibits a much stronger positive Cotton effect in the isoborneol (see Fig. 11-5) than in the borneol series (Fig. 11-4).[13,15,16]

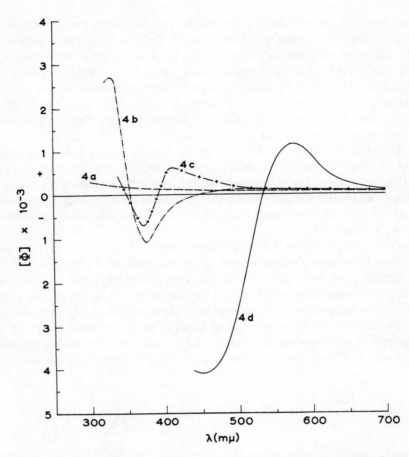

Fig. 11-4. RD curves of (+)-borneol (4a), bornyl methyl xanthate (4b), bornyl trityl xanthathe (4c), and bornyl N-phenyl-N-thiobenzoyl-thiourethane (4d) [modified from B. Sjöberg, D. J. Cram, L. Wolf, and C. Djerassi, <u>Acta Chem. Scand.</u>, **16**, 1079 (1962)].

11-3. COTTON EFFECT ASSOCIATED WITH SUGARS AND THEIR DERIVATIVES

The search for a convenient way to assign the stereochemistry in carbohydrates has been a subject of concern for a long time. By 1930, rotatory dispersion had already been suggested for the resolution of this intriguing problem.[3,4,17] However, recent improvements in instrumentation, as well as the wide variety of "optically active chromophoric derivatives" now permit a greater insight into the configurational and conformational aspects of this important class of naturally occurring substances.[17]

Figure 11-6 shows the dispersion curves for D-glucose (6) and D-sorbitol (7) measured on a Cary Model 60 recording spectropolarimeter.[18] No Cotton effect is observed down to 190 mμ. D-galactose (8), also represented in

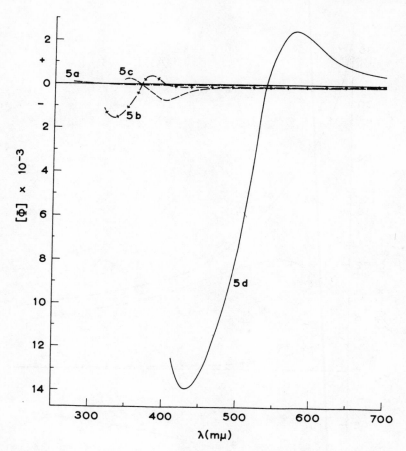

Fig. 11-5. RD curves of (-)-isoborneol (5a), isobornyl methyl xanthate (5b), iso-bornyl trityl xanthate (5c), and isobornyl N-phenyl-N-thiobenzoyl-thiourethane (5d) [modified from B. Sjöberg, D. J. Cram, L. Wolf, and C. Djerassi, <u>Acta Chem. Scand.</u>, **16**, 1079 (1962)].

Figure 11-6, shows a plain dispersion curve immediately after dissolving, but when equilibrium in the mutarotation reaction has been reached, the curve shows a peak at about 208 mμ.[18] The reason for this effect is not known at present, but might arise from the furanoside form, known to be present in sugars of the galacto configuration.[18] Also reproduced in Figure 11-6 is the rotatory dispersion curve of L-fucose (9), which is essentially the mirror image of the curve of D-galactose (8).

Whenever a carboxyl or acyl group is present in the sugar molecule a Cotton effect is observed.[18,19] This has been discussed in detail in a recent optical rotatory dispersion study of five-membered sugar lactones.[19] The authors of that study reached important conclusions, which can be summarized as follows: **When the hydroxyl group situated on the carbon atom adjacent to**

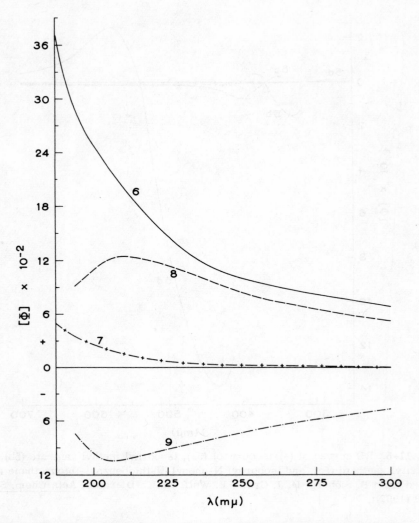

Fig. 11-6. RD curves of D-glucose (6), D-sorbitol (7), and D-galactose (8) at equilibrium and L-fucose (9) at equilibrium, in water solution [adapted from N. Pace, C. Tanford, and E. A. Davidson, J. Am. Chem. Soc., **86**, 3160 (1964)].

the carbonyl function of the γ-lactone ring has the S-configuration according to Cahn's convention,[20] the Cotton effect associated with the weak n – π* transition around 220-230 mμ will be positive. Conversely, a negative Cotton effect is associated with a secondary alcohol grouping in such a situation presenting the R-configuration.[19] This rule is quite welcome, since it constitutes an important complement to "Hudson's lactone rule,"[21] which makes possible the assignment of the absolute configuration of an asymmetric carbon situated at C-4 or C-5 in a lactone ring. Moreover, Hudson's rule relates the optical rotation of a lactone to the configuration of the lactone-forming hydroxyl group. A lactone of type (A) is positive, while lactone (B) would be more negative.[21]

This rule is illustrated in Figure 11-7, which shows the positive Cotton effect of D-arabono-γ-lactone (10), whose configuration at C-2 is S, and the negative dispersion curve of D-glucono-γ-lactone (11) (C-2-R[19]).

Recent careful examination has suggested[21c] that from a consideration of molecular orbitals one should look at the asymmetry of the compound containing the carbonyl (or ester or lactone) group as in (C). If the ester or lactone group is to some extent a resonance hybrid between (C) and (D), one must consider both carbon-oxygen bonds as having a certain amount of double-bond character. If one then applies the octant idea to **each** of these C=O double bonds in turn and combines the results, one gets a system of **sectors**, similar to but not identical with the octants of the ordinary ketone treatment.[5] † The important fact emerges that the contributions of alkyl groups in the various sectors are, broadly speaking, opposite in sign to those for the same substituents in ordinary ketones. A considerable number of lactones have given Cotton effect curves[6a,b] at about 220 mμ the sign of which essentially supports this hypothesis.[21c] Further development of this work will be awaited with interest.

10

11

A   B   C   D

---

†These proposals are based on theoretical studies by Dr. A. Moscowitz, University of Minnesota.

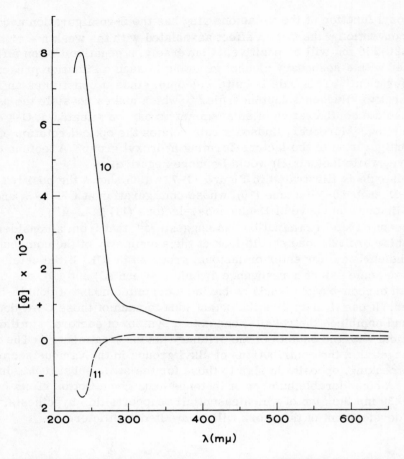

Fig. 11-7. RD curves of D-arabono-γ-lactone (10) and D-glucono-γ-lactone (11), in methanol solution [adapted from T. Okuda, S. Harigaya, and A. Kiyomoto, <u>Chem. Pharm. Bull. Japan</u>, **12**, 504 (1964)].

As indicated in the beginning of this section, when the molecule is devoid of a chromophore, hydroxy compounds such as sugars usually exhibit plain dispersion curves in the spectral range which can be examined at present. Therefore it is sometimes desirable to convert the hydroxyl group(s) of a sugar into a derivative presenting a Cotton effect which can then be properly investigated. Such an example has already been mentioned in Section 11-2, where the Cotton effect exhibited by a xanthate derivative of α-D-glucopyranose (3) was discussed.[14,15] Several recent similar studies have been published[17] which indicate optical rotatory dispersion and circular dichroism to be convenient methods for the investigation of the configuration of hydroxyl groupings in derivatives of glucose as well as anomeric pyranoses[22] (see also Sec. 11-7).

The rotatory dispersion curves of the α-D-(12) and β-D-(13) glucopyranosyl ethylxanthates are represented in Figure 11-8.[22] The dispersion curves of

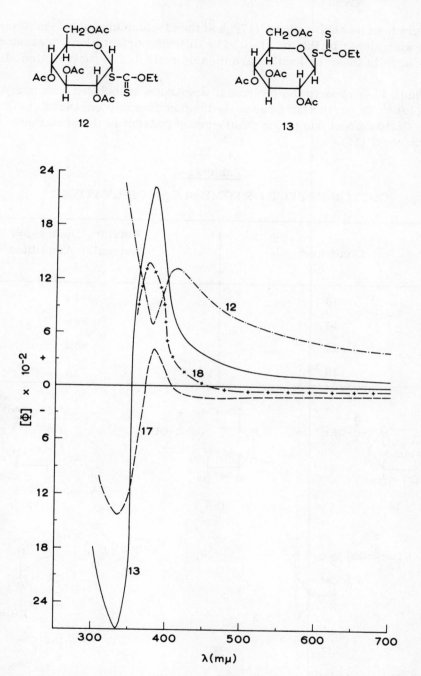

Fig. 11-8. RD curves of 2,3,4,6-tetra-O-acetyl-α-D-glucopyranosyl ethylxanthate (12), 2,3,4,6-tetra-O-acetyl-β-D-glucopyranosyl ethylxanthate (13), 1,2-O-isopropylidene-D-xylofuranose 5-ethylxanthate (17), and 1,2,5,6-O-diisopropylidene-D-glucofuranose-3-(S-methyl) xanthate (18) [adapted from Y. Tsuzuki et al., <u>Bull. Chem. Soc. Japan</u>, **37**, 162, 730 (1964)].

D-xylofuranose 5-ethylxanthate (17) and the D-glucofuranose 3-methylxanthate (18) are also shown in Figure 11-8. The different orientations presented by the chromophore in these molecules are clearly reflected in their Cotton effect curves.[22]

Table 11-3 reports the molecular amplitude associated with compounds (13) to (16).[22] Of particular interest is the considerable enhancement of the positive Cotton effect due to the amido-group present in the acetamido-glucopyranosyl (16).

Table 11-3

COTTON EFFECT OF SOME SUGAR DERIVATIVES[22]

Compound	Rotatory Dispersion Molecular Amplitude a
13	+49
14	+45
15	+46
16	+71

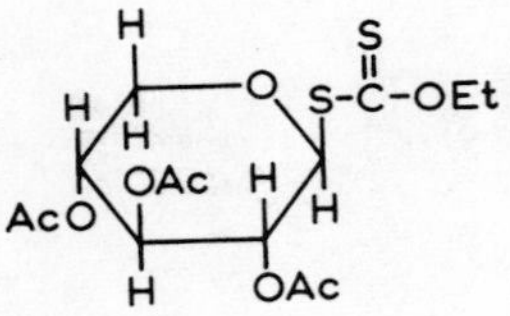

14

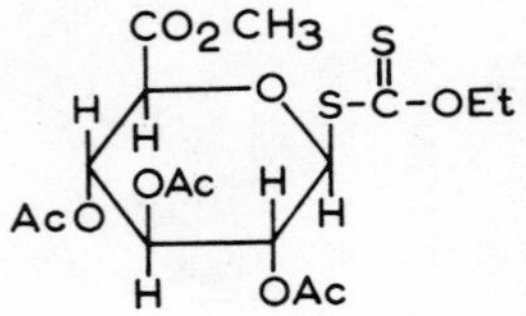

15

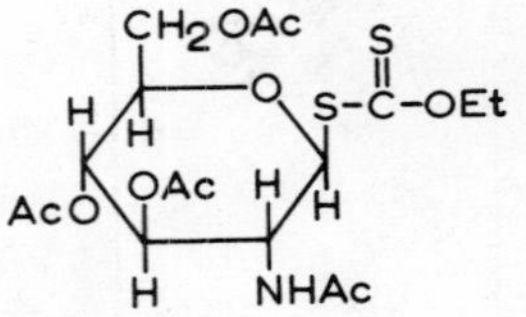

16

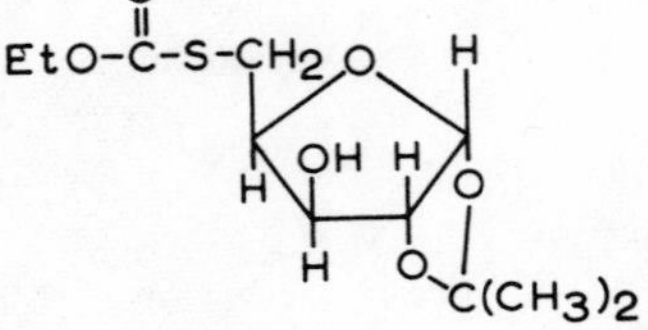

17

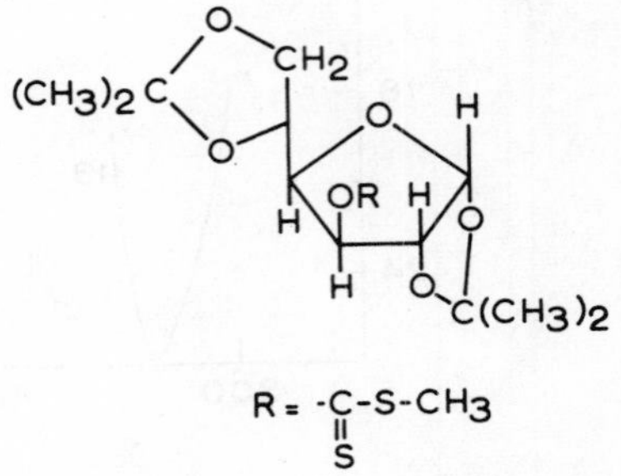

R = -C-S-CH₃

18

An interesting phenomenon was observed recently[23] in the optical properties of the two 1-nitro-2-acetamido-1,2-dideoxy-D-hexitols (19) and (20). While both compounds are levorotatory at the sodium D-line, compound (19) shows a trough at 334 mμ and its epimer (20) a peak at 346 mμ. This marked difference obviously reflects the opposite absolute configuration at the carbon atom adjacent to the nitro-methyl group.

CH$_2$NO$_2$ | CH$_2$NO$_2$
AcHN—C—H | H—C—NHAc
HO—C—H | HO—C—H
H—C—OH | H—C—OH
H—C—OH | H—C—OH
CH$_2$OH | CH$_2$OH

[Φ] = -620   [Φ] = +30

19   20

A Cotton effect associated with the nitro chromophore has long been recognized.[24] This particular point will be discussed with more detail in Section 11-4. It may be noted here, however, that the nitro group shows an ultra-violet absorption band in the 270 - 280 mμ region and that this band is optically active. Thus the rotatory dispersion curves of some epimeric pairs of carbohydrated C-nitro-alcohols have been obtained recently, leading to interesting results.[25] Indeed, the sign of Cotton effect is directly related to the absolute configuration of the substituent on the carbon atom situated next to the nitromethyl group, in a manner similar to the lactone rule stated above. The compounds with the R-configuration[20] at this center exhibit negative Cotton effect curves, while those carrying a substituent at C-2 with the S-configuration[20] show positive dispersion curves.[25] The other asymmetric centers remote from the nitro-group seem to have little or no effect on the sign of the curves. Furthermore, the observed Cotton effect is also independent of the nature of the substituent at C-2; for example, compounds (19) to (22) are in good agreement with the above rule. From a quantitative point of view, however, new measurements with an apparatus reaching lower wavelengths seem desirable, since there might be a relationship between the molecular amplitude of these curves and the nature of the substituent at C-2, as suggested by a comparison of the curves of compounds (19) to (20).[23,25] Circular dichroism would probably be more valuable for such quantitative studies, eliminating the substraction of the background rotation due to the other asymmetric centers of the molecule.

11-4. AMINES AND DERIVATIVES — THE NITRO AND NITROSO CHROMOPHORES

Amines and aminoketals do not exhibit any absorption band in the spectral range usually investigated by optical rotatory dispersion and circular dichroism techniques. For configuration assignments one has then to refer to specific derivatives, presenting a chromophore absorbing in the 220-700 mμ region.

$$[\Phi] = -600$$

21

$$[\Phi] = +600$$

22

Various derivatives, such as N-salicylidene derivatives,[26] N-phthalyl derivatives,[27] nitrosoamines,[28-30] nitroso nitrites,[31] N-nitrosoamides,[28] alkyl-nitrites,[11,32] have already been suggested.

For example, as indicated in Figure 11-9, optically active Schiff bases exhibit Cotton effects sometimes readily analyzed by rotatory dispersion and circular dichroism.[26] The N-salicylidene derivative of the 20α-amino steroid (23a) displays a positive circular dichroism curve at 315 mμ, while its 20β-epimer (23b) exhibits a negative Cotton effect at the same wavelength.[26a] The very weak Cotton effect associated with the n - π* transition at 400 mμ has been commented upon elsewhere.[12,26c] That this band is optically active is illustrated in Figure 11-9, which also reproduces the multiple Cotton effect rotatory dispersion curve of (S)-(+)-N-salicylidene-α-phenylethylamine (24).[26c] Two positive Cotton effects, an intense one centered near 315 mμ and another much weaker at about 410 mμ, have been shown to be associated with the ultraviolet absorption bands near 315 and 403 mμ. A third absorption band, around 280 mμ, is also optically active, as indicated by the tailing of the circular dichroism curves of (23a) and (23b).[26a] The optical properties of these Schiff bases are solvent-dependent, and this has been discussed in detail by Smith and coworkers.[26c]

23a, R$_1$ = N=CH—⟨⟩; R$_2$ = H

b, R$_1$ = H; R$_2$ = N=CH—⟨⟩

24

Recently, it has been suggested that rotatory dispersion and circular dichroism measurements of the N-phthalyl derivative of secondary amines would

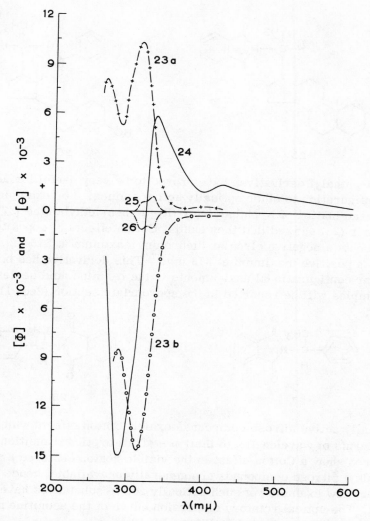

Fig. 11-9. RD curve of (S)-(+)-N-salicylidene-α-phenylethylamine (24) and CD curves of N-salicylidene-20α-amino-5α-pregnan-3β-ol (23a), N-salicylidene-20β-amino-5α-pregnan-3β-ol(23b), N-phthalyl-20α-amino-5α-pregnan-3β-ol (25), and the corresponding 20β-isomer (26).

easily permit an assignment of their configuration.[27] A relatively weak positive Cotton effect is associated with the 20α-stereochemistry (25), and a negative Cotton effect with the 20β-N-phthalyl chromophore (26), in the steroid molecule. This is shown in Figure 11-9, which also reproduces the circular dichroism curves of these compounds. Although the sign of the Cotton effects is identical for the Schiff base and the N-phthalyl derivatives, Figure 11-9 clearly indicates a marked difference in the molecular ellipticity associated with the chromophore characterizing these compounds.

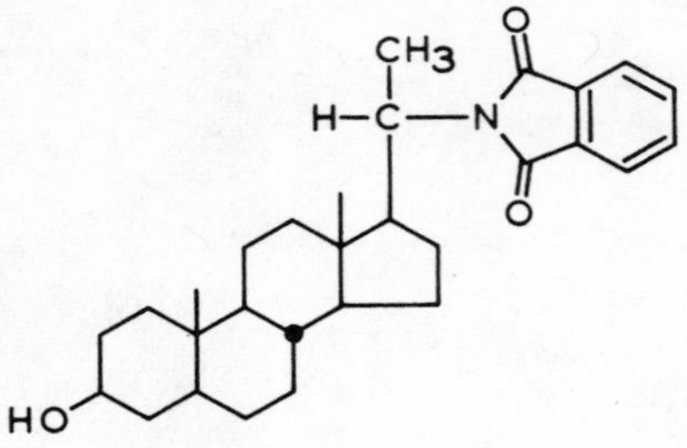

25

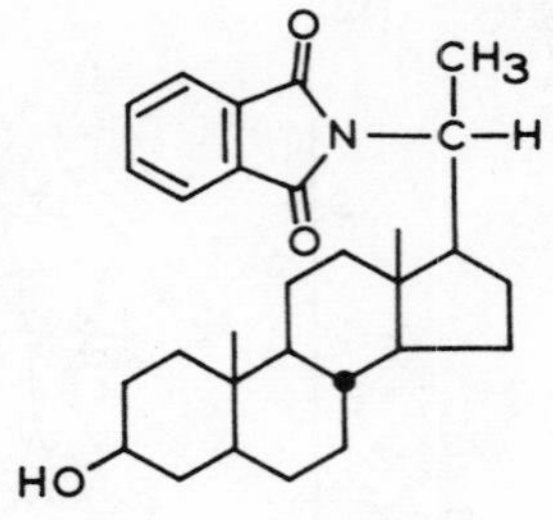

26

The N-phthalyl derivatives have proved to be very useful for assigning the absolute configuration to other optically active amines. For example, circular dichroism examination of N-phthalyl-(+)-(R)-α-phenylethylamine (27) and its (-)-(S)-isomer (28) showed that they exhibit Cotton effects of opposite sign. The former presents a negative circular dichroism maximum at 315 mμ, while the latter gives a positive maximum at 313 mμ.[27] This derivative has been success-fully used for configurational assignments in the α-amino acid series, and some further examples will be reported in the appropriate section (Sec. 11-9).

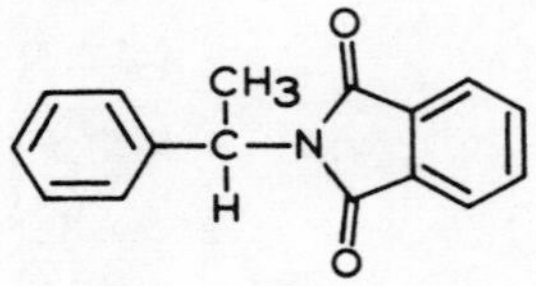

27

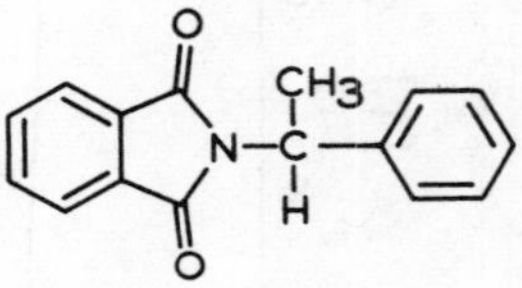

28

Optically active nitroso compounds exhibit Cotton effects which can be related in terms of wavelengths to their n - π* absorption transition. C-Nitroso chromophores show a Cotton effect in the visible region centered around 675 mμ. However, alkyl nitroso compounds are generally unavailable, hence the Cotton effect of very few examples of such optically active substances have been examined.[28] The optical rotatory dispersion curve of the aconitine nitroso derivative (29)[29] is represented in Figure 11-10.[28]

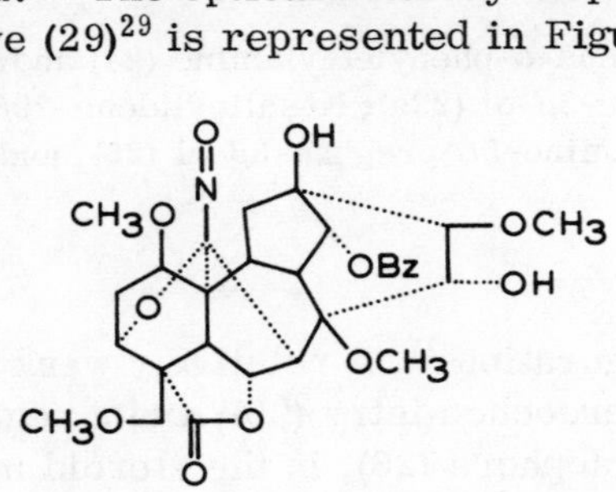

29

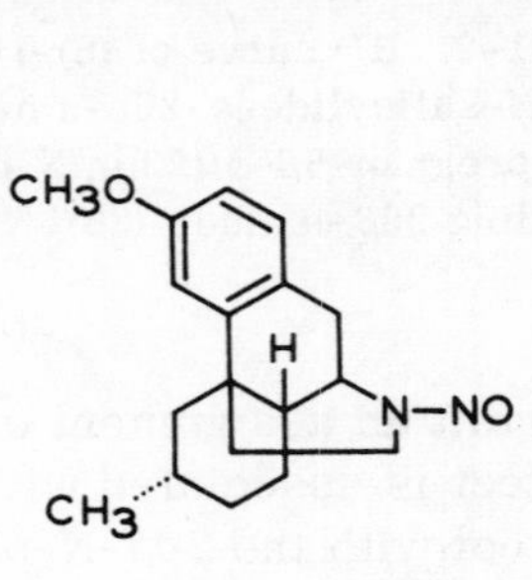

30

N-Nitrosodialkylamines exhibit a Cotton effect between 350 and 400 mμ, as shown in Figure 11-10 for the N-nitroso derivative (30).[30] The rotatory disper-sion curves of this substance (30) were shown to be solvent-dependent, since

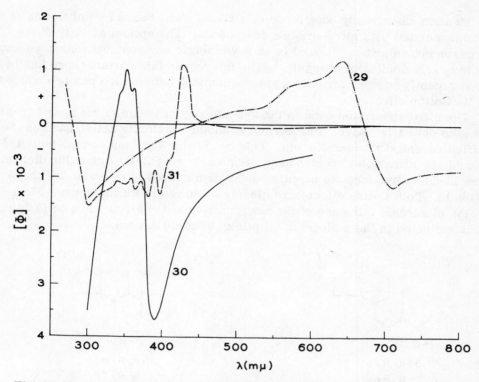

Fig. 11-10. RD curves of the aconitine nitroso derivative (29), the tetracyclic N-nitroso compound (30), and N-nitroso-N-acetyl-L-leucine methyl ester (31).

marked differences in the position and intensity of the extrema were observed in changing the polarity of the solvent.[30]

Circular dichroism examination of bornylene and caryophyllene nitrosites (nitroso nitrites) performed by Mitchell[31] led him to conclude that the 680 mμ transition in the chromophore is optically active.

Djerassi et al.[28a] have obtained the rotatory dispersion curves of several N-nitrosoamides, such as N-nitroso-N-acetyl-L-leucine methyl ester (31) also reproduced in Figure 11-10, and showed that optically active N-nitrosoamides exhibit multiple Cotton effect curves in the region of 300 to 450 mμ. A series of four maxima and shoulders is usually observed in the 375-430 mμ region, a characteristic feature reminiscent of the fine structure observed by Kuhn in the spectra of alkyl nitrites.[11,32]

$$O=N \quad CO_2CH_3$$
$$CH_3-\overset{\underset{\displaystyle O}{|}}{C}-N-\overset{\underset{\displaystyle CH_2-CH-CH_3}{|}}{C}-H$$
$$\underset{\displaystyle CH_3}{}$$

31

Mention has already been made (see Chap. 8 and Sec. 11-3) of Cotton effects associated with nitro-organic compounds. The optical activity of the nitro chromophore, when situated in an asymmetric environment, has been known since the early studies of Mitchell.[24] The interest in this chromophore has been revived recently,[3,10,33,34] for useful stereochemical information can be deduced from its Cotton effect.

The nitro absorption band in the 280 mμ region is due to the n - π^* transition and is optically active. Furthermore, another optically active band has been identified recently[10,34] near 330 mμ. This band, which had not been detected previously by ultraviolet spectroscopy, is clearly revealed by circular dichroism. Figure 11-11 reproduces the circular dichroism curves of compounds (32a,b) and (33a,b). Both Cotton effects are clearly observed in these curves. Moreover, the electronic influence of the newly introduced chlorine atom in (32b) and (33b) is reflected in the molecular ellipticity of these curves.

32a, R = H
b, R = Cl

33a, R = H
b, R = Cl

The optical rotatory dispersion or circular dichroism curves of various nitro-steroids (with a nitro group at C-3, C-4, C-6, C-7, and C-17) have been measured and commented upon.[3,10,34] Recent low-temperature circular dichroism measurements conducted on such derivatives indicated substantial changes in the Cotton effect curves. This has been interpreted as a reflection of conformational equilibria existing in these compounds.[34]

Conjugated nitroolefin steroids have also been investigated.[3,10,34] For instance, Figure 11-12 shows the relevant information on 6-nitro-pregn-5-en-3β-ol-20-one-acetate (34).[10] This compound also contains the saturated 20-keto group with its positive Cotton effect (see Sec. 6-6). The long-wavelength band of the conjugated nitro chromophore is recognizable by the shoulder (320-350 mμ) in the ultraviolet spectrum, as well as by the negative Cotton effect observed in the dispersion and circular dichroism curves (see Fig. 11-12).[10] The n - π^* transition of the 20-keto chromophore is completely obliterated in the ultraviolet spectrum by the stronger 258 mμ absorption band of the nitro group. Its presence is nevertheless unequivocally demonstrated by the strong positive Cotton effect around 300 mμ which is detected by circular and rotatory dispersion. The separation between the two Cotton effects is also superior in the dichroism curve to that found in the rotatory dispersion curve.

While the optical properties of the dithiourethane derivative of some cyclic amines, and the N-chloro amines and N-chloro aminoketals have also been

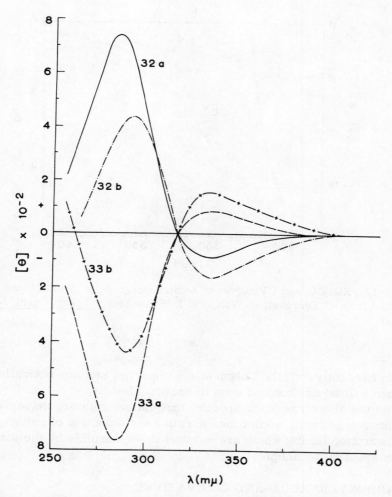

Fig. 11-11. CD curves of 4β-nitro-5α-cholestane (32a), 4α-chloro-4β-nitro-5α-cholestane (32b), 6β-nitro-5α-cholestane (33a), and 6α-chloro-6β-nitro-5α-cholestane (33b) in methyl-cyclohexane-isopentane solution [adapted from G. Snatzke, D. Becher, and J. R. Bull, <u>Tetrahedron</u>, **20**, 2443 (1964)].

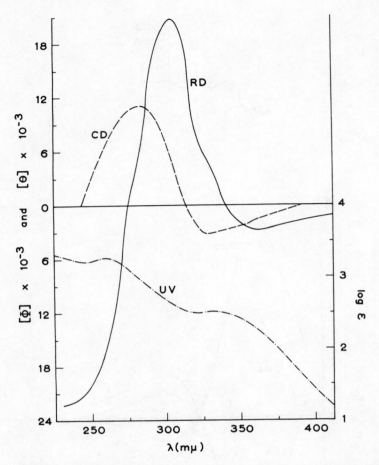

Fig. 11-12. RD, CD, and UV curves of 6-nitro-pregn-5-en-3β-ol-20-one-acetate (34) [modified from C. Djerassi, H. Wolf, and E. Bunnenberg, J. Am. Chem. Soc., **85**, 2835 (1963)].

investigated recently,[34bis] the Cotton effect observed in some optically active aryl amines will be commented upon in Section 11-6.

From the above results it appears that optical rotatory dispersion, circular dichroism, or both, sometimes permit easy detection of hidden or overlapping absorption bands, which are not readily discernible by the standard ultraviolet spectral techniques.

11-5. CARBOXYLIC ACIDS AND DERIVATIVES

The optical rotatory dispersion curves of various optically active carboxylic acids, esters, and other derivatives have been measured recently with a Bellingham and Stanley automatic spectropolarimeter.[6] The salient feature of most of the curves is a Cotton effect, with its first extremum appearing at about 225 mμ, related to the carbonyl absorption band at about 210 mμ (see Sec. 11-3). This is illustrated by the dispersion curve of methyl etiocholanate (35), exhibiting a peak ([Φ] = +5000°) around 225 mμ.[6]

35

In Section 5-2 mention was made of Sjöberg's rotatory dispersion study of α-substituted carboxylic acids.[35] The instrument available at the time did not permit one to reach the wavelength where the Cotton effects appear. A new investigation of the Cotton effect associated with the carboxyl group in substituted succinic acids (at about 225 mμ) shows that, in the D-series, α-alkyl, α-aryl and α-halogeno-succinic acids give a positive Cotton effect, while D-α-hydroxy-succinic acid (malic acid) and its O-alkyl ethers exhibit negative Cotton effect curves.[36]

Another approach to the stereochemical study of carboxylic acid is suggested by the examination of the anomalous rotatory dispersion and circular dichroism curves of the thionamide function.[37] In these compounds, the thione is adjacent to the asymmetric center, rendering the situation favorable and reliable for stereochemical studies, since the Cotton effects are rather pronounced. A correlation can thus be made between the absolute configuration (R or S)[20] of the asymmetric center closest to the chromophore and the sign of the Cotton effect associated with the low-extinction ultraviolet absorption maximum (about 330 mμ). Table 11-4, giving the circular dichroism maximum for some of the compounds examined, illustrates the important stereochemical information this derivative can provide.[37]

All the thionamides which were examined exhibited Cotton effects around 340 mμ, thus showing the n - π^* band to be optically active. Moreover, in this instance, circular dichroism measurements proved to be more useful than the optical rotatory dispersion curves, because in rotatory dispersion the second extremum is sometimes completely hidden by the background effects arising from the high-intensity $\pi - \pi^*$ band at 265 mμ.

It can be seen from Table 11-4 that in the cases in which the asymmetric center closest to the N-methylthionamide chromophore is composed only of carbon and hydrogen atoms, an R-configuration produces a negative Cotton effect and an S-configuration leads to a positive one. The N-methylthionamide of O-acetyllactic acid (41), which has the S-configuration, constitutes an exception to the rule, since it produces a negative Cotton effect (Table 11-4).[37]

The Cotton effect exhibited by some of these compounds also proved to be solvent-dependent. This is illustrated by the last substance listed in Table 11-4. The validity of the attempted correlation between Cotton effect and configuration

Table 11-4

COTTON EFFECT SHOWN BY SOME OPTICALLY ACTIVE
THIONAMIDES[37]

Compound	Absolute Configuration of Asymmetric Center Closest to the Chromophore	Circular Dichroism Molecular Ellipticity
36	S	$[\theta]_{342}$ +2457 (methanol solution)
37	R	$[\theta]_{340}$ -1293 (methanol solution)
38	R	$[\theta]_{353}$ -352 (methanol solution)
39	S	$[\theta]_{343}$ +539 (methanol solution)
40	S	$[\theta]_{340}$ +3460 (methanol solution)
41	S	$[\theta]_{342}$ -1113 (methanol solution)
42	R	$[\theta]_{360}$ -604 (dioxane solution)

in N-thion-cholanyl-morpholine (42) could be questioned, since the measurements
of the circular dichroism curve were performed in dioxane (and not in methanol,
as they were for the other compounds listed in Table 11-4) for solubility reasons.
Such a change of solvent has been shown to be sometimes accompanied by an inversion of the Cotton effect.[37] Finally, circular dichroism measurements over
the range -192° to +168° indicated that free rotation occurs in these thionamides[37]

Acylthioureas may also be prepared in order to examine the Cotton effect associated with the asymmetry surrounding the carboxylic function, and some such examples have been reported[38] (see also Sec. 11-9).

Lactones, which are intramolecular esters, also exhibit specific Cotton effects, a function of their asymmetric environment. This has already been illustrated with γ-lactones in Figures 5-8 and 11-7 and commented upon in the corresponding sections (Secs. 5-2 and 11-3).

The Cotton effects of some α,β-unsaturated carboxylic acids have been examined recently by Weiss and Ziffer.[39] They focused their attention on the weak n - π^* transition of the conjugated carbonyl group occurring at about 250 mμ. Figure 11-13 reproduces the circular dichroism curves for shikimic acid (43), 5-epi-shikimic acid (44), shellolic acid (45), and 3β-hydroxy-etio-chola-5,16-dienic-acid-acetate (46).[39] In the examples examined, circular dichroism proved to be more sensitive than rotatory dispersion, for which the background rotation sometimes hides completely the Cotton effect associated with this system. Apart from the important fact that the Cotton effect is clearly observed, as indicated in the case of shikimic (43) and epi-shikimic acid (44), inversion of the configuration of the asymmetric center situated next to the double bond inverts the sign of the Cotton effect. As illustrated in Figure 11-13, acids (43) and (44) exhibit opposite circular dichroism maxima whose molecular ellipticities are also considerably different.[39]

43   44   45   46

This observation has recently been extrapolated to α,β-unsaturated γ-lactones.[40] Indeed, it has been shown that while the steroid lactone (47) exhibits a strong positive Cotton effect ($[\theta]_{250}$ = +26400), lactone (48) obtained from fusidic acid[41] presents an intense negative circular dichroism maximum ($[\theta]_{250}$ = -29700).

47   48

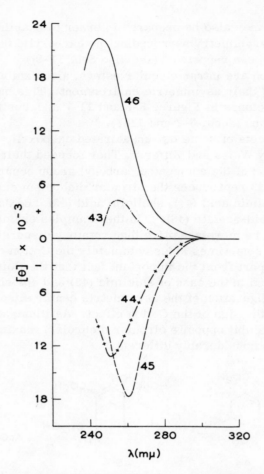

Fig. 11-13. CD curves of shikimic acid (43), 5-epi-shikimic acid (44), shellolic acid (45), and 3β-hydroxy-etiochola-5,16-dienic-acid-acetate (46) in ethanol solution [adapted from U. Weiss and H. Zifter, J. Org. Chem., **28**, 1248 (1963)].

A further example of application of the rotatory dispersion method to optically active unsaturated γ-lactone is suggested by the stereochemical studies performed with the alkaloids securinine (49) and virosecurinine (50).[42] These compounds were found to be optical antipodes by comparison of their dispersion curves (see Fig. 11-14), which are mirror images.[42] The long-wavelength position of the Cotton effect in these compounds is attributed to their highly conjugated chromophoric system.

The same applies to α-aryl substituted γ-lactones. During the study of the absolute configuration of α- and β-narcotine, various optical rotatory dispersion curves were obtained.[43] Figure 11-15 gives the dispersion curves of ℓ-α-narcotine (1R, 9S) (51), ℓ-β-narcotine (1R, 9R) (52), ℓ-α-hydrastine (1R, 9R) (53), and ℓ-β-hydrastine (1R, 9S) (54).[43] The opposite absolute stereochemistry

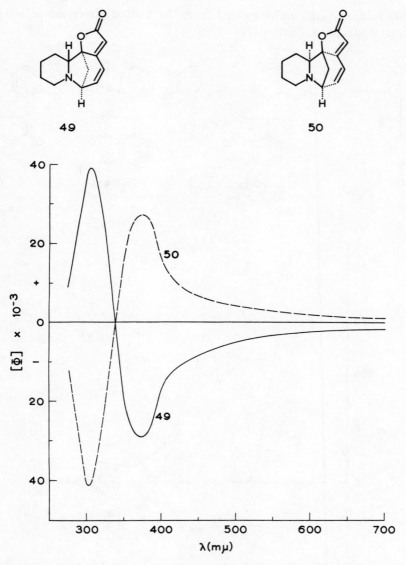

Fig. 11-14. RD curves of securinine (49) and virosecurinine (50) [adapted from Z. Horii, T. Tanaka, Y. Tamura, S. Saito, C. Matsumura, and N. Sugimoto, <u>Yakugaku Zasshi</u>, **83**, 602 (1963)].

which differentiates (51) and (52) and (53) from (54) is immediately apparent in their rotatory dispersion curves. Moreover, the "partial" Cotton effect which can be observed at about 260 mμ, as well as the weaker Cotton effect occurring at higher wavelength, express the different configurations charac-terizing these α-aryl-γ-lactones. It is the aim of the next section to emphasize that valuable information can be gained from the Cotton effect associated with optically active aromatic derivatives.

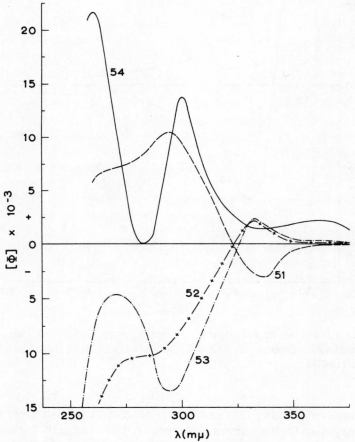

Fig. 11-15. RD curves of ℓ-α-narcotine (51), ℓ-β-narcotine (52), ℓ-α-hydrastine (53), and ℓ-β-hydrastine (54) in 2N hydrochloric acid solution [adapted from M. Ohta, H. Tani, S. Morozumi, and S. Kodaira, <u>Chem. Pharm. Bull.</u> Japan, **12**, 1080 (1964)].

11-6. AROMATIC COMPOUNDS

A. Applications of Optical Rotatory Dispersion to Configurational Problems

Kuhn and Biller[11b] have shown that certain derivatives of mandelic acid (55) and atrolactic acid (56) exhibit Cotton effects. This has been confirmed recently by an extensive study of α-aryl-substituted carboxylic acids undertaken by Sjöberg[35] (see Sec. 11-5), as well as in more recent rotatory dispersion studies[44-46] devoted to the determination of absolute configuration of asymmetric centers in the vicinity of an aromatic ring.

$$C_6H_5-CH(OH)-CO_2H$$

$$C_6H_5-\overset{\overset{\displaystyle CH_3}{|}}{\underset{\underset{\displaystyle OH}{|}}{C}}-CO_2H$$

55

56

Optical rotatory dispersion has been applied to assign the absolute configuration to threo-2-amino-1,2-diphenylethanol (57) .[46] As in the case of phenyl-carbinol examined by Mateos and Cram[45] (Sec. 5-2), it seems that in these series the Cotton effect of the threo and erythro isomers does not occur at the same wavelength. Nevertheless, a correlation between the strongly negative multiple Cotton effect associated with threo-2-amino-1,2-diphenylethanol (57) and those of ephedrines, such as (-)-ephedrine (58),[46] enabled the investigators[46] to assign the correct absolute configuration to this amino-diphenylethanol (57). Although valuable information could be obtained from "partial" dispersion curves of optically active aralkylamines and alcohols,[46] it seems desirable to gain further insight into the complete Cotton effect of such compounds with the presently available instrumentation. A quantitative evaluation of these Cotton effects would indeed probably lead to more general and secure conclusions. In the meantime, one may refer to specific derivatives of the amino group, such as N-nitroso,[28,46b] N-nitroso-N-acetyl,[28,44c] phthalyl,[27,46d] maleyl[46d] and dithio-carbamates,[46b] known to exhibit absorption bands in regions easily investigated by rotatory dispersion and circular dichroism (see also Sec. 11-4).

An optical rotatory dispersion study of several natural rotenoids has shown that they have the same absolute stereochemistry (6a S, 12a S)[47] as in rotenone (59).[48]

57

58

59

B. Aromatic Alkaloids

The application of the rotatory dispersion technique to alkaloids containing one or several aromatic rings and their derivatives has so far been limited to a relatively small number of compounds.[3,4] For instance, the rotatory dispersion curves have been published for narcotines, hydrastines (see Sec. 11-5), garryfoline, cuauchichicine, and their dihydro derivatives,[49] yohimbane and related compounds,[49,50,51] jervine[49] and isojervine,[52a] rubijervine[52b] tetrahydropalmatine,[45] seredone,[50] 18-dehydrotetramethylholarrhimine,[53] haemanthamine, buphanisine,[54] (-)-demethylgalanthamine and (+)-demethyldihydrogalanthamine,[54bis] emetine and isoemetine,[55] lysergic acid derivatives,[56] and benzylisoquinoline alkaloids,[57] as well as various alkaloids belonging to the morphine, codeine, and thebaine series.[3,58] Unfortunately, most of these curves were obtained at a time when instrumentation did not allow complete evaluation of the Cotton effects. In the present case, also, it seems desirable that some of these compounds be reexamined with the new spectropolarimeters now allowing investigation of a broader spectral range.

Indeed, when correctly interpreted, the Cotton effect can be of primary utility for solving stereochemical problems encountered in this broad class of natural products. Some recent examples will now be mentioned to illustrate the possibilities offered by rotatory dispersion and circular dichroism in alkaloid stereochemical problems.

The absolute configuration of calycanthine (60), whose structure and relative stereochemistry were established by X-ray diffraction studies,[59] could be assigned from an examination of its circular dichroism curve.[60]

60

61a, R = H
b, R = OCH$_3$

Recently, a new class of heptacyclic indole alkaloids has been discovered.[61] While the structures of two of its members, neblinine (61a) and obscurinervidine (61b), have been assigned by chemical degradation as well as by mass spectrometry and nuclear magnetic resonance examination, optical rotatory dispersion played an important role in permitting stereochemical correlations to be made. Indeed, the dispersion curves of neblinine (61a) and obscurinervidine (61b), which are reported in Figure 11-16 and are of completely the same type and sign through two Cotton effects, indicate their stereochemical identity.[61] The Cotton effect occurring above 300 mμ is presumably due to the aromatic ring, while the intense negative extremum appearing in the 260 mμ region is attributed to the γ-lactone system present in these alkaloids (see Sec. 11-3). It is apparent

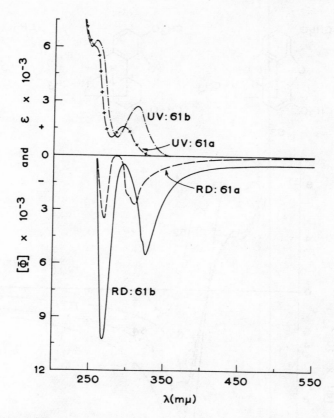

Fig. 11-16. RD and UV curves of neblinine (61a) and obscurinervidine (61b) [adapted from K. S. Brown and C. Djerassi, J. Am. Chem. Soc., **86**, 2451 (1964)].

from Figure 11-16, where the ultraviolet spectra of (61a) and (61b) are also reported, that the Cotton effect in the 300 mμ region is due to the benzene chromophore.

The benzene chromophore situated in asymmetric surroundings induces a Cotton effect which is revealed by rotatory dispersion. This is best exemplified by the rotatory dispersion curves of benzoquinolizidine (62) (see Fig. 11-17), obtained by degradation of securinine (49), which exhibits a negative Cotton effect in that region.[62] Furthermore, from the dispersion curves the R-configuration could be assigned to the asymmetric center in this compound (62).[62] These curves agree in sign with those for some 1-alkyl-tetrahydro-isoquinolines.[57]

As already mentioned, several alkaloids belonging to the morphine, codeine, and thebaine groups have been submitted to rotatory dispersion inspection[58] (see also Sec. 10-2). Recent measurements have permitted investigation of a broader wavelengths range, leading to important observations.[30,62bis] Figure 11-17 reproduces the dispersion curves of dehydrothebaine (63) and its parent compounds (64) and (65).[30] The negative Cotton effect appearing at about 290 mμ is clearly identified. Also, quite typical of such compounds is the shoulder

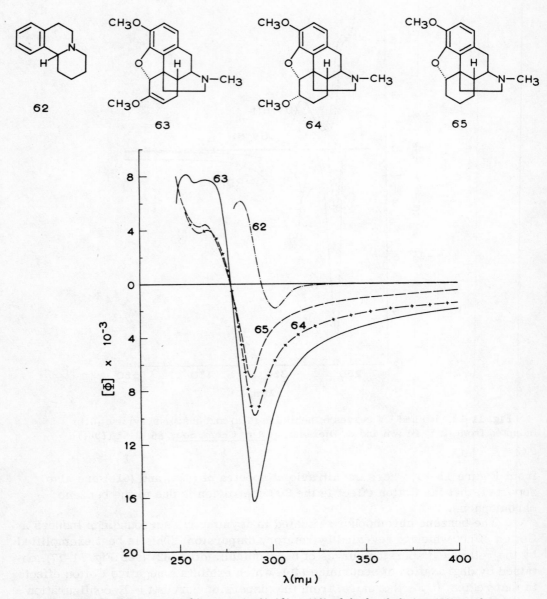

Fig. 11-17. RD curves of benzoquinolizidine (62), dehydrothebaine (63), and its parent compounds (64) and (65) in methanol solution.

situated in the 260 mμ region (see Fig. 11-17). Reduction of the enol ether double bond in (63) and demethoxylation result in a substantial decrease of the Cotton effect.

Somewhat related to the above compounds are the tetracyclic alkaloids (66) to (69), whose rotatory dispersion curves are reproduced in Figure 11-18.

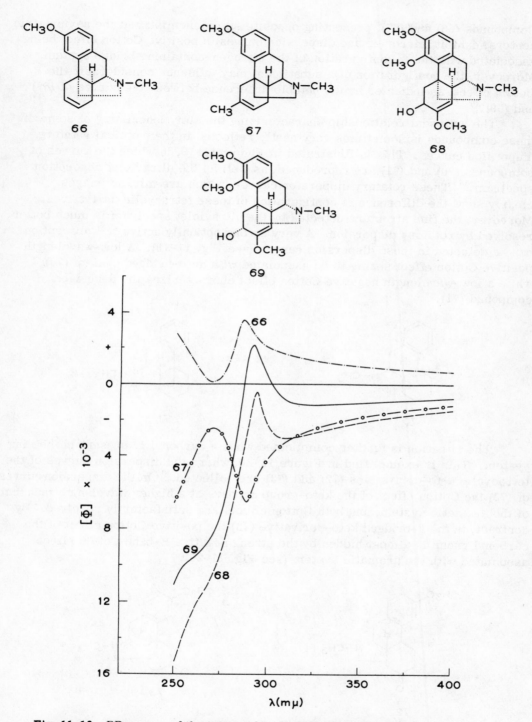

Fig. 11-18. RD curves of the tetracyclic alkaloids (66) to (69) [courtesy of Dr. K. Kuriyama, the Shionogi Research Laboratory].

Compounds (66) and (67), presenting opposite stereochemistry at the asymmetric centers, exhibit mirror-image dispersion curves, a positive Cotton effect being associated with the α-configuration of the nitrogen-containing bridge system. Moreover, the configuration of a substituent may influence considerably the Cotton effect, as indicated by the notable difference between the curves of (68) and (69).[30]

The antipodal relationship characterizing the stereochemistry of some of these compounds is sometimes very neatly reflected in their optical rotatory dispersion curves. This is illustrated in Figure 11-19, in which the curves of compounds (70) and (71) are reproduced, as well as the ultraviolet absorption spectrum.[30] These rotatory dispersion curves, which are mirror images, clearly show the difference of configuration of these tetracyclic derivatives. Moreover, the fine structure detected by the ultraviolet spectrum is much better resolved by rotatory dispersion. A very strong optically active tail absorption can be detected in these dispersion curves (see Fig. 11-19). A low-wavelength positive Cotton effect seems to be associated with an α-bridged system (70), while a low-wavelength negative Cotton effect characterizes the β-bridged compound (71).

70

71

The situation is further complicated when a carbonyl is present in the ring system. This is exemplified in Figure 11-20, where the dispersion curves of the tetracyclic keto-derivatives (72) and (73) are collected.[30] In the dispersion curves of (72) the Cotton effect of the keto-group appears at a higher wavelength than that of the aromatic system, and both Cotton effects are satisfactorily resolved. By contrast, in the β-bridged keto-derivative (73) the positive Cotton effect of the carbonyl group is almost hidden by the strong negative B-band Cotton effect associated with the aromatic system (see Fig. 11-20).[30]

72

73

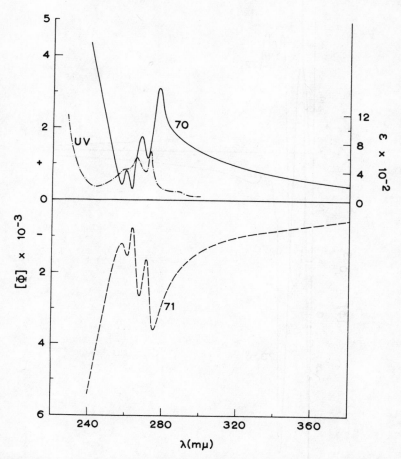

Fig. 11-19. RD and UV curves of the enantiomeric tetracyclic methylamines (70) and (71) in methanol solution [courtesy of Dr. K. Kuriyama, the Shionogi Research Laboratory].

An application of the rotatory dispersion technique for the assignment of configuration of the asymmetric center situated next to the quinoxaline ring in cinchona alkaloids has been suggested recently.[63]

Optical rotatory dispersion has also been applied, for configurational assignments, to the aporphine alkaloids.[64] The very intense Cotton effect sometimes observed, for example, in the case of bulbocapnine (74; a = +340) indicates that they belong to the class of compounds with an inherently dissymmetric chromophore. The chirality of these twisted biphenyls is uniquely determined by the absolute configuration of the asymmetric carbon atom.[64] The situation encountered in these compounds is thus reminiscent of the optically active conjugated dienes and styrenes discussed in Chapter 10. Some colchicine alkaloids have also been examined recently by optical rotatory dispersion.[65] In these compounds the twisted system is of a special type, because one ring is a tropolone.

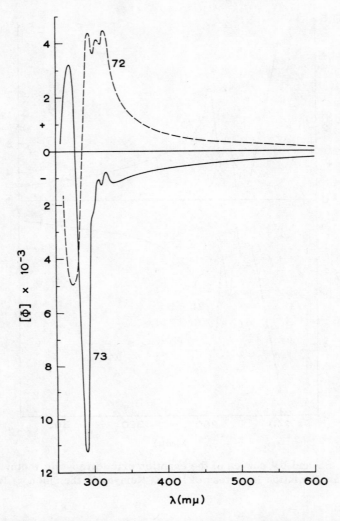

Fig. 11-20. RD curves of the tetracyclic ketones (72) and (73) in dioxane solution [courtesy of Dr. K. Kuriyama, the Shionogi Research Laboratory].

74

C. Aromatic Steroids

So far little attention has been paid to aromatic steroids and terpenes. Useful information can, however, be obtained from the Cotton effect exhibited by such compounds. This is illustrated in the case of the 9α-aromatic steroid (75) and its 9β-isomer (76).[66,67] Figure 11-21 clearly indicates that while a positive Cotton effect in the 235 mμ region is associated with the 9α-configuration (75), the 9β-stereoisomer (76) exhibits a negative curve whose Cotton effect occurs at a low wavelength. Moreover, in both curves a shoulder is apparent at about 260 mμ which corresponds to the aromatic B-band absorption. Further work is desirable in order to obtain the full Cotton effect curves of such compounds.

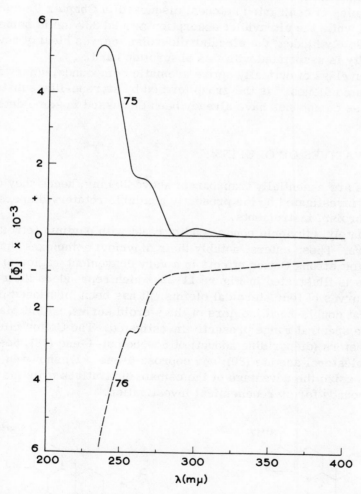

Fig. 11-21. RD curves of 3,17α,20β-trihydroxy-19-norpregna-1, 3, 5(10)-triene (75) and 3,17α,20β-trihydroxy-19-nor-9β-pregna-1, 3, 5(10)-triene (76) in methanol solution.

75   76   77

The rotatory dispersion and circular dichroism spectra of several ketones conjugated with an aromatic ring have also been examined recently.[68] These compounds, exhibiting a Cotton effect in the 300-350 mμ region, constitute special examples of conjugated ketones, discussed in Chapter 9. Suffice it to say here that while the ultraviolet absorption around 330 mμ is sometimes almost completely hidden, the circular dichroism curves clearly reveal that an optical activity is associated with this absorption band.

Another class of optically active aromatic compounds, somewhat related to skewed cisoid dienes,[69] is the group formed by styrene-like substances such as (77). These compounds have already been discussed in some detail in Section 10-4.

11-7. DERIVATIVES OF OLEFINS

Olefins are essentially transparent above 200 mμ, hence they cannot be conveniently investigated by the presently available rotatory dispersion and circular dichroism instruments.

Fortunately, ethylenic bonds readily react with osmium tetroxide to form osmate esters. These esters, notably their dipyridyl complexes, have been found to exhibit strong Cotton effects in a very convenient region of the spectrum.[70] This is illustrated in Figure 11-22, which reproduces the rotatory dispersion curves of four steroidal olefins. It has been mentioned previously (Sec. 4-2) that double-bond isomers of the steroid series exhibit plain dispersion curves in the spectral range presently investigated. The Cotton effect curves of the osmate esters (di-pyridine adduct) of 5α-cholest-1-ene (78), 5α-cholest-2-ene (79), cholesterol acetate (80), and coprost-6-ene (81), shown in Figure 11-22,[70] clearly emphasize the advantage of the osmate derivatives over the ethylenic parent compounds for stereochemical investigation.[70]

78   79

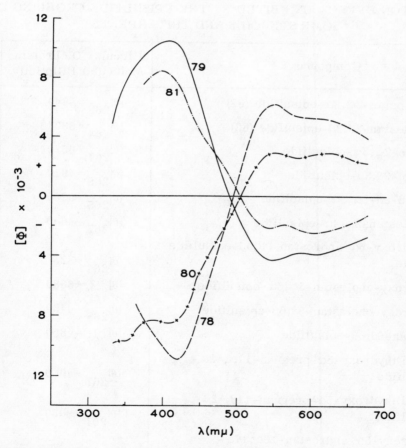

Fig. 11-22. RD curves of the di-pyridine adduct of the osmate ester of 5α–cholest-1-ene (78), 5α–cholest-2-ene (79), cholesterol acetate (80), and coprost-6-ene (81) in methylene dichloride [adapted from E. Bunnenberg and C. Djerassi, J. Am. Chem. Soc., **82**, 5953 (1960)].

Another derivative of olefins which has interesting spectroscopic properties is the episulfide. Early spectroscopic measurements with simple episulfides have shown the existence of a low-intensity absorption maximum in the 260 mμ region which appears to resemble the n - π^* absorption of the carbonyl chromophore.[71] Djerassi, Takeda, and their collaborators[72] taking advantage of these favorable spectroscopic properties, have undertaken an extensive optical rotatory dispersion and circular dichroism study of steroidal episulfides. Cookson, McGhie, and their coworkers[73] recently confirmed these findings and extended the observations to other such derivatives. The circular dichroism molecular ellipticity for various episulfides situated in different locations of the steroid and lanostane molecules is reported in Table 11-5.

Table 11-5

COTTON EFFECT EXHIBITED BY THE EPISULFIDE GROUPING IN SOME STEROIDS AND TRITERPENES

Compound	Circular Dichroism Molecular Ellipticity	Ref.
5α-Cholestan-2α,3α-episulfide (82)	$[\theta]_{268}$ -3840	72, 73
5α-Cholestan-2β,3β-episulfide (83)	$[\theta]_{264}$ +630	72, 73
Lanostan-2α,3α-episulfide	$[\theta]_{267}$ -6530	73
Lanostan-2β,3β-episulfide	$[\theta]_{265}$ +1910	73
Lanost-8-en-2α,3α-episulfide	$[\theta]_{265}$ -5250	73
5α-Cholestan-3α,4α-episulfide	$[\theta]_{267}$ -4600	72
17β-Hydroxy-5α-androstan-3β,4β-episulfide-acetate	$[\theta]_{266}$ +325	72
3β-Hydroxy-cholestan-5α,6α-episulfide	$[\theta]_{272}$ +6680	72
3β-Hydroxy-cholestan-5β,6β-episulfide	$[\theta]_{268}$ -4460	72
Cholestan-5β,6β-episulfide	$[\theta]_{267}$ -4850	72
3β,20β-Dihydroxy-5α-pregnan-11α,12α-episulfide	$[\theta]_{267}$ +4060	72
3β,20β-Dihydroxy-5α-pregnan-11β,12β-episulfide	$[\theta]_{261}$ +3460	72
3β-Hydroxy-5α-androstan-16α,17α-episulfide-acetate	$[\theta]_{264}$ +700	72
3β-Hydroxy-5α-androstan-16β,17β-episulfide-acetate	$[\theta]_{268}$ +5370	72

From these data (Table 11-5) it is apparent that in some cases, such as (82) and (83), either the sign or the rotational strength, or both parameters, can be utilized for differentiating between the position and the configuration of the episulfide function. From a theoretical point of view, it should be noted that the isolated episulfide group, like the isolated carbonyl function, represents a type of chromophore classified as "inherently symmetric" (see Sec. 2-4). Hence the observed Cotton effect results only from the asymmetry induced in the episulfide group by the rest of the molecule. Furthermore, whereas the magnetic dipole moment of an n - π^* transition is directed along the internuclear axis (e.g., C=S in a thione, vide infra), it may be at right angle in an n - σ^* transition, as in a sulfide. Cookson et al.[73] discussed the shape of episulfide orbitals and the conformational factors responsible for the Cotton effect associated with some of these compounds. The dependence of the sign and the magnitude of the rotatory power associated with the n - σ^* absorption of episulfides on the stereochemistry of dissymmetric substituents has been tentatively analyzed by these authors. They also emphasized that the n - σ^* transition of the episulfide group has the advantage of absorbing in an accessible region of the spectrum (about 260 mμ) and that this function has no conformational freedom. However, the episulfide group presents the complications of two possible σ^* orbitals, each with three nodes not exactly at right angles to the straight line between the carbon and sulfur atoms.[73]

82   83

When episulfides are reacted with potassium alkyl xanthates, trithiocarbonates are obtained. These compounds exhibit a low-intensity maximum near 430 mμ, a high-intensity maximum in the 305 mμ region, and finally, a medium-intensity maximum around 235 mμ. These properties make the trithiocarbonate an appropriate function for optical rotatory dispersion and circular dichroism investigation.[72] Indeed, the above absorption bands are optically active and readily examined by these techniques.

This is exemplified in Figure 11-23, where the circular dichroism, rotatory dispersion, and ultraviolet absorption curves of (+)-trans-9-methyl-decalin-2β,3α-trithiocarbonate (84) are reproduced.[72] The ultraviolet transitions, which are optically active, are clearly resolved by circular dichroism. The long-wavelength maximum gives rise to a positive Cotton effect which is associated with the 315 mμ absorption band. The circular dichroism curve also indicates a negative maximum in the 250 mμ region.[72]

A trithiocarbonate grouping can therefore be used as a "chromophoric" derivative for olefins. In cyclic systems this derivative permits one to assign the correct absolute stereochemistry. For instance, the absolute configuration

298   Other Chromophores

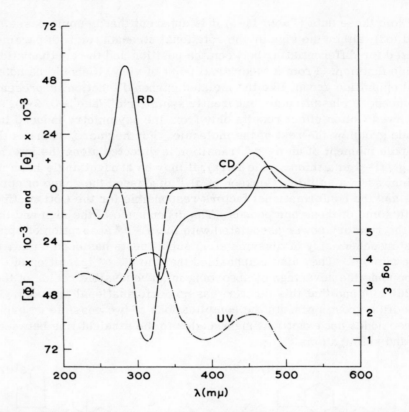

Fig. 11-23. RD, CD, and UV curves of (+)-<u>trans</u>-9-methyl-decalin-2β, 3α-trithio-carbonate (84) in dioxane solution [adapted from C. Djerassi, H. Wolf, D. A. Lighter, E. Bunnenberg, K. Takeda, T. Komeno, and K. Kuriyama, <u>Tetrahedron</u>, **19**, 1547 (1963)].

84

85

of (+)-<u>trans</u>-9-methyl-octalin-2 [the starting material of the trithiocarbonate (84)], if unknown, could be determined by comparison of the optical rotatory dispersion or circular dichroism curve of (84) with the curve of, say, the 2,3-trithiocarbonate (85) of established absolute configuration.[72]

The same derivative has also been used successfully in the sugar series. This is illustrated in Figure 11-24, where the spectral properties of 5,6-dideoxy-1,2;3,4-di-O-isopropylidene-L-gulitol-5,6-trithiocarbonate (86) are shown.[72] In this example, the long-wavelength Cotton effect is negative, and the 300 mμ Cotton effect is positive.

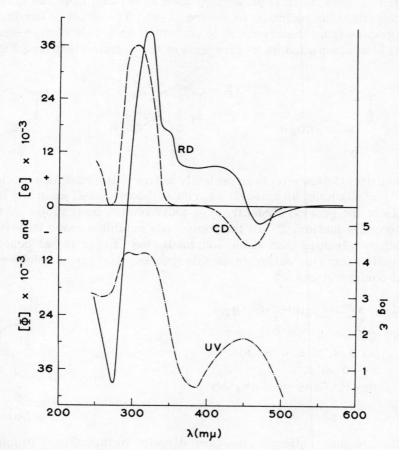

Fig. 11-24. RD, CD, and UV curves of 5,6-dideoxy-1,2; 3,4-di-O-isopropylidene-L-gulitol-5,6-trithiocarbonate (86) in dioxane solution [from C. Djerassi, H. Wolf, D. A. Lightner, E. Bunnenberg, K. Takeda, T. Komeno, and K. Kuriyama, Tetrahedron, **19**, 1547 (1963); reproduced by permission of the editor].

11-8. OTHER OPTICALLY ACTIVE SULFUR AND SELENIUM DERIVATIVES

The anomalous rotatory dispersion of a variety of sulfur containing chromophores, such as dithiocarbamates,[74] xanthates,[13,14,15,74] thionocarbalkoxy derivatives,[75] thiohydantoins,[75] and acylthiourea[76] have been recorded. Disulfides and diselenides were also investigated.[3,77] The steric relations of analogous disulfides and diselenides could be correlated by means of their dispersion curves, the same sign of the Cotton effect implying identical configuration. This is illustrated in Figure 11-25, where the optical rotatory dispersion curves of (+)-1,2-dithiane-3,6-dicarboxylic acid (87), (+)-1,2-diselenane-3,6-dicarboxylic acid (88) (see also Fig. 4-14), and (-)-1,2-dithiane-4-carboxylic acid (89) are reproduced.[77] The disulfide (87) shows an anomalous curve with a positive Cotton effect, related to the ultraviolet absorption band at 280 mμ. The diselenide (88), which exhibits its first absorption band at 341 mμ, presents a strong positive Cotton effect, as indicated in Figure 11-25. The effect of moving the disulfide group away from the asymmetric center, as in 1,2-dithiane-4-carboxylic acid (89), is accompanied by an inversion of the Cotton effect (see Fig. 11-25).

87   88   89

Recently, Cotton effects in optically active sulfoxides have been investigated.[78] For example, an extensive series of homologous, naturally derived sulfoxides of the general structure type (90) has also been subjected to rotatory dispersion examination.[78b] All the compounds exhibited more negative rotations at shorter wavelengths than at the sodium D-line. Hence it was concluded that the naturally occurring sulfoxide-isothiocyanates thus far encountered possess identical configurations.[78b]

$CH_3-S-[CH_2]_n-NH-C-NH-R_2$

n= 3, 4, 5, 8, 9 or 10
R$_1$ = O or S
R$_2$ = H, C$_6$H$_5$ or C$_6$H$_4$CH$_3$

90

91a, Δ^5
b, 5αH

More recently, attention has been directed to thioketones (thiones).[79] These compounds present in the visible region a Cotton effect which is associated with the low-intensity absorption occurring about 490 mμ. Figure 11-26 shows the rotatory dispersion curve of 3β-hydroxy-androst-5-en-17-thione (97a) and the circular dichroism curve of 3β-hydroxy-5α-androstan-17-thione (91b). Insofar

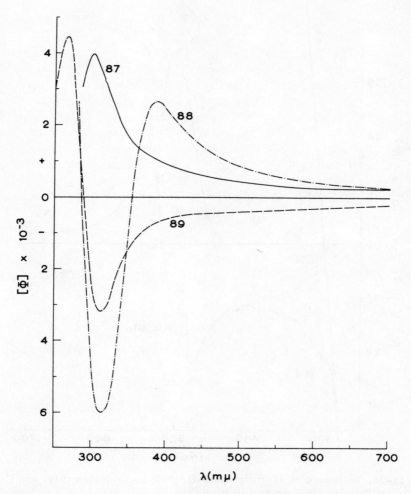

Fig. 11-25. RD curves of (+)-1, 2-dithiane-3,6-dicarboxylic acid (87), (+)-1, 2-diselenane-3,6-dicarboxylic acid (88), and (-)-1, 2-dithiane-4-carboxylic acid (89) [from C. Djerassi, A. Fredga, and B. Sjöberg, <u>Acta Chem. Scand.</u>, **15**, 417 (1961); reproduced by permission of the editor].

as results are available, the n - π^* absorption of the thiocarbonyl group at about 490 mμ conforms to the octant rule.[5]

Several optically active trithiones have also been prepared and submitted to rotatory dispersion and circular dichroism examination[80] because the trithione chromophore exhibits several absorption maxima which all are optically active. This is exemplified in Figure 11-27, in which the ultraviolet absorption spectrum and the optical rotatory dispersion and circular dichroism curves of (+)-camphor-trithione (92) are reproduced.[80b]

A positive Cotton effect is associated with the weak absorption detected in the 480-520 mμ region, as indicated in the rotatory dispersion and circular

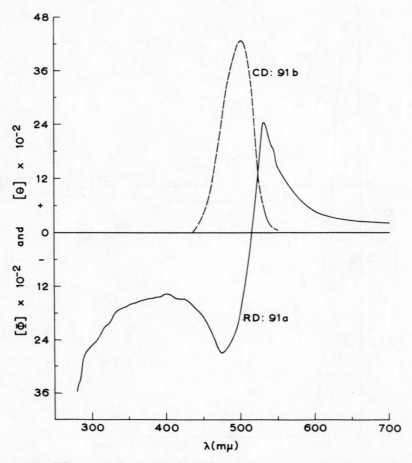

Fig. 11-26. RD curve of 3β –hydroxy-androst-5-en-17-thione (91a) and CD curve of 3β –hydroxy-5α–androstan-17-thione (91b).

92

dichroism curves of (92), reproduced in Figure 11-27.[80b] The circular dichroism negative maximum at 415 mμ clearly indicates the 417 mμ ultraviolet absorption band to be optically active and to exhibit a negative Cotton effect. A third optically active absorption band appears at about 343 mμ, and, as shown in Figure 11-27, it presents a positive Cotton effect. The fourth positive maximum

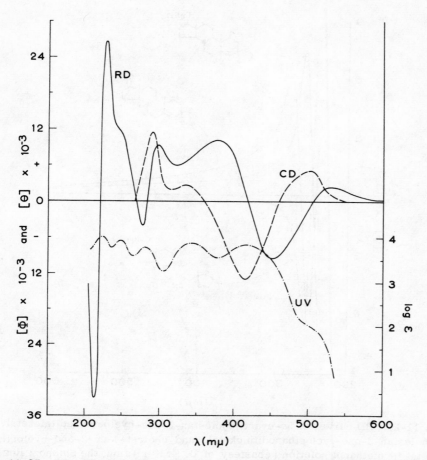

Fig. 11-27. RD, CD, and UV curves of (+)-camphor trithione (92) [adapted from H. Wolf, E. Bunnenberg, C. Djerassi, A. Lüttringhaus, and A. Stockhausen, <u>Ann. Chem.</u>, **674**, 62 (1964)].

observed on the circular dichroism curve (see Fig. 11-27) indicates the 280 mμ absorption band also to be optically active. The rotatory dispersion curve clearly shows a shoulder between 255 and 235 mμ and, at a lower wavelength (about 228 mμ), a peak which is followed by a trough at 212 mμ. These Cotton effects thus reflect the optical activity of the low-wavelength absorption bands observed in the ultraviolet spectrum of (92).

The optical rotatory dispersion and circular dichroism properties of a number of steroidal thiolacetates have also been investigated,[80bis] and a long wavelength low intensity optically active absorption band near 270 mμ has been detected.[80bis]

As indicated in Figure 11-28, cycloethylenethioketal derivatives of saturated and unsaturated ketones also exhibit typical Cotton effect curves.

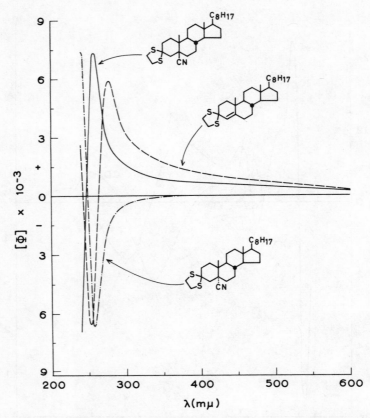

Fig. 11-28. RD curves of 5α–cyano–cholestan–3–one–cycloethanedithioketal, 5β–cyano–cholestan–3–one–cycloethanedithioketal, and cholest–4–en–3–one–cycloethane-diothioketal in methanol solution [courtesy of D. K. Kuriyama, the Shionogi Research Laboratory].

Noteworthy in the present case are the signs of the Cotton effects, which are opposite to those of the corresponding 3-keto derivatives.[30]

Finally, recent applications of the optical rotatory dispersion technique to other asymmetric sulfur[78] and to asymmetric silicon derivatives should also be mentioned.[80]

11-9. α-HYDROXY AND α-AMINO ACIDS

Until very recently the configuration of α-substituted optically active acids, such as α-hydroxy and α-amino acids, could not be investigated easily by rotatory dispersion or circular dichroism, because of the low wavelength at which they absorb in the ultraviolet. Hence, although several optical rotatory dispersion studies of α-amino acids have been described in the literature,[3,4,81] these have all been carried out with instruments which did not permit the measurement of the curves below about 250 mμ. The chromophore of longest-wavelength absorption in hydroxy and amino acids is the carboxyl group, the n - π^* transition of which occurs at about 220 mμ. The new instruments permit one to reach the region of this absorption band (see Secs. 11-3 and 11-5). This is the reason that lately several important studies of the Cotton effect associated with the n - π^* carbonyl absorption of α-hydroxy and α-amino acids have appeared.[82,83,84,84bis] These studies have shown the existence of a Cotton effect around 215 mμ. The rotatory dispersion values for a few pairs of D- and L-amino acids, as well as for some L-α-hydroxy-acids, are reported in Table 11-6.[82,83]

It is evident from these data that all L-amino acids and L-hydroxy acids (unless presenting unusual substituents in the neighborhood of the α-substituted acid function, or other chromophores absorbing at higher wavelength) exhibit a positive Cotton effect, with a peak in the 215 mμ region. Moreover, the change from water to dilute hydrochloric acid as solvent is generally accompanied for α-amino acids by an increase in molecular rotation at the peak and a bathochromic shift of around 10 mμ of this peak. This observation is in agreement with the Lutz-Jirgensons rule for the molecular rotation at the sodium D-line.[85]

These observations and results are obviously of importance. However, a recent rotatory dispersion examination of aliphatic amino acids, carried out on a Cary Model 60 recording spectropolarimeter, has permitted evaluation of the complete Cotton effect.[84] All five amino acids, when examined in an acid medium (see Table 11-7), show a long-wavelength first extremum at 225 mμ, a crossover at 210-212 mμ, and a second extremum at 195-200 mμ.[84] The molecular amplitudes follow the pattern of alkyl substitution. L-Alanine, the most symmetrical amino acid studied,[84] shows the lowest amplitude (Table 11-7). Substitution of the alkyl group leads to intermediate amplitudes for L-valine and L-α-amino-n-butyric acid. Further substitution gives higher amplitudes for L-leucine and L-norleucine (Table 11-7).[84] In other recent optical rotatory dispersion studies of L-amino acids,[84bis] the presence of a positive Cotton effect near 210 mμ was confirmed. Moreover, tyrosine and tryptophan showed an additional Cotton effect near 275 mμ attributed presumably to their aromatic ring.[84bis]

Until easy access to the complete Cotton effect exhibited by such compounds is possible, one may refer to specific derivatives of these functions, in which the optically active absorption band is shifted toward somewhat higher wavelengths.[3] It has been shown that dithiocarbamate derivatives of α-amino acids, such as the dithiocarbamate of L-(+)-alanine (93), absorb near 330 mμ with a low extinction, and that these derivatives exhibit Cotton effect curves (see Fig. 11-29).[74] The same applies to the xanthates of α-hydroxy acids, whose low-intensity ultraviolet absorption maximum falls near 356 mμ. This is shown in Figure 11-29, where the rotatory dispersion curve of the dithiocarbamate of L-(+)-lactic acid (94) is represented.[86]

As illustrated in Figure 11-29, the curve of the lactic acid derivative (94) is displaced toward the visible; its ultraviolet absorption maximum occurs approximately 30 mμ closer to the red than that of the thiocarbamate (93). Furthermore, the nature of the α-alkyl or α-aryl substituent is not important,

Table 11-6

COTTON EFFECT OF SOME α-AMINO AND α-HYDROXY ACIDS

Compound		First Optical Rotatory Dispersion Extremum	
Name	Formula	Water	Dilute HCl
L-Alanine	$CH_3-CH-CO_2H$ $\underset{NH_2}{\vert}$	$[\Phi]$ +750° (P)†	$[\Phi]$ +1610° (P)
D-Alanine		-740° (T)†	+159° (T)
L-Phenylalanine	$C_6H_5CH-CO_2H$ $\underset{NH_2}{\vert}$	+3240° (ENR)†	+5180° (P)
D-Phenylalanine		-3040° (ENR)	-5040° (T)
L-Serine	$HO-CH_2-CH-CO_2H$ $\underset{NH_2}{\vert}$	+1070° (P)	+2080° (P)
D-Serine		-1150° (T)	-2170° (T)
L-Threonine	$CH_3-CH-CH-CO_2H$ $\underset{OH\ \ NH_2}{\vert\ \ \ \vert}$	-40° (P)	+1730° (P)
D-Threonine		±0° (T)	-1710° (T)
L-Lactic acid	$CH_3-CHOH-CO_2H$	+1530° (P)	+1530° (P)
L-β-Isopropyl lactic acid	$(CH_3)_2-CH-CH_2-CHOH-CO_2H$		+2400° (P)
L-Tartaric acid	$HO_2C-CHOH-CHOH-CO_2H$		+7900° (P)
L-Mandelic acid	$C_6H_5-CHOH-CO_2H$		+20700° (P)

†P = peak; T = trough; ENR = extremum not reached.

Table 11-7

ROTATORY DISPERSION MOLECULAR AMPLITUDE
OF SOME L-AMINO ACIDS

Compound		Rotatory Dispersion Molecular Amplitude a
Name	Formula	
L-Alanine	$CH_3-CH-CO_2H$ $\quad\quad\; \vert$ $\quad\quad NH_2$	+49
L-α-Amino-n-butyric acid	$CH_3-CH_2-CH-CO_2H$ $\quad\quad\quad\quad\; \vert$ $\quad\quad\quad\quad NH_2$	+51
L-Valine	$(CH_3)_2-CH-CH-CO_2H$ $\quad\quad\quad\quad\; \vert$ $\quad\quad\quad\quad NH_2$	+60
L-Norleucine	$CH_3-(CH_2)_3-CH-CO_2H$ $\quad\quad\quad\quad\quad\; \vert$ $\quad\quad\quad\quad\quad NH_2$	+64
L-Leucine	$(CH_3)_2-CH-CH_2-CH-CO_2H$ $\quad\quad\quad\quad\quad\quad\; \vert$ $\quad\quad\quad\quad\quad\quad NH_2$	+81

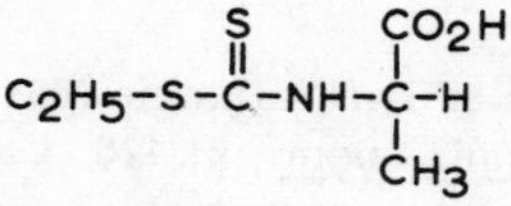

93

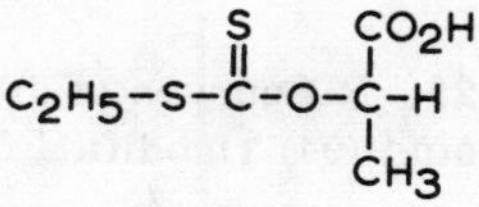

94

because α-hydroxy acids such as L-(-)-malic acid and L-(+)-mandelic acid
behave in an identical manner, their respective xanthates (95) and (96) exhibiting
positive Cotton effect curves, even though the parent acids show molecular
rotations of opposite sign at 589 mμ.[74,86]

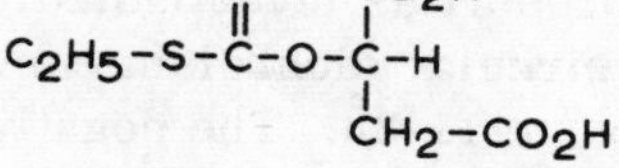

95

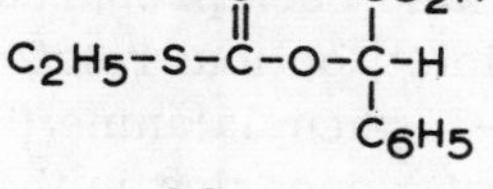

96

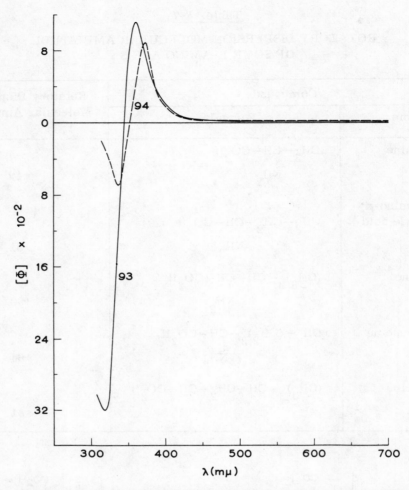

Fig. 11-29. RD curves of dithiocarbamate derivatives of L-(+)-alanine (93) and L-(+)-lactic acid (94) [modified from C. Djerassi, <u>Pure Appl. Chem.</u>, **2**, 475 (1961)].

The rotatory dispersion curves of a number of N-nitroso derivatives of N-acetyl- or N-benzoyl-α-amino acids have also been investigated, and their Cotton effects can be used for stereochemical assignments.[28] The same applies to acylthioureas,[38,76,87] as well as to 3-phenyl-2-thiohydantoins and N-thiono-carbethoxy amino acids.[75] N-phthalyl derivatives of a large number of amino acids have also been prepared and their optical properties investigated.[27,28,88] The ultraviolet, optical rotatory dispersion, and circular dichroism curves of N-phthalyl-L-phenylalanine (97) are shown in Figure 11-30. The negative Cotton effect, appearing in the 300 mμ region, corresponds to the ultraviolet transition of the phthalimide chromophore.[27] Furthermore, the circular dichroism curve, obtained in dioxane solution, shows a weak negative maximum, which did not appear either in the ultraviolet spectrum or in the rotatory dispersion curve.

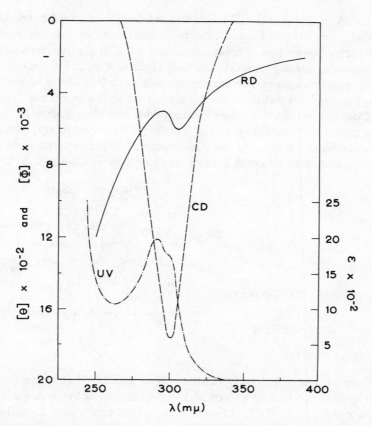

Fig. 11-30. RD, CD, and UV curves of N-phthalyl-L-phenylalanine (97) [modified from H. Wolf, E. Bunnenberg, and C. Djerassi, <u>Chem. Ber.</u>, **97**, 533 (1964)].

97   **98**

The very intense specific rotation associated with some of the recently described dimedone-amino acid condensation products,[89] such as the L-leucine methyl ester derivative (98; a = -261), induced a more thorough investigation of the optical properties of such compounds.[90] The nuclear magnetic resonance spectra[89] show that these enamines have a vinylogous amide grouping —CO—CH═CH—NH—; they have unexpected stability to both acid and alkali, attributed to resonance of the conjugated system.[89,91]

As indicated in Table 11-8,[90] these dimedone-amino acid condensation products display very strong Cotton effects reminiscent of the inherently dissymmetric chromophores (see Chaps. 8, 9, and 10). In the present case, however, the presence of an asymmetric carbon atom in the immediate vicinity of the chromophore is necessary for strong optical activity, since dimedoneglycyl-L-leucine ethyl ester (99) exhibits no Cotton effect in the spectral range examined.[90] Conversely, in the other compounds, listed in Table 11-8, a center of asymmetry is directly attached to the vinylogous amide group, which makes the situation somewhat similar to the electronic distribution encountered in d-urobilin (100), known to present a very intense Cotton effect (a $\cong$ +300).[92]

or isomer with x,y= double bond
z = vinyl

99   100

It has been shown previously (Tables 11-6 and 11-7) that the free L-amino acids present a positive Cotton effect and the D-amino acids a negative one. From the data reported in Table 11-8 it is apparent that most L-amino acid-dimedone condensation products display negative Cotton effect curves,[66] and that the same enamine derivatives obtained from D-amino acids exhibit positive Cotton effects. The position of the extrema and the breadth of the curves (see Sec. 2-5) vary substantially with the nature of the amino acid and the ester group. However, still much more characteristic are the amplitudes presented by these compounds. Extraordinary high values were sometimes obtained; for instance for dimedone-L-valine thiophenyl ester (101; a = -1018), dimedone-L-leucine thiophenyl ester (102; a = -646) and dimedone-L-tyrosine O-benzyl-methyl ester (103; a = +2011), as indicated in Table 11-8.[90]

101   102

Compound (103), although a derivative of an L-amino acid, shows a positive Cotton effect. This inversion in sign has been found to characterize all such enamines bearing a benzyl grouping (or derivative) on the asymmetric carbon

Table 11-8

COTTON EFFECT EXHIBITED BY SOME DIMEDONE-AMINO ACID CONDENSATION COMPOUNDS

| Dimedone-Condensation Compound | Optical Rotatory Dispersion | | | | Molecular Amplitude a |
| Amino Acid | First Extremum | | Second Extremum | | |
	Wavelength (mμ)	Molecular Rotation [Φ]	Wavelength (mμ)	Molecular Rotation [Φ]	
L-Leucine methyl ester (98)	276	-12600°(T)†	241	+13500°(P)†	-261
D-Leucine methyl ester	308	+6900°(P)	250	-7270°(T)	+142
L-Alanine thiophenyl ester	312	-31300°(T)	266	+47200°(P)	-785
L-Phenylalanine methyl ester	283	+24600°(P)	252	-13900°(T)	+385
L-Valine thiophenyl ester (101)	313	-33400°(T)	267	+68400°(P)	-1018
L-Leucine thiophenyl ester (102)	310	-33000°(T)	264	+31600°(P)	-646
L-Tyrosine-O-benzyl methyl ester (103)	284	+68100°(P)	253	-133000°(T)	+2011

†P = peak; T = trough.

103

atom situated next to the —CO—CH=CH—NH—chromophore.[90] The positive
Cotton effect associated with L-phenylalanine methyl ester (Table 11-8) constitutes a further illustration of this observation.

In conclusion, the dimedone-amino acid condensation products present
very interesting optical activities, obviously related to their unusual spectroscopic properties. A detailed discussion of the physical properties of such
derivatives, as well as of similar dihydroresorcinol condensation products of
some amino acids, will appear elsewhere. It may be noted, however, that the
position of the rotatory dispersion extrema and the amplitude of the Cotton
effects seem to be very sensitive to the nature of the amino acid (or ester)
forming the enamine system. It is hoped that these specific properties will be
of some help in the structural and synthetic studies performed in the protein
and peptide fields.

In connection with these observations, a closer examination of the optical
properties of the related β-dicarbonyl condensation products described by
Dane et al.[93] seems desirable, since their rotatory dispersion curves could
perhaps also provide valuable information.

11-10. MISCELLANEOUS

Various pyrromycinones, rhodomycinones, isorhodomycinones, and their
derivatives have recently been examined by circular dichroism.[94] From the
Cotton effects observed, the authors could show that all these pigments possess
the same absolute configuration at their asymmetric centers. The intense
absorption coefficients which characterize the highly conjugated system present
in these compounds (104), led the investigators to choose circular dichroism for
such examination.

where   R = H, OH, CO$_2$CH$_3$

104

Several rotatory dispersion[95] and circular dichroism[96] studies of metal-loporphyrin compounds have been published. Moreover, a comprehensive survey of the optical phenomena in metal chelates has recently appeared.[97] Since this survey also implies organo-metallic derivatives, the optical properties associated with these substances will not be reviewed here. Only a few comments about very recent works will be mentioned.

It may be said that in general the long-wavelength absorption band of transition metal complexes is due to an electronic transition of the magnetic-dipole type. The optical activity of numerous metal complexes with symmetries lower than dihedral, as well as those with three bidentate ligands, have been measured recently for the purpose of assigning spectroscopic transitions and absolute configurations. In addition, the origin of the rotatory power of metal complexes has been studied theoretically, and experimental work aimed at distinguishing among several theories has been reported.[98] The contribution played by rotatory dispersion has been quite important in this field, since the sign of the rotation at a particular wavelength (e.g., the sodium D line) cannot be used to relate the configurations of various substances because of their different absorption bands.[97]

A method for determining the chirality of metal complexes containing conjugated ligands and based on their Cotton effects has also been proposed. For example, the assignment of absolute configuration has been made for $(-)$-Ru $(phen)_3^{2+}$, which contains three noncoplanar O-phenanthroline chromophores.[99] In that respect, Mason and his collaborators[100] draw one's attention to the fact that antimonyl (+)-tartrate isomers of tris-2,2'-bipyridyl and the tris-1,10-phenanthroline complexes of Ni(II), Fe(II), Ru(II), Ru(III), Os(II), or Os(III) give circular dichroism curves which are virtually mirror images over the whole of the accessible wavelength region, although these isomers probably have the same absolute configuration.

Because of the importance of amino acids, mention should also be made of the recent optical rotatory dispersion study of metal chelates of pyridoxyliden-aminoacids,[101] in which it was shown that while the pyridoxylidene complex of L-valine with copper ions (at pH 8.7) exhibits a negative Cotton effect curve at about 400 mμ, the D-valine metal complex displays a mirror-image curve in the same spectral region. The authors attributed the strong Cotton effect to restricted rotation due to the metal chelate which is formed.[101]

The last example of this section reports the investigation of helical polymerization of pseudo-isocyanine by circular dichroism.[102] It has been shown that while the salts of 1,1'-diethyl-2,2'-cyanine (105) are monomeric in ethyl alcohol solution, addition of a concentrated ethanol solution of the dye (105) to an aqueous (+)-tartrate solution produces an optically active polymer. This work further suggests that the polymer of pseudo-isocyanin (105) chooses a helix conformation formed by eight monomers per turn. The general theory for helical polymers, predicted by Moffitt,[103] has been used to determine the chirality and structure of such dissymmetric polymers.

105

In the next chapter Moffitt's theory, as well as the helical conformation adopted by proteins and polypeptides, will be briefly discussed in the light of the information gained from recent optical rotatory dispersion and circular dichroism studies.

11-11. TABLE OF FUNCTIONAL GROUPS AND CHROMOPHORIC DERIVATIVES

In Table 11-9, taken mainly from Djerassi,[104] are listed most of the functional groups and chromophoric derivatives which can easily be investigated by optical rotatory dispersion and circular dichroism. The position of the main optically active absorption bands and the appropriate references are also reported.

Table 11-9

Functional Group	Chromophoric Derivative	Absorption Maxima (mμ)	Ref.
—NH$_2$ (and amino acids)	—NHC($=$S)SR	330	14, 74
—NH$_2$ (and amino acids)		300	27, 88
$>$NH	$>$NNO	370	28
—NHCOR	—N(NO)COR	350–450	28
RCHCO$_2$H | NH$_2$		310	14, 75
RCHCO$_2$H | NH$_2$	RCHCO$_2$H | NHC($=$S)OC$_2$H$_5$	280	14, 75
RCHCO$_2$H | NH$_2$	RCHCO$_2$H | NHC($=$S)C$_6$H$_5$	290, 380	104, 105
RCHCO$_2$H | NH$_2$	RCHCO$_2$H | NHC($=$S)CH$_2$C$_6$H$_5$	270, 335	104, 105
R—CH—CO$_2$R$_1$ | NH$_2$		240–320	90
—OH	—OC($=$S)SR	350	8, 14, 15, 74

Table 11-9 (Continued)

Functional Group	Chromophoric Derivative	Absorption Maxima (mμ)	Ref.
$-OH$	$C=O$	280–310	3, 4, 5
$-OH$	$-ONO$	325–390	8, 9, 10
$-OH$	$-O-\overset{\overset{\displaystyle O}{\|\|}}{C}-R$	200–230	6, 7
$-CO_2H$	$-CO_2R$	200–230	6, 7, 84
$-CO_2H$	$-CONHC(=S)NR_2$	340	14, 87
$-CO_2H$	$-C(=S)NRR$	325–360	104
$-C=C-$	(thiirane ring, S)	260	72, 73
$-C=C-$	(1,3-dithiole-2-thione ring)	235, 305, 430	72
$-C=C-$	(osmate ester, OsO$_4$ adduct)	450, 550	70

REFERENCES

1. (a) A. E. Gillam and E. S. Stern, An Introduction to Electronic Absorption
    Spectroscopy in Organic Chemistry, E. Arnold, London, 1958; (b) A. I. Scott,
    Interpretation of the Ultraviolet Spectra of Natural Products, Pergamon Press,
    Oxford, 1964; (c) R. C. Cookson, J. Chem. Soc., 282 (1964); (d) R. C. Cookson
    and S. H. Dandegaonker, J. Chem. Soc., 352 (1955); (e) R. B. Woodward, J. Am.
    Chem. Soc., 63, 1123 (1941) and 64, 76 (1942).

2. (a) L. J. Bellamy, The Infra-red Spectra of Complex Molecules, Wiley, New York,
    1958; (b) A. D. Cross, Introduction to Practical Infra-red Spectroscopy,
    Butterworths, London, 1960; (c) E. N. Jones and F. Herling, J. Org. Chem., 19,
    1252, (1954). (d) K. Nakanishi, Infrared Absorption Spectroscopy, Holden-Day,
    San Francisco, 1964.

3. C. Djerassi, Optical Rotatory Dispersion; Applications to Organic Chemistry,
    McGraw-Hill, New York, 1960.

4. W. Klyne in Advances in Organic Chemistry (R. A. Raphael, E. C. Taylor, and
    H. Wynberg, eds.), Vol. I, p. 239, Interscience, New York, 1960.

5. W. Moffitt, R. B. Woodward, A. Moscowitz, W. Klyne, and C. Djerassi, J. Am.
    Chem. Soc., 83, 4013 (1961).

6. (a) J. P. Jennings and W. Klyne, Biochem. J., 86, 12 P (1963); (b) P. M. Scopes,
    J. P. Jennings, and W. Klyne, unpublished results; (c) J. C. Danilewicz,
    D. C. F. Garbutt, A. Horeau, and W. Klyne, J. Chem. Soc., 2254 (1964).

7. J. C. Danilewicz and W. Klyne, J. Chem. Soc., in press.

8. C. Djerassi, I. T. Harrison, O. Zagneetko, and A. L. Nussbaum, J. Org. Chem.,
    27, 1173 (1962).

9. M. Legrand and R. Viennet, Comptes rendus, 255, 2985 (1962); see also ref. 40.

10. C. Djerassi, H. Wolf, and E. Bunnenberg, J. Am. Chem. Soc., 85, 2835 (1963).

11. (a) W. Kuhn and H. L. Lehmann, Z. physik. Chem., B 18, 32 (1932); (b) W. Kuhn and
    H. Biller, Z. physik. Chem., B 29, 1 (1935); (c) W. Kuhn, Ann. Rev. Phys. Chem.,
    9, 417 (1958).

12. P. Crabbé, Tetrahedron, 20, 1211 (1964).

13. T. M. Lowry and H. Hudson, Phil. Trans. Roy. Soc. London, 232A, 117 (1933).

14. C. Djerassi, H. Wolf, and E. Bunnenberg, J. Am. Chem. Soc., 84, 4552 (1962).

15. B. Sjöberg, D. J. Cram, L. Wolf, and C. Djerassi, Acta Chem. Scand., 16, 1079 (1962).

16. L. Tschugaeff and A. Ogorodnikoff, Z. Physik. Chem. 74, 503 (1910); Z. Physik.
    Chem., 85, 481 (1913).

318   Other Chromophores

17. See for example (a) C. S. Hudson, M. L. Wolfrom, and T. M. Lowry, J. Chem. Soc., 1179 (1933), and references therein; (b) W. C. G. Baldwin, M. L. Wolfrom, and T. M. Lowry, J. Chem. Soc., 696 (1935), and related papers; (c) T. L. Harris, E. L. Hirst, and C. E. Wood, J. Chem. Soc., 848 (1937), and related papers; (d) W. A. Bonner, J. Am. Chem. Soc., 71, 3384 (1949); (e) W. Kauzmann, F. B. Clough, and I. Tobias, Tetrahedron, 13, 57 (1961); (f) R. U. Lemieux and M. Hoffer, Can. J. Chem., 39, 110 (1961); (g) M. L. Wolfrom, A. Thompson, and D. R. Lineback, J. Org. Chem., 27, 2563 (1962); (h) V. S. R. Rao and J. F. Foster, Nature, 200, 570 (1963); (i) R. J. Abraham, L. D. Hall, L. Hough, K. A. McLauchlan, and H. J. Miller, J. Chem. Soc., 748 (1963); (j) R. U. Lemieux and J. W. Lown, Can. J. Chem., 41, 889 (1963); (k) G. J. F. Chittenden and R. D. Guthrie, J. Chem. Soc., 1045 (1964); (l) R. J. Ferrier and N. R. Williams, Chem. and Ind., 1696 (1964), and references cited therein.

18. N. Pace, C. Tanford, and E. A. Davidson, J. Am. Chem. Soc., 86, 3160 (1964).

19. T. Okuda, S. Harigaya, and A. Kiyomoto, Chem. Pharm. Bull. Japan, 12, 504 (1964).

20. R. S. Cahn, C. K. Ingold, and V. Prelog, Experientia, 12, 81 (1956).

21. (a) C. S. Hudson, J. Am. Chem. Soc., 32, 338 (1910); (b) P. M. Scopes and W. Klyne, Biochem. J. 86, 13P. (1963); (c) Private communication from Professor W. Klyne, University of London, cf. J. P. Jennings, W. Klyne and P. M. Scopes, Proc. Chem. Soc., December (1964).

22. (a) Y. Tsuzuki, K. Tanaka, and K. Tanabe, Bull. Chem. Soc. Japan, 35, 1614 (1962), and references cited therein; (b) Y. Tsuzuki, K. Tanabe, M. Akagi, and S. Tejima, Bull. Chem. Soc. Japan, 37, 162 (1964); (c) Y. Tsuzuki, K. Tanaka, K. Tanabe, M. Akagi, and S. Tejima, Bull. Chem. Soc. Japan, 37, 730 (1964).

23. C. Satoh and A. Kiyomoto, Chem. Pharm. Bull. Japan, 12, 615 (1964).

24. S. Mitchell and R. R. Gordon, J. Chem. Soc., 853 (1936).

25. C. Satoh, A. Kiyomoto, and T. Okuda, Chem. Pharm. Bull. Japan, 12, 518 (1964).

26. (a) D. Bertin and M. Legrand, Comptes rendus, 256, 960 (1963); (b) H. E. Smith, M. E. Warren, and A. W. Ingersoll, J. Am. Chem. Soc., 84, 1513 (1962); (c) H. E. Smith, S. L. Cook, and M. E. Warren, J. Org. Chem., 29, 2265 (1964).

27. (a) J. H. Brewster and S. F. Osman, J. Am. Chem. Soc., 82, 5754 (1960); (b) H. Wolf, E. Bunnenberg, and C. Djerassi, Chem. Ber., 97, 533 (1964).

28. (a) C. Djerassi, E. Lund, E. Bunnenberg, and B. Sjöberg, J. Am. Chem. Soc., 83, 2307 (1961); (b) K. Schreiber, H. Ripperger, C. Horstmann, K. Heller, and G. Snatzke, in preparation.

29. F. W. Bachelor, R. F. C. Brown, and G. Büchi, Tetrahedron Letters, No. 10, 1 (1960).

30. The rotatory dispersion curves of these compounds prepared at the Shionogi
     Research Laboratory, Osaka, were obtained through the kindness of Dr. Karu
     Kuriyama.

31. (a) S. Mitchell, J. Chem. Soc., 3258 (1928); (b) S. Mitchell and S. B. Carmack,
     J. Chem. Soc., 415 (1932).

32. H. B. Elkins and W. Khun, J. Am. Chem. Soc., 57, 296 (1935).

33. G. Jacob, G. Ourisson, and A. Rassat, Bull. Soc. Chim. France, 1374 (1959).

34. (a) G. Snatzke, Tetrahedron, in press; (b) G. Snatzke, D. Becker, and J. R. Bull,
     Tetrahedron, 20, 2443 (1964); (c) J. R. Bull, J. P. Jennings, W. Klyne, G. D.
     Meakins, P. M. Scopes, and G. Snatzke, J. Chem. Soc., in press.

34 bis. (a) H. Ripperger and K. Schreiber, Tetrahedron, in press; (b) H. Ripperger,
     K. Schreiber, and G. Snatzke, Tetrahedron, in press.

35. B. Sjöberg, Acta Chem. Scand., 14, 273 (1960), Arkiv Kemi, 15, 451 (1960).

36. Private communication from Dr. B. Sjöberg, Astra Aktiebolaget, Södertälje, cf.
     A. Fredga, J. P. Jennings, W. Klyne, P. M. Scopes, B. Sjöberg, and S. Sjöberg,
     J. Chem. Soc., in press.

37. J. V. Burakevich and C. Djerassi, J. Am. Chem. Soc., 87, 51 (1965).

38. (a) J. Sandström, Acta Chem. Scand., 17, 678 (1963); (b) M. J. Janssen, Rec. Trav.
     Chim. 79, 454, 464 (1960); see also refs. 76 and 87.

39. U. Weiss and H. Ziffer, J. Org. Chem., 28, 1248 (1963).

40. R. Bucourt, M. Legrand, M. Vignau, J. Tessier, and V. Delaroff, Comptes rendus,
     257, 2679 (1963).

41. D. Arigoni, W. von Daehne, W. O. Godtfredsen, A. Melera, and S. Vangedal,
     Experientia, 20, 344 (1964), and references therein.

42. (a) Z. Horii, T. Tanaka, Y. Tamura, S. Saito, C. Matsumura, and N. Sugimoto,
     Yakugaku Zasshi, 83, 602 (1963); (b) S. Saito, K. Kotera, N. Shigematsu, A. Ide,
     Z. Horii, and Y. Tamura, Chem. and Ind., 689 (1963); (c) Z. Horii, M. Ikeda,
     Y. Yamawaki, Y. Tamura, S. Saito, and K. Kotera, Chem. Pharm. Bull. Japan,
     11, 817 (1963); (d) S. Saito, K. Kotera, N. Shigematsu, A. Ide, N. Sugimoto,
     Z. Horii, M. Hanaoka, Y. Yamawaki, and Y. Tamura, Tetrahedron, 19, 2085 (1963);
     (e) J. Parello, A. Melera, and R. Goutarel, Bull. Soc. Chim. France, 898 (1963);
     (f) T. Nakano, T. H. Yang, S. Terao, and L. J. Durham, Chem. and Ind., 1034, 1763
     (1963); (g) Z. Horii, M. Ikeda, Y. Tamura, S. Saito, M. Suzuki, and K. Kotera,
     Chem. Pharm. Bull. Japan, 12, 1118 (1964); (h) T. Nakano, T. H. Yang, and S. Terao,
     J. Org. Chem., 29, 3441 (1964).

43. (a) M. Ohta, H. Tani, S. Morozumi, and S. Kodaira, Tetrahedron Letters, No. 27,
     1857 (1963); (b) M. Ohta, H. Tani, S. Morozumi, and S. Kodaira, Chem. Pharm.
     Bull. Japan, 12, 1080 (1964).

44. (a) G. G. Lyle, J. Org. Chem., 25, 1779 (1960); (b) W. M. Potapov and A. P. Terentev, Zh. Obshch. Khim., 34, 516 (1964); (c) A. La Manna and V. Ghislandi, Il Farmaco (Milan), 17, 355 (1962).

45. J. L. Mateos and D. J. Cram, J. Am. Chem. Soc., 81, 2756 (1959).

46. (a) G. G. Lyle and W. Lacroix, J. Org. Chem., 28, 900 (1963); (b) I. P. Dirkx and Th. J. de Boer, Rec. Trav. Chim., 83, 535 (1964), see also ref. 74; (c) A. La Manna and V. Ghislandi, Il Farmaco (Milan), 19, 378 (1964); (d) A. La Manna and V. Ghislandi, Il Farmaco (Milan), 19, 480 (1964).

47. C. Djerassi, W. D. Ollis, and R. C. Russell, J. Chem. Soc., 1448 (1961).

48. G. Büchi, L. Crombie, P. J. Godin, and J. S. Kaltenbronn, J. Chem. Soc., 2843 (1961).

49. C. Djerassi, R. Riniker, and B. Riniker, J. Am. Chem. Soc., 78, 6362 (1956).

50. J. Poisson, N. Neuss, R. Goutarel, and M. M. Janot, Bull. Soc. Chim. France, 1195 (1958).

51. J. A. D. Jeffreys, J. Chem. Soc., 3077 (1959).

52. (a) T. Masamune, M. Takasugi, M. Gohda, H. Suzuki, S. Kawahara, and T. Irie, J. Org. Chem., 29, 2282 (1964); (b) S. W. Pelletier, and D. M. Locke, J. Am. Chem. Soc., 79, 4531 (1957).

53. C. Djerassi, O. Halpern, V. Halpern, O. Schindler, and C. Tamm, Helv. Chim. Acta, 41, 250 (1958).

54. W. C. Wildman and H. M. Fales, J. Am. Chem. Soc., 80, 6465, (1958).

54 bis. S. M. Laiho and H. M. Fales, J. Am. Chem. Soc., 86, 4434 (1964).

55. E. E. van Tamelen and J. H. Hester, J. Am. Chem. Soc., 81, 507 (1959).

56. H. G. Leemann and S. Fabbri, Helv. Chim. Acta, 42, 2696 (1959).

57. A. R. Battersby, I. R. C. Bick, J. P. Jennings, W. Klyne, P. M. Scopes, and M. J. Vernengo, J Chem. Soc., in press.

58. J. M. Bobbitt, U. Weiss, and D. D. Hanessian, J. Org. Chem. 24, 1582 (1959).

59. T. A. Hamor and J. M. Robertson, J. Chem. Soc., 194 (1962).

60. S. F. Mason, Proc. Chem. Soc., 362 (1962).

61. K. B. Brown and C. Djerassi, J. Am. Chem. Soc., 86, 2451 (1964).

62. Z. Horii, M. Ikeda, Y. Yamawaki, T. Tamura, S. Saito, and K. Kotera, Tetrahedron, 19, 2101 (1964).

62 bis. (a) Y. K. Sawa, N. Tsuji, and S. Maeda, Tetrahedron, 15, 144, 154 (1961);
         (b) Y. K. Sawa and S. Maeda, Tetrahedron, 20, 2247 (1964); (c) Y. K. Sawa, N. Tsuji,
         and S. Maeda, Tetrahedron, 20, 2255 (1964); (d) Y. K. Sawa and S. Maeda, Tetra-
         hedron, 20, 2259 (1964).

63.   G. G. Lyle and W. Gaffield, Tetrahedron Letters, No. 21, 1371 (1963) and No. 29,
       1990 (1964); see also V. Prelog, Tetrahedron Letters, No. 30, 2037 (1964), and
       references therein.

64.   (a) C. Djerassi, K. Mislow, and M. Shamma, Experientia, 18, 53 (1962); (b)
       J. C. Craig and S. K. Roy, Tetrahedron, in press.

65.   J. Hrbek, J. P. Jennings, W. Klyne, and F. Šantavy, Coll. Czech. Chem. Commun.,
       29, 2822 (1964).

66.   These rotatory dispersion tracings have been obtained on a Bellingham and
       Stanley-Bendix-Ericsson automatic recording spectropolarimeter at the University
       of London through the kind cooperation of Prof. W. Klyne.

67.   These compounds have been prepared by Dr. J. Siddall of the Syntex Research
       Laboratories.

68.   R. C. Cambie, L. N. Mander, A. K. Bose, and M. S. Manhas, Tetrahedron, 20,
       409 (1964).

69.   A. Moscowitz, E. Charney, U. Weiss, and H. Ziffer, J. Am. Chem. Soc., 83,
       4661 (1961).

70.   E. Bunnenberg and C. Djerassi, J. Am. Chem. Soc., 82, 5953 (1960).

71.   (a) R. E. Davis, J. Org. Chem., 23, 216, 1380 (1958); (b) A. M. Creighton and
       L. N. Owen, J. Chem. Soc., 1024 (1960).

72.   C. Djerassi, H. Wolf, D. A. Lightner, E. Bunnenberg, K. Takeda, T. Komeno, and
       K. Kuriyama, Tetrahedron, 19, 1547 (1963).

73.   D. E. Bays, R. C. Cookson, R. R. Hill, J. F. MacGhie, and G. E. Usher, J. Chem.
       Soc., 1563 (1964).

74.   B. Sjöberg, A. Fredga, and C. Djerassi, J. Am. Chem. Soc., 81, 5002 (1959).

75.   C. Djerassi, K. Undheim, R. C. Sheppard, W. G. Terry, and B. Sjöberg, Acta
       Chem. Scand., 15, 903 (1961).

76.   C. Djerassi and K. Undheim, J. Am. Chem. Soc., 82, 5755 (1960); See also ref. 87.

77.   C. Djerassi, A. Fredga, and B. Sjöberg, Acta Chem. Scand., 15, 417 (1961).

78. (a) K. Mislow, A. L. Ternay Jr., and J. T. Melillo, J. Am. Chem. Soc., 85, 2329 (1963); (b) W. Klyne, J. Day, and A. Kjaer, Acta Chem. Scand., 14, 215 (1960); (c) E. B. Fleischer, M. Axelrod, M. Green, and K. Mislow, J. Am. Chem. Soc., 86, 3395 (1964); (d) K. Mislow, M. M. Green, P. Laur, and D. R. Chisholm, J. Am. Chem. Soc., in press; (e) K. K. Andersen, W. Gaffield, N. E. Papanikolaou, J. W. Foley, and R. I. Perkins, J. Am. Chem. Soc., 86, 5637 (1964).

79. (a) C. Djerassi and D. Herbst, J. Org. Chem., 26, 4675 (1961); (b) R. E. Ballard and S. F. Mason, J. Chem. Soc., 1624 (1963).

80. (a) C. Djerassi and A. Lüttringhaus, Chem. Ber., 94, 2305 (1961); (b) H. Wolf, E. Bunnenberg, C. Djerassi, A. Lüttringhaus, and A. Stockhausen, Ann. Chem., 674, 62 (1964).

80 bis. K. Takeda, K. Kuriyama, T. Komeno, D. A. Lightner, R. Records, and C. Djerassi, J. Am. Chem. Soc., in press.

80 ter. L. H. Sommer, C. L. Frye, M. C. Musolf, G. A. Parker, P. G. Rodewald, K. W. Michael, Y. Okaya, and R. Pepinsky, J. Am. Chem. Soc., 83, 2210 (1961).

81. Inter alia (a) P. Karrer and W. Kaase, Helv. Chim. Acta, 2, 436 (1919); (b) J. W. Patterson and W. R. Brode, Arch. Biochem., 2, 247 (1943); (c) E. Brand, E. Washburn, B. F. Erlanger, E. Ellenbogen, J. Daniel, F. Lippmann, and M. Scheu, J. Am. Chem. Soc., 76, 5037 (1954); (d) M. C. Otey, J. P. Greenstein, M. Winitz, and S. M. Birnbaum, J. Am. Chem. Soc., 77, 3112 (1955); (e) N. Izumiya, R. Wade, M. Winitz, M. C. Otey, S. M. Birnbaum, R. J. Koegel, and J. P. Greenstein, J. Am. Chem. Soc., 79, 652 (1957); (f) J. A. Schellman in ref. 3, p. 210; (g) J. Strem, Y. S. R. Krishna-Prasad, and J. A. Schellman, Tetrahedron, 13 176 (1961); (h) J. W. Cornforth, G. Ryback, G. Popjak, C. Donninger, and G. Schroepfer, Biochem. Biophys. Res. Commun., 9, 371 (1962); (i) M. Sprecher, M. J. Clark, and D. B. Sprinson, Biochem. Biophys. Res. Commun., 15, 581 (1964); (j) L. I. Katzin, and E. Gulyas, J. Am. Chem. Soc., 86, 1655 (1964); (k) See also refs. 74 to 77; (l) V. M. Potapov, A. P. Terentiev, and Dang Ni Tai, Dokl. Akad. Nauk.S.S.S.R., 158, 1136 (1964).

82. J. P. Jennings, W. Klyne, and P. M. Scopes, J. Chem. Soc., in press; see also ref. 6a.

83. I. P. Dirkx and F. L. J. Sixma, Rec. Trav. Chim., 83, 522 (1964).

84. W. Gaffield, Chem. and Ind., 1460 (1964).

84 bis. (a) D. W. Urry and H. Eyring, J. Am. Chem. Soc., 86, 4574 (1964); (b) E. Iizuka and J. T. Yang, Biochemistry, 3, 1519 (1964); (c) J. Brahms and W. F. H. Mommaerts, J. Mol. Biol., 10, 73 (1964); (d) G. D. Fasman, E. Bodenheimer, and C. Lindblow, Biochemistry, 3, 1665 (1964); (e) S. Beychok and G. D. Fasman, Biochemistry, 3, 1675 (1964).

85. O. Lutz and B. Jirgensons, Chem. Ber., 63, 448 (1930); Chem. Ber., 64, 1221 (1931).

86. C. Djerassi, Pure Appl. Chem., 2, 475 (1961).

87.   C. Djerassi, K. Undheim, and A. M. Weidler, Acta Chem. Scand., 16, 1147 (1962).

88.   C. Djerassi, E. Lund, E. Bunnenberg, and J. C. Sheehan, J. Org. Chem., 26, 4509 (1961).

89.   B. Halpern and L. B. James, Nature, 202, 592 (1964).

90.   P. Crabbé and B. Halpern, Chem. and Ind., in press.

91.   (a) B. Halpern and L. B. James, Aust. J. Chem. 17, 1282 (1964); (b) B. Halpern and A. D. Cross, forthcoming publication; (c) B. Halpern, Aust. J. Chem., in press.

92.   (a) C. H. Gray, P. M. Jones, W. Klyne, and D. C. Nicholson, Nature, 184, 41 (1959); (b) A. Moscowitz, W. C. Krueger, I. T. Kay, G. Skewes, and S. Buckenstein, Proc. Natl. Acad. Sci. U.S., in press.

93.   E. Dane, F. Drees, and P. Konrad, Angew. Chem., 74, 873 (1962).

94.   H. Brockmann Jr. and M. Legrand, Tetrahedron, 19, 395 (1963).

95.   (a) G. L. Eichhorn, Tetrahedron, 13, 208 (1961); (b) B. Ke and R. M. Miller, Naturwiss; 51, 436 (1964), and references therein.

96.   (a) L. Velluz, M. Legrand, and R. Viennet, Comptes rendus, 255, 15 (1962); (b) M. Legrand and R. Viennet, Bull. Soc. Chim. France, 1435 (1962).

97.   (a) A. M. Sargeson in Chelating Agents and Metal Complexes (F. P. Dwyer and D. P. Mellor, eds.), chap. 5, p. 183, Academic Press, New York, 1964; (b) See also: Proceedings of the 8th. International Conference on Coordination Chemistry (V. Gutman, ed.), Springer-Verlag, Vienna, 1964, especially pp. 101-111.

98.   S. F. Mason, Chem. and Ind., 1286 (1964), and references cited therein.

99.   A. J. McCaffery and S. F. Mason, Proc. Chem. Soc., 211 (1963), and references therein.

100. A. J. McCaffery, S. F. Mason, and B. J. Norman, Proc. Chem. Soc., 259 (1964).

101. I. M. Torchinskii and L. G. Koreneva, Dokl. Akad. Nauk. S.S.S.R., 155, 961 (1964); see also: P. W. Schneider and H. Brintzinger, Helv. Chim. Acta, 47, 1717 (1964).

102. S. F. Mason, Proc. Chem. Soc., 119 (1964).

103. W. Moffitt, Proc. Nat. Acad. Sci. U.S., 42, 736 (1956), J. Chem. Phys., 25, 467 (1956).

104. C. Djerassi, Proc. Chem. Soc., 314 (1964).

105. B. Sjöberg, B. Hansson, and R. Dahlbom, Acta Chem. Scand., 16, 1057 (1962).

12

Polypeptides, Proteins, and Nucleic Acids

12-1. INTRODUCTION

This chapter is a brief survey of some observations made in the fields of polypeptides, proteins, and nucleic acids. It will be seen that optical rotatory dispersion and, more recently, circular dichroism have provided valuable information for the investigators interested in this important field of natural products.

For more thorough discussions, the reader should refer to the detailed articles and reviews written by specialists in these fields. More specifically, the work of Blout[1,2] and Doty,[3] as well as the recent articles of Jirgenson,[4] Kauzmann,[5] Tinoco,[6] and Yang[7] and their collaborators should be consulted.

Polypeptides and proteins are polymers composed of α-amino acids joined through secondary amide linkages (peptide bond). Apart from glycine, the amino acids constituting the protein molecules are all optically active as they possess one or several asymmetric centers. The configuration around the carbon atom situated next to the carboxyl in most naturally occurring amino acids of proteins is identical, and these amino acids belong to the L-series. Nevertheless, a few D-amino acids have been found in naturally occurring low-molecular-weight polypeptides, such as the gramicidins and polymixins.[1]

Since high-molecular-weight polypeptides and proteins consist of many amino acid residues, it is apparent that the atoms in a molecule of the general type shown in Figure 12-1[1] can occupy several positions in space, since greater freedom in rotation is possible around each $-CH-\overset{\overset{O}{\|}}{C}-$ and $-CH-NH-$ bond of the "backbone" than around the planar $-\overset{\overset{O}{\|}}{C}-NH-$ bonds.

Hence to specify the structure of such molecules it is necessary not only to ascertain the configuration of the atoms or molecular groups around the asymmetric carbon atoms but also to specify the conformation or spatial relationship of the various groups comprising the whole molecule (see Sec. 5-1). Thus, in these fields, the fundamental contrinution of rotatory dispersion and circular dichroism will be for the study of polypeptide and protein conformations.

In that respect it may be mentioned that Prelog and his collaborators[7 bis] have already discussed the cycloenantiomerism and the rotatory dispersion properties of cyclopeptides.

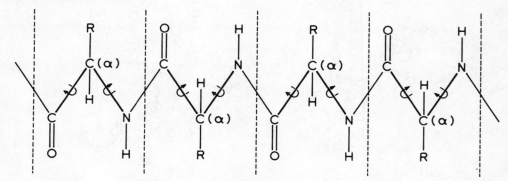

Fig. 12-1. Schematic representation of a portion of a polypeptide or protein molecule [adapted from E. R. Blout in C. Djerassi, <u>Optical Rotatory Dispersion: Applications to Organic Chemistry</u>, McGraw-Hill, New York, 1960].

12-2. HELICAL CONFORMATION OF POLYPEPTIDES: MOFFITT'S THEORY.

Soon after the suggestion by Pauling and Corey[8] that a totally intramolecularly hydrogen-bonded structure, the α-helix represented in Figure 12-2, might be the important structural feature in many synthetic polypeptides and in proteins, Cohen[9] pointed out that the changes in optical rotation that accompany the unfolding or denaturation of proteins may be due to changes from helical structure to more random conformations.

Moffitt[10] developed a theory of optical rotation, associated with a polypeptide helix, using a quantum-mechanical treatment. This author expressed the specific rotation of the helices in a two-term equation:

[1]
$$[m']_\lambda \equiv \frac{M_0}{100} \times \frac{3}{n^2 + 2} \qquad [\alpha]_\lambda = \frac{a_0 \lambda_0{}^2}{\lambda^2 - \lambda_0{}^2} + \frac{b_0 \lambda_0{}^4}{(\lambda^2 - \lambda_0{}^2)^2}$$

where $[m']_\lambda$ is the mean residue rotation (i.e., monomer unit rotation) at wavelength λ; M_0 is the molecular weight per residue (or monomer unit); n is the refractive index of the solvent; a_0, b_0, and λ_0 are constants characteristic of the helix; and the a_0 term contains both helix and residue contributions.

Moffitt's quantitative calculation has proved to be oversimplified, and this theory has been revised,[11] so that a rigorous treatment of this problem requires the introduction of additional terms. Moffitt predicted correctly that the α-helix conformation of polypeptides derived from L-amino acids is right-handed. Moreover, while Moffitt originally claimed[10] the rotational strength for light incident parallel to the helix axis to be zero, he later indicated[11] that in his original treatment important terms had been neglected and, therefore, that this rotational strength was not zero. That is, he introduced the important notion

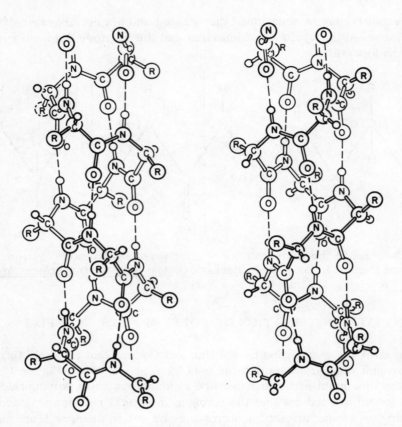

Fig. 12-2. Drawing showing two possible forms of the α-helix. The one on the left is a left-handed helix, the one on the right a right-handed helix. In both the amino-acid residues have the L-configuration [adapted from R. B. Corey and L. Pauling, <u>Rend. ist</u>. <u>lombardo sci</u>., P 1, **89**, 10 (1955)].

that the rotational strength is also significantly dependent upon the pitch of the helix.[11],[12] This contention has been supported by Tinoco's recent work,[13] although Mason[14] claims that Moffitt's early assumption[10] is correct. Tinoco et al.[13] also emphasized that the pitch-dependent rotational strengths are important in oligomers and are paramount in polymers containing chromophores with transition moments directed perpendicular to the helix axis, such as deoxyribonucleic acid. In high polymers belonging to the polypeptide α-helix type, however, the monomer transitions moments are neither parallel nor perpendicular to the axis of the helix, so that the pitch-dependent rotational strengths mutually cancel to a greater degree than the radius dependent terms.

The optical rotatory dispersion curves of several polypeptides in weakly hydrogen-bond-breaking solvents (sometimes called helical solvents) have been measured. The experimental curves do not fit a simple Drude equation (see

Chap. 2), but are anomalous. However, such dispersion results may be plotted in the form suggested by Moffitt.[10] This implies multiplication of both sides of equation [1] with $(\lambda^2 - \lambda_0^2)$ and then plotting $(\lambda^2 - \lambda_0^2) [m']_\lambda$ against $1/(\lambda^2 - \lambda_0^2)$, with λ_0 as a parameter. If a correct λ_0 value is chosen, one obtains a straight line.

Figures 12-3 and 12-4 illustrate this concept. In Figure 12-3 the rotatory dispersion curves of poly-γ-benzyl-L-glutamate (1) and poly-α,L-glutamic acid (2) are represented, while Figure 12-4 shows a Moffitt plot of the optical rotatory dispersion of poly-γ-benzyl-L-glutamate (1) and poly-β-benzyl-L-aspartate (3).[1,15]

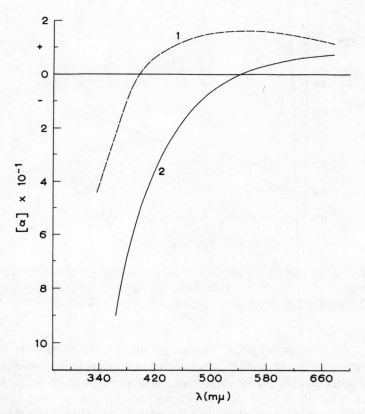

Fig. 12-3. RD curves of poly-γ-benzyl-L-glutamate (1) and poly-α,L-glutamic acid (2) [adapted from E. R. Blout, in C. Djerassi, <u>Optical Rotatory Dispersion: Applications to Organic Chemistry</u>, McGraw-Hill, New York, 1960].

An α-helix can have two senses of twist. The right- and left-handed polypeptide helices are nonsuperimposable, and with the exception of polyglycine, they are not even mirror images of each other.[7] Furthermore, from the earlier Moffitt's work[10] if follows that, from the derivation of equation [1], the sign of b_0 is negative for right-handed helices and positive for left-handed helices.

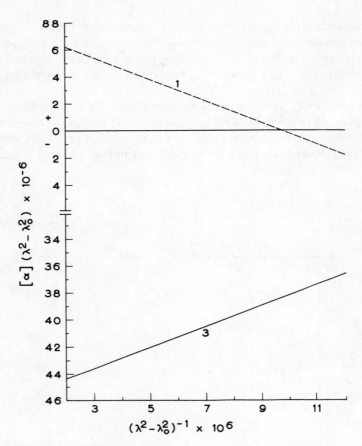

Fig. 12-4. Moffitt plot of the RD data of poly-γ-benzyl-L-glutamate (1) and poly-β-benzyl-L-aspartate (3) [modified from E. R. Blout, in C. Djerassi, <u>Optical Rotatory Dispersion: Applications to Organic Chemistry</u>, McGraw-Hill, New York, 1960].

Mason[14] supports this assumption, which was withdrawn by Moffitt in his later paper with Fitts and Kirkwood.[11a]   The question has probably been partly resolved by the X-ray structure of myoglobin, which has right-handed helices and is known to have a negative b_0.[16] However, positive b_0 values have been reported for substances known to have right-handed helices.[16] Therefore the sign of b_0 per se does not necessarily indicate the handedness of the helix. Recent studies of poly-L-tyrosine and related copolymers seem to confirm this view.[16bis]

The sense of twist of polybenzyl-L-aspartate (3) is opposite to that of polybenzyl-L-glutamate (1), as indicated by the rotatory dispersion curves reproduced in Figure 12-5.[2,17]

Blout has emphasized[1] that the important influences on the optical rotatory dispersion properties of polypeptides are of three types: the conformation of the polypeptide chain, the nature of the side chains attached to the β-carbon atom of the component amino acids, and the length of the polypeptide chain.

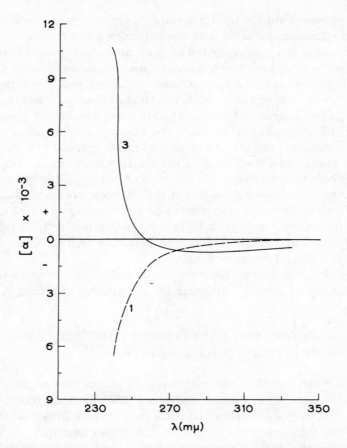

Fig. 12-5. RD curves of poly-β-benzyl-L-aspartate (3) and poly-γ-benzyl-L-glutamate (1) [adapted from R. H. Karlson, K. S. Norland, G. D. Fashman, and E. R. Blout, J. Am. Chem. Soc., **82**, 2268 (1960)].

As far as the conformation of the polypeptide chain is concerned, Moffitt's equation permits one to estimate the helix contents of some of these macromolecules.

With respect to the nature of the side chains attached to the β-carbon atom of the amino acid function, it has been shown[1] that the nature of this substituent plays a direct role in the optical rotatory dispersion properties of polypeptides. Nevertheless, it appears that with proteins the dominating factor is the conformation of the molecule, and thus careful analysis of the optical rotatory dispersion data will permit the general conformation to be assigned, whatever the nature of the substituent of the peptide units.

Finally, since the molecular weight of the polypeptide markedly affects its optical properties, it follows that its optical rotatory dispersion curve is dependent upon the chain length.[1]

These results indicate the importance of rotatory dispersion in the study of the conformations associated with polypeptides and proteins. However, the goal of determining the conformation of such macromolecules from their dispersion curves has not yet been achieved. Indeed, many factors are involved in these measurements, such as interactions of the solvent, sometimes implying denaturation processes and thus conformational changes. Before protein conformations can be determined with certainty from rotatory dispersion measurements, it will be necessary to evaluate the effects of many other possible polypeptide conformations, the effects of chain length, and the effects of cross-linkages.[1] A great amount of work is presently under way, attempting to establish a correlation between the dispersion curves of polypeptides and proteins and their conformations. There is no doubt that the new rotatory dispersion and circular dichroism instruments, which allow a broader spectral examination, will lead to important observations. Solvent-dependent and temperature-dependent circular dichroism and rotatory dispersion studies will also certainly provide valuable information in the near future.

In any event, the latest information indicates that proteins seem to prefer a right-handed sense of twist, although the possibility of mixed helices cannot be ruled out.[7]

12-3. COTTON EFFECTS IN POLYPEPTIDES AND PROTEINS: APPLICATIONS OF THE MULTITERM DRUDE EQUATION

An important result of the improvement in instrumentation mentioned in the previous section is the recent analysis of Shechter and Blout[18] of the Cotton effects exhibited by polypeptides and proteins. This analysis of the visible and near-ultraviolet rotations not only allows the determination of α-helix content of proteins in solution, but also provides a basis for the differentiation of α-helix-containing proteins from proteins involving other structures. This treatment[18] was greatly aided by knowledge of the rotations in the 185-240 mμ region.

In Chapter 2 it was mentioned that for most organic chemical problems, the Drude equation could be limited to the first term. However, the new mathematical analysis of rotatory dispersion data of polypeptides and proteins performed by Blout and his coworkers[18,19] indicates the two-term and several-term Drude equation to be more appropriate. The necessity of applying a multi-term Drude equation for polypeptide and protein conformational analysis had been recognized earlier by several investigators.[5,20] It was found[18] that a two-term Drude equation with one term fixed at 193 mμ gives a good fit of visible and near-ultraviolet rotatory dispersion if the second term is fixed at 225 mμ. The second term includes the contributions of all the Cotton effects which influence the optical activity in the visible and near-ultraviolet region except the Cotton effect centered at 193 mμ. If, on the one hand, only two Cotton effects influence the rotation, then the second term involves the contribution of only one Cotton effect centered at 225 mμ. If, on the other hand, more than two Cotton effects are responsible for the rotation in the visible and near-ultraviolet region, then the second term is the sum of the contributions from several Cotton effects, one of the major contributors to this second term being probably the n - π* transition.[18]

Table 12-1 summarizes the rotatory dispersion data of L-polypeptides in various conformations.[18] The random conformation, i.e., a conformation with no periodic but with possible fixed arrangement of peptide groups, shows at least two Cotton effects, a negative Cotton effect with its crossover point at about 198 mμ and a very weak Cotton effect around 225 mμ.[18]

Table 12-1

ROTATORY DISPERSION DATA OF L-POLYPEPTIDES
IN VARIOUS CONFORMATIONS[18]

Structure	Crossover Point (mμ)	Peak (mμ)	Trough (mμ)	Sign
α-Helix †	225		233	−
	193	198	185	+
Random †			233	−
	198	190	204	−
Poly-L-proline-II †	203	194	216	−
Poly-L-proline-I ††	210	218	202	+
β form ††	198	207	190	+

† In solution.

†† In oriented solid state.

Figure 12-6 reproduces the circular dichroism curve and the ultraviolet absorption spectrum of the α-helix form of poly-L-glutamic acid (5), as well as the circular dichroism and ultraviolet absorption curves of the random coil form (6).[14,21] From this figure it is apparent that only one Cotton effect was observed in the circular dichroism curve of the random coil form.

Also worth mentioning is the fact that polyproline helices and β (extended) forms of polypeptides show quite different Cotton effects from those exhibited by α-helices or random forms.[16,19]

From an extensive mathematical analysis of the rotatory dispersion data of polypeptides and proteins in α-helical and random conformations it was concluded that an estimate can be made, at least in some cases, of α-helix content in synthetic polypeptides and proteins. Moreover, some proteins suspected of being non-α-helical did not fit the equation found for α-helical conformations.[18] These findings are of fundamental importance, since they now permit a conformational study of polypeptides and proteins on a safer basis.

Recently, Jirgensons[4c] studied a series of proteins by rotatory dispersion. It was found that all native globular proteins can be classified into two groups.

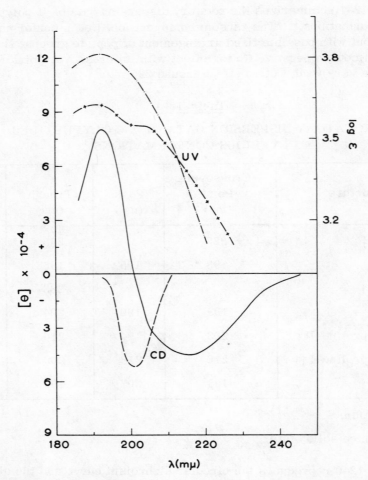

Fig. 12-6. CD (————) and UV (-+-+-+) curves of the α-helix form of poly-L-glutamic acid, and the CD (_____) and UV (_.._.._) curves of the random coil form [adapted from S. F. Mason, <u>Nature,</u> **199,** 139 (1963)].

The first group comprises the proteins showing a negative Cotton effect with a sharp trough in the dispersion curve at 233 mμ. The second group includes the proteins showing a dispersion curve typified by a flat minimum at 220-233 mμ. To the first class belong the proteins which have a strongly negative Moffitt's constant (b_0 in equation [1]) and whose polypeptide chains probably have the α-helical conformation to a large extent. The native proteins of the second group ($b_0 = 0$) are probably devoid of the α-helix or have it only in relatively insignificant amounts.[4c]

    Before closing this section, one additional remark must be made. The effect of solvent on the optical rotatory dispersion and circular dichroism data of molecules containing the peptide group is of the utmost importance. This point has been emphasized by all investigators working in these fields and is best illustrated in Figure 12-7, which shows the dramatic variations observed in the rotatory dispersion curves of N-acetyl-L-glutamic acid in dioxane-water mixtures.[22]

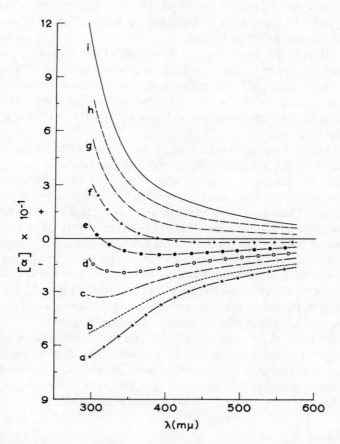

Fig. 12-7. RD curves of N-acetyl-L-glutamic acid in dioxane-water mixtures: (a) 100% water; (b) 10% dioxane in water; (c) 20% dioxane; (d) 30% dioxane; (e) 40% dioxane; (f) 50% dioxane; (g) 60% dioxane; (h) 70% dioxane; (i) 80% dioxane in water. [from C. Tanford, J. Am. Chem. Soc., **84,** 1747 (1962); reproduced by permission of the editor].

12-4. A NEW APPROACH TO THE CONFORMATIONAL STUDY OF THE HELIX IN POLYPEPTIDES AND PROTEINS

It is known that proteins and other macromolecules bind dyes, and this property may lead to a new way to investigate the conformation of macromolecules of the polypeptide and protein type.[2]

If basic dyes, such as acriflavine or acridine orange (see Table 12-2), are added to solutions of polyglutamic acid, the polyglutamic acid binds the basic dyes over the pH range 4 to 7. At pH 7, polyglutamic acid exists mainly as the charged polyion, and because of its charge this polypeptide attains random conformations at this pH. Measurements of the optical rotatory dispersion of basic dyes bound to polyglutamic acid in the random conformation show curves identical to those of the polypeptide alone. Since the dyes contain no asymmetric center this finding is not surprising. However, if the optical rotatory dispersion is measured on solutions of the dye-polypeptide complexes in which the polypeptide is in a helical conformation, a markedly anomalous Cotton effect curve is observed,[23] the Cotton effects being centered at the dye absorption bands. The spectral data on the binding of several basic dyes with poly-L-glutamic acid are reported in Table 12-2.[2]

Since acridine orange shows a negative Cotton effect with L-polyglutamic acid, and since L-polyglutamic acid molecules presumably have only one sense of twist, it was of interest to inquire what the effect of a polypeptide substrate of the opposite sense of twist would be on the rotatory dispersion of a dye-polypeptide complex. Thus poly-D-glutamic acid was chosen. Whatever the absolute sense of twist of poly-L-glutamic acid, poly-D-glutamic acid should have the opposite sense of twist. The experimental rotatory dispersion curves are collected in Figure 12-8.[23] As can be seen, the acridine orange-L-polyglutamic acid complex exhibits a negative Cotton effect, whereas the D-polyglutamic acid complex shows a positive Cotton effect. Thus the Cotton effect associated with dye-polypeptide complexes may serve as a simple and effective method for the determination of the relative helix sense in polypeptides.[2,23]

The same type of investigation has been initiated with proteins.[2] When acridine orange was bound to the tobacco mosaic virus, the rotatory dispersion curve was anomalous and a Cotton effect was observed. Furthermore, from the sign of the Cotton effect it was deduced that the sense of helix in tobacco virus mosaic was the same as that in L-polyglutamic acid.[2,23bis]

12-5. MISCELLANEOUS

Apart from the basic concepts set forth previously, numerous important studies have been devoted to conformational problems associated with polypeptides, proteins, and polynucleotides.

For instance, circular dichroism measurements were recently applied to the studies of homopolyribonucleotide compounds in order to correlate the helical conformation with the optical activity observed in these substances.[24] The experimental results are in qualitative agreement with the previous rotatory dispersion observations made in the nucleic acid series.[25] The observations resulting from the circular dichroism examination of homopolynucleotides indicated the sensitivity of the method for the study of macromolecular conformations and emphasized the conformational mobility characterizing these polynucleotides at higher temperatures.

Table 12-2

SPECTRAL DATA ON THE BINDING OF SEVERAL BASIC DYES TO POLY-L-GLUTAMIC ACID†

Dye	Dye Structure	pH	Carboxyl: Dye Ratio	Inflection Point of Cotton Effect (mμ)	Absorption Maxima of Dye (mμ)
Acriflavine		4.9	185	458	457
Acridine Orange		4.5	915 2435	470 ~475	467 and shoulder at 497
Rhodamine B		4.7	1476	558 and 588	556 and shoulder at 585
Rhodamine 6G		4.6	2640 1320	491,502,533 492,506,537	496,529 498,530
Thiazole Magenta-T		4.5	190	480	478

† Reproduced from E. R. Blout, Tetrahedron, 13, 123 (1961), by permission of the editor.

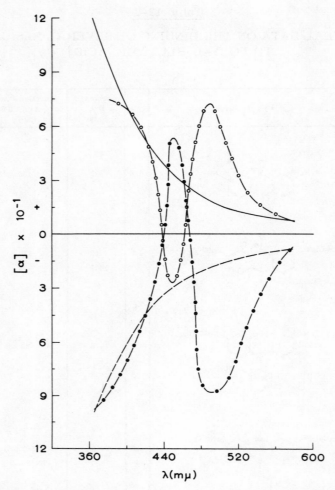

Fig. 12-8. RD curves of acridine orange: D-polyglutamic acid complex (-o-o-o-) and L-polyglutamic acid complex (-.-.-.-), with the plain RD curves of the corresponding free acids: D- (———) and L-polyglutamic acid (-----), respectively [modified from E. R. Blout, Tetrahedron, **13**, 123 (1961)].

From a recent optical rotatory dispersion examination of deoxyribonucleotides, Yang et al.[26] were able to deduce important information not available from other spectroscopic data. Furthermore, they concluded that rotatory dispersion promises a quantitative approach to the study of the structures of synthetic polynucleotides and natural nucleic acids, since the β-deoxyribonucleotides which were examined exhibited Cotton effects in the region of 260 mμ and because an important difference was observed between the pyrimidine and purine compounds, showing positive and negative Cotton effects, respectively. This study was soon followed by similar work by Klyne and his coworkers,[27] who brought out the important finding that the members of an anomeric pair of nucleosides give rotatory dispersion curves of opposite sign. These investigators also showed that the presence or absence of a 2-hydroxy group in the sugar moiety (ribose or 2-deoxyribose) makes no major difference in the rotatory dispersion curves. Furthermore, the rotatory dispersion properties of carbonyl addition compounds with nicotinamide adenine dinucleotide in frozen solution have also been reported recently,[28a] as well as a conformational examination of nucleic acids in solution.[28b]

The helical conformations of polycytidylic acid[29] and the conformation of various globular proteins,[4b] such as β-lactoglobulins,[30] have also been investigated by rotatory dispersion. The same technique has provided important information regarding the conformation of various pituitary hormones.[31] For example, the low rotatory dispersion values observed for the globular protein luteinizing hormone has been interpreted as due to some specific conformation of the polypeptide chain differing considerably from the α-helical conformation which otherwise would have been assumed.[31]

During a recent rotatory dispersion study of liver alcohol dehydrogenase and its complexes,[32] considerable increases of Moffitt's b_0 values have been observed for some ternary complexes, and these have been attributed to protein conformational changes.

An optical rotatory dispersion and circular dichroism study of hemocyanin and oxyhemocyanin has indicated that no appreciable change in protein conformation occurs on oxygenating hemocyanin.[33]

Finally, rotatory disperson has also proved useful in a study of thrombin-induced conversion of fibrinogen to fibrin monomer[34] during an examination of the effects of detergents on the conformation of proteins,[35] as evidence for conformational changes in α-chymotrypsin-catalyzed reactions,[36] as well as for a study of aspartic amino transferase.[37]

For the conformational problems cited in this chapter rotatory dispersion and circular dichroism have been of less help than for those in earlier chapters. This is mainly due to the complexity of the molecules under investigation and to the fact that little is known about their stereochemistry. However, the very recent results, which have been briefly reviewed, seem to indicate that these physico-chemical methods are bound to make in the very near future an important contribution to the stereochemical elucidation of polypeptides, proteins, and nucleic acids. Thus one can be certain that rotatory dispersion and circular dichroism will soon demonstrate their power in a field which is perhaps the most important one from the biochemical point of view, since a better knowledge of the structure of proteins and nucleic acids will lead to a better understanding of the origin and nature of life.

REFERENCES

1. E. R. Blout, Chap. 17 in C. Djerassi, Optical Rotatory Dispersion: Applications to Organic Chemistry, McGraw–Hill, New York, 1960.

2. E. R. Blout, Tetrahedron, 13, 123 (1961).

3. P. Doty, Rev. Mod. Phys., 31, 107 (1959), and in Proceedings of the Fourth International Congress of Biochemistry, O. Kratky (ed.), Symposium IX, Pergamon Press, New York (1959); see also: G. Holzwarth and P. Doty, J. Am. Chem. Soc., 87, 218 (1965).

4. (a) B. Jirgensons, Tetrahedron, 13, 166 (1961); (b) B. Jirgensons, J. Biol. Chem., 238, 2716 (1963); (c) B. Jirgensons, Makrom. Chem., 72, 119 (1964).

5. W. Kauzmann, Ann. Rev. Phys. Chem., 8, 413 (1957).

6. I. Tinoco, R. W. Woody, and K. Yamaoka, Tetrahedron, 13, 134 (1961), and references cited therein.

7. Jen Tsi Yang, Tetrahedron, 13, 143 (1961), and references therein.

7bis. V. Prelog and H. Gerlach, Helv. Chim. Acta, 47, 2288 (1964), and H. Gerlach, J. A. Owtschinnikow, and V. Prelog, Helv. Chim. Acta, 47, 2294 (1964).

8. (a) L. Pauling and R. B. Corey, J. Am. Chem. Soc., 72, 5349 (1950); (b) R. B. Corey and L. Pauling, Rend. ist. lombardo sci., P 1, 89, 10 (1955).

9. C. Cohen, Nature, 175, 129 (1955).

10. (a) W. Moffitt, J. Chem. Phys., 25, 467 (1956); (b) W. Moffitt and J. T. Yang, Proc. Nat. Acad. Sci. U.S., 42, 596 (1956); (c) W. Moffitt, Proc. Nat. Acad. Sci. U.S., 42, 756 (1956).

11. (a) W. Moffitt, D. D. Fitts, and J. G. Kirkwood, Proc. Nat. Acad. Sci. U.S., 43, 723 (1957); (b) D. D. Fitts and J. G. Kirkwood, Proc. Nat. Acad. Sci. U.S., 43, 1046 (1957); (c) P. Doty and R. D. Lundberg, Proc. Nat. Acad. Sci. U.S., 43, 213 (1957); (d) I. Tinoco and R. W. Woody, J. Chem. Phys., 32, 461 (1960); See also ref. 6.

12. (a) A. Moscowitz, A. E. Hansen, L. S. Forster, and K. Rosenheck, Biopolymers, 1, 75 (1964); (b) S. F. Mason, Chem. and Ind., 1286 (1964).

13. (a) I. Tinoco, Radiation Res., 20, 133 (1963); (b) I. Tinoco, J. Am. Chem. Soc., 86, 297 (1964); (c) I. Tinoco, R. W. Woody, and D. F. Bradley, J. Chem. Phys., 38, 1317 (1963); (d) I. Tinoco, R. W. Woody, and D. F. Bradley, Biopolymers, 1, 239 (1963); (e) I. Tinoco and R. W. Woody, J. Chem. Phys., 40, 160 (1964).

14.   S. F. Mason, Nature, 199, 139 (1963).

15.   P. Doty, A. Wada, J. T. Yang, and E. R. Blout, J. Polymer Sci., 23, 851 (1957).

16.   Private communication from Professor E. R. Blout and Mr. J. P. Carver, Harvard University.

16bis.   G. D. Fasman, E. Bodenheimer, and C. Lindblow, Biochemistry, 3, 1665 (1964); S. Beychok and G. D. Fasman, Biochemistry, 3, 1675 (1964).

17.   R. H. Karlson, K. S. Norland, G. D. Fasman, and E. R. Blout, J. Am. Chem. Soc., 82, 2268 (1960).

18.   E. Shechter and E. R. Blout, Proc. Nat. Acad. Sci. U.S., 51, 695 (1964), and references cited therein.

19.   (a) N. S. Simmons and E. R. Blout, Biophys. J., 1, 55 (1960); (b) N. S. Simmons, C. Cohen, A. G. Szent-Györgyi, D. B. Wetlaufer, and E. R. Blout, J. Am. Chem. Soc., 83, 4766 (1961); (c) E. R. Blout, I. Schmier, and N. S. Simmons, J. Am. Chem. Soc., 84, 3193 (1962); (d) E. R. Blout, J. P. Carver, and J. Gross, J. Am. Chem. Soc., 85, 644 (1963); (e) E. R. Blout and E. Shechter, Biopolymers, 1, 565 (1963); (f) E. Shechter and E. R. Blout, Proc. Nat. Acad. Sci. U.S., 51, 794 (1964); (g) E. Shechter, J. P. Carver, and E. R. Blout, Proc. Nat. Acad. Sci. U.S., 51, 1029 (1964).

20.   (a) J. T. Yang and P. Doty, J. Am. Chem. Soc., 79, 761 (1957); (b) L. I. Katzin and E. Gulyas, J. Am. Chem. Soc., 86, 1655 (1964).

21.   (a) I. Rosenheck and P. Doty, Proc. Nat. Acad. Sci. U.S., 47, 1775 (1961); (b) G. Holzwarth, W. B. Gratzer, and P. Doty, J. Am. Chem. Soc., 84, 3194 (1962).

22.   C. Tanford, J. Am. Chem. Soc., 84, 1747 (1962).

23.   L. S. Stryer and E. R. Blout, J. Am. Chem. Soc., 83, 1411 (1961).

23 bis. S. F. Mason and A. J. McCaffery, Nature, 204, 468 (1964).

24.   J. Brahms, J. Am. Chem. Soc., 85, 3298 (1963).

25.   J. R. Fresco, A. M. Lesk, R. Gorn, and P. Doty, J. Am. Chem. Soc., 83, 3155 (1961).

26.   J. T. Yang and T. Samejima, J. Am. Chem. Soc., 83, 4039 (1963).

27.   T. L. V. Ulbricht, J. P. Jennings, P. M. Scopes, and W. Klyne, Tetrahedron Letters, No. 13, 695 (1964).

28.   (a) M. I. Dolin and K. B. Jacobson, J. Biol. Chem., 239, 3007 (1964); (b) J. Brahms and W. F. H. M. Mommaerts, J. Mol. Biol., 10, 40 (1964).

29.   G. D. Fasman, C. Lindblow, and L. Grossman, Biochemistry, 3, 1015 (1964).

30.   T. T. Herskowits, R. Townend, and S. N. Timasheff, J. Am. Chem. Soc., 86, 4445 (1964).

31.   B. Jirgensons, Arch. Biochem. Biophys., 91, 123 (1960).

32.   H. Theorell and T. Yonetani, Nature, 203, 755 (1964).

33.   J. G. Foss, Biochim. Biophys. Acta, 79, 41 (1964).

34.   C. M. Kay and M. M. Marsh, Nature, 189, 307 (1961).

35.   B. Jirgensons, Arch. Biochem. Biophys., 94, 59 (1961).

36.   B. H. Havsteen and G. P. Hess, J. Am. Chem. Soc., 85, 791 (1963).

37.   P. Fasella and G. G. Hammes, Biochemistry, 3, 530 (1964).

Appendix

Automatic Processing of Circular Dichroism Data [†]

It is often worthwhile to automate routine measurements, particularly if the automation does not cause a decrease in accuracy. Thus most commercial spectrophotomers are automatic recording instruments. In the determination and evaluation of circular dichroism data, it is necessary to correct for the baseline with a reference scan, to convert the raw data to molecular ellipticity, and to replot the data in a more convenient form. Furthermore, evaluation of the rotational strength, which involves an integrated area, and determination of quantities related to variation of the rotational strength with temperature can give significant information. Finally, statistical treatment of the raw data to minimize the noise results in more easily interpreted curves.

Although each of these operations can be accomplished by hand, it is unquestionably faster, more accurate, and less expensive to carry them out with a computer. In addition, storage of data in a digital computer offers the possibility of attempting empirical correlations in a rapid manner. Consequently, apparatus has been obtained for digitalizing output data from the circular dichroism spectrometer, and a digital computer and its associated equipment have been programmed to process these data. The techniques involved in this procedure are applicable to handling most types of spectral data.

Data were obtained with the Jouan Dichrograph (see Chap. 3). The conversion was accomplished by means of a Perkin-Elmer digital data recorder, model DDR-1, a device which, by means of a shaft encoder, converts the analog output of the spectrometer recorder at specified intervals to digital information on punched paper tape. The information on the paper tape was then transferred to standard IBM cards, collated with the appropriate control cards (which contained identifying information, molecular weight, and so on), and placed in the computer, in this case a Burroughs B-5000. The computer output consisted of

[†]This section is a contribution from Gerry J. Elman and John I. Brauman, Department of Chemistry, Stanford University.

printed material and a magnetic tape, which, when run on a Calcomp plotter, produced a graphical output. It was possible to obtain previously written subprograms which caused this plotter to draw straight lines through specified points and to label the axes of the graphs. Since the data were obtained every 0.5 mμ, a series of straight lines drawn point to point gave a good approximation to a smooth curve.

A pictorial representation of the procedures outlined above is shown in Figure A-1. Modification of the encoder to produce punched cards directly would eliminate the necessity of a tape-to-card converter.

The computer program itself is relatively straightforward. It consists of a number of more or less independent procedures (subroutines or subprograms), each of which performs one type of operation. These are called in proper sequence during execution of the program. Figure A-2 is a diagram of the program, showing the direction of the flow and the operation performed by each subroutine. The proper choice of parameters on the control cards will cause the computer to read in data, subtract out a reference scan, normalize the data to molecular ellipticity, calculate the rotational strength, plot the data on a graph with appropriate scale factors for optimum positioning, "smooth" the curve any desired number of times, and determine the value of ΔF^0 which gives the best least-squares fit to the equation relating R_0^T and ΔF^0, assuming two conformers in mobile equilibrium, if data for more than two temperatures have been given.

The smoothing operation, adapted from a program of George,[1] uses standard mathematical methods involving least-squares curve fitting.[2,3] The effect of smoothing a typical curve is shown in Figures A-3 and A-4; the unsmoothed curve is shown in Figure A-3.

The rotational strength is defined as

$$R_T^0 \cong 6.96 \times 10^{-43} \int \frac{[\theta]}{\lambda} \, \Delta\lambda$$

The integral was evaluated as the sum of rectangles of area $([\theta]/\lambda)\Delta\lambda$, where $\Delta\lambda = 0.5$ mμ, the interval between measurements. The magnitude of uncertainty in the measurements makes unnecessary the use of a more exact integration technique, such as a Simpson's rule parabolic approximation. Modifications would, however, be simple.

The procedure for determining the best value of ΔF^0 to fit rotational strength data at various temperatures makes use of an optimization method developed by Wilde,[4] which involves Fibonacci numbers.

The value of ΔF^0 chosen gives the best least-squares fit for R_a and R_b. The effectiveness of this program is shown by calculating exact values of R_0^T at temperatures from -194 to +100° from given values of ΔF^0, R_a, and R_b. These values of R_0^T were then used to recalculate ΔF^0, R_a, and R_b. The results are shown in Table A-1 after a search over the range $\Delta F^0 = 0$ to 2000 cal.

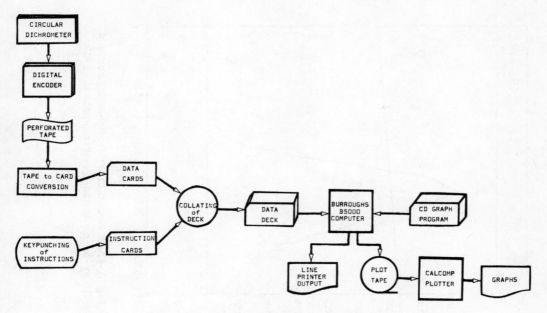

Fig. A-1. Flow chart for data processing

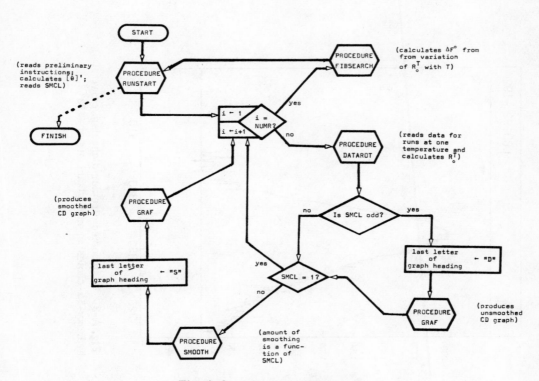

Fig. A-2. CD graph program

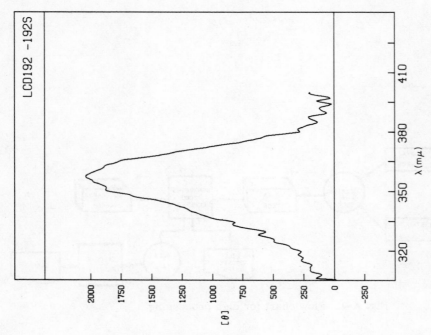

Fig. A-4. Smoothed circular dichroism curve of 3β-hydroxy-5α-cholestan-methylxanthate at -192°.

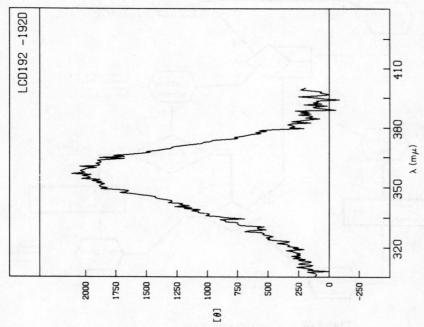

Fig. A-3. Unsmoothed circular dichroism curve of 3β-hydroxy-5α-cholestan-methylxanthate at -192°.

Table A-1

CALCULATION OF GIVEN QUANTITIES

Parameter	Given Value	Calculated Value
ΔF^0	1000.0	1001 ±6
R_a	100.00	100.2 ±1
R_b	-50.000	-49.99 ±0.1

The fit of data has a variance of 5×10^{-5}.

In order to show their over-all structures, the programs actually used are reproduced below. The language in which they are written is Algol; a Fortran program would be similar. The exact construction of such programs depends on the calling sequence for the plotting subroutine locally available and on the particular computer to be used. Similarly, input data specifications will depend on the facilities at local installations.

These results serve as an example of the type of automatic processing which can be accomplished with circular dichroism data. Modification to any specific system and computer installation should be straightforward.

ACKNOWLEDGMENT

The authors are grateful to Dr. A. Savitzky and the Perkin-Elmer Corporation for suggesting the application and use of equipment and techniques, and for making the Digital Data Recorder available for this work. We also thank Mr. Larry Breed of the Stanford Computation Center for help with tape to card conversion, and most particularly, Dr. E. Bunnenberg for implementing the electronic and mechanical techniques and carrying out the measurements, and for helpful discussions. The Stanford University Computation Center generously provided free computer time.

REFERENCES

1.   R. George, Communications of the Association for Computing Machinery, 6, 663 (1963).

2.   C. Lanczos, Applied Analysis, pp. 316-320, Prentice-Hall, Englewood Cliffs, N. J., 1956.

3.   A. Savitzky and M. J. E. Golay, Anal. Chem., 36, 1627 (1964).

4.   D. J. Wilde, Optimum Seeking Methods, pp. 10-37, Prentice-Hall, Englewood Cliffs, N. J., 1964.

```
BEGIN COMMENT CD GRAPH PROGRAM

PLOTTING PROCEDURES ARE INSERTED HERE;


BEGIN
    INTEGER I, N, NUMR, SWNO, SMCL;
    REAL THPRIM, XZ, XST;
    ARRAY THETA, X[0:800];
    ALPHA ARRAY CDNO[0:1];
    LABEL AGAIN, FINISH;


    PROCEDURE RUNSTART (NUMR, THPRIM, CDNO, FINISH, SMCL);
        REAL THPRIM;
        INTEGER NUMR, SMCL;
        ALPHA CDNO;
        LABEL FINISH;
        BEGIN
            INTEGER I, C1, C2, C3, C4, C5, C6, C7, C8, C9, C10, C11, C12,
        C13;
            REAL CH11, CH12, CH13, MOLWT, SEN, CON, PER, LEN, PHLAG;
            ALPHA ARRAY TITLE[0:10];
            LABEL RED1;
            DEFINE FIZU = FOR I + 0 STEP 1 UNTIL#;
            FORMAT
                OF1 (/X10, A6, X20, 11A6),
                OF2 (X10, "MOLECULAR WEIGHT = ", F9.3/),
                OF3 (X10, "CALCULATED THETAPRIME = ", E11.4///),
                FM1 (I2, X1, A6, X1, 11A6),
                FM2 (X1,I2,X1,I3,4(X1,I1),2(X2,I1),2(X1,I1),3(F8.3,X1,I1));
    RED1:       READ (PHLAG);
                IF PHLAG ≠ 1111 THEN GO TO RED1;
                READ (FM1, NUMR, CDNO, FIZU 10 DO TITLE[I]);
                WRITE (OF1, CDNO, FIZU 10 DO TITLE[I]);
                IF NUMR < 1 THEN GO TO FINISH;
                READ (FM2, C1, C2, C3, C4, C5, C6, C7, C8, C9, C10, CH11,
        C11, CH12, C12, CH13, C13);
                MOLWT + 12.011×C1 + 1.008×C2 + 14.008×C3+16×C4 + 32.066×C5
        + 30.975×C6 + 35.457×C7 + 79.916×C8 + 126.91×C9 + 19.00×C10
        + CH11×C11 + CH12×C12 + CH13×C13;
                WRITE (OF2, MOLWT);
                READ (CON, PER, LEN, SEN, SMCL);
                THPRIM + 0.1008 × SEN × PER/CON /LEN × MOLWT;
                WRITE (OF3, THPRIM);
        END RUNSTART;


    PROCEDURE DATAROT (THETA, X, N, THPRIM, TEMP, XZ, XST, CDNO, ROT);
        ARRAY THETA, X[0];
        REAL THPRIM, TEMP, XZ, XST, ROT;
        INTEGER N;
        ALPHA CDNO;
        BEGIN
            INTEGER I, J, L, M, Q, BLANKS, RUNS;
            REAL PHLAG, DL, DELTA, THFAC, LZ1, LZ2, LE1, LE2, DILFAC;
            DEFINE FIZN = FOR I + 0 STEP 1 UNTIL N DO#;
            FORMAT
                OF4 (X10, "TEMPERATURE DESIGNATION:", X3, A6/X10, "TEMPERAT
    URE FACTOR:", F9.4/X10, "NUMBER OF BLANKS TAKEN:",I4, X10,"NUMBER OF RUN
    S MADE:", I4/),
                FM3 (I4, X1, A6, F6.4, X2, I2, X1, I2, X5, I3, X1, I3, X1,
        F6.4);
            LABEL RED2;
    RED2:    READ (PHLAG);
             IF PHLAG ≠ 1111 THEN GO TO RED2;
             READ (FM3, TEMP, CDNO, THFAC, BLANKS, RUNS, LZ1, LE1, DL);
             WRITE (OF4, CDNO, THFAC, BLANKS, RUNS);
             N + (LZ1 - LE1)/DL;
             XZ + 2.5 × ENTIER ((LZ1 - LE1)/45 + 1);
```

```
                XST + 5 × ENTIER (LE1/5);
                BEGIN
                    ARRAY TH[0:1, 0:N];
                    INTEGER ARRAY SH[0:N];
                    LABEL RED3, RED4;
                    FOR Q + 0, 1 DO FIZN
                     TH[Q,I] + 0;
                    FIZN SH[I] + 0;
                    FOR J + 1 STEP 1 UNTIL BLANKS DO
                     BEGIN
RED3:                  READ (PHLAG);
                       IF PHLAG ≠ 1111 THEN GO TO RED3;
                       READ (LZ2, LE2);
                       L + (LZ1 - LZ2)/DL;
                       M + (LE1 - LE2)/DL + N;
                       READ (FOR I + L STEP 1 UNTIL M DO THETA[I]);
                       FOR I + L STEP 1 UNTIL M DO
                        BEGIN
                           TH[0,I] + TH[0,I] + THETA[I];
                           SH[I] + SH[I] + 1;
                        END;
                     END;
                    FIZN TH[0,I] + TH[0,I]/SH[I];
                    FIZN SH[I] + 0;
                    FOR J + 1 STEP 1 UNTIL RUNS DO
                     BEGIN
RED4:                  READ (PHLAG);
                       IF PHLAG ≠ 1111 THEN GO TO RED4;
                       READ (LZ2, LE2, DILFAC);
                       L + (LZ1 - LZ2)/DL;
                       M + (LE1 - LE2)/DL + N;
                       READ (FOR I + L STEP 1 UNTIL M DO THETA[I]);
                       FOR I + L STEP 1 UNTIL M DO
                        BEGIN
                           TH[1,I] + (THETA[I] -TH[0,I]) × DILFAC + TH[1,I];
                           SH[I] + SH[I] + 1;
                        END;
                     END;
                    THPRIM + THPRIM × THFAC;
                    DELTA + DL × 6.96@-03;
                    ROT + 0;
                    FIZN
                     BEGIN
                        THETA[I] + TH[1,I]/SH[I] × THPRIM;
                        X[I] + -I × DL + LZ1;
                        ROT + THETA[I]/X[I] × DELTA + ROT;
                     END;
                END;
            END DATAROT;


        PROCEDURE MINIMAX (A, B, M, MAX, MIN, LMAX, LMIN); VALUE M;
            ARRAY A, B[0];
            .INTEGER M;
            REAL MAX, MIN, LMAX, LMIN;
            BEGIN
                INTEGER I;
                MAX + MIN + A[0];
                LMAX + LMIN + B[0];
                FOR I + 1 STEP 1 UNTIL M DO
                 IF A[I] > MAX THEN
                    BEGIN
                        MAX + A[I];
                        LMAX + B[I];
                    END
                 ELSE IF A[I] < MIN THEN
                    BEGIN
                        MIN + A[I];
                        LMIN + B[I];
                    END;
            END MINIMAX;
```

```
    PROCEDURE GRAF (THETA, X, N, XZ, XST, CDNO, SWNO);
        ALPHA ARRAY CDNO[O];
        ARRAY THETA, X[O];
        REAL XZ, XST;
        INTEGER SWNO, N;
        BEGIN
            BOOLEAN BOO;
            ARRAY XP, YP[O:N], XLIN1, YLIN1[O:4], XLIN2, YLIN2, XLIN3,
        YLIN3, XTIC, YTIC[O:1];
            REAL MAX, MIN, Z1, LMAX, LMIN, XNUM, YNUM;
            INTEGER I, J, L, Z2, Z3, NBR;
            FORMAT
                OF6 (X35, 2A6//),
                OF7 ("WAVELENGTH", X4, F5.1, 9(X6,F5.1)/"THETA        ",
        10E11.3/);
            LABEL FIRST, THEREAFTER;
            DEFINE
                FIZU = FOR I + O STEP 1 UNTIL#,
                BOL = I + J < N AND J ≤ 9#;
            SWITCH INITPLTSW + FIRST, THEREAFTER;
            GO TO INITPLTSW [SWNO];
FIRST:      SWNO + 2;
            PLOT (O, O, +1019);
THEREAFTER:
            WRITE (OF6, CDNO[O], CDNO[1]);
            FOR I + O STEP 10 UNTIL N - 10 DO
             WRITE (OF7, FOR J + O STEP 1 WHILE BOL DO X[I+J],
                         FOR J + O STEP 1 WHILE BOL DO THETA[I+J]);
            MINIMAX (THETA, X, N, MAX, MIN, LMAX, LMIN);
            Z1 + MAX - MIN;
            Z2 + ENTIER (LN(Z1/21)/0.6932) + 1;
            Z3 + 2*Z2;
            Z3 + IF Z3 > 1024 THEN Z3
                    ELSE IF Z3 > 64 THEN 25 × ENTIER (Z3/25)
                    ELSE IF Z3 > 2 THEN 5 × ENTIER ((Z3 + 2)/5)
                    ELSE Z3;
            L + ENTIER (6.25 - (MAX + MIN)/4/Z3) × 2;
                FILL XLIN2 [*] WITH O, O ;
                FILL YLIN2 [*] WITH O, 1;
                LINE (XLIN2, YLIN2, 2, TRUE);
                FILL XLIN2 [*] WITH 0.75, 0.75;
                LINE (XLIN2, YLIN2, 2, FALSE);
                FILL XLIN1 [*] WITH 1.936, 9.05, 9.05, 1.936, 1.936;
                FILL YLIN1 [*] WITH 0.4, 0.4, 10.2425, 10.2425, 0.4;
                LINE (XLIN1, YLIN1, 5, TRUE);
                FILL XLIN2 [*] WITH 1.936, 9.05;
                FILL YLIN2 [*] WITH 9.4551, 9.4551;
                LINE (XLIN2, YLIN2, 2, TRUE);

                SYMBOL (6.8, 9.8, 0.21, CDNO, O, 12);
                YLIN3[O] + YLIN3[1] + L/2.54 + 0.4;
                LINE (XLIN2, YLIN3, 2, FALSE);
                FILL XTIC [*] WITH 1.936, 2.1;
                FOR I + 10 STEP -1 UNTIL 1 DO BEGIN
                YTIC [O] + YTIC [1] + I × 0.7874 + 0.4;
                BOO + I/2 = ENTIER (I/2);
                LINE (XTIC, YTIC, 2, BOO);   END;
                FILL YTIC [*] WITH 0.4, 0.564;
                FIZU 7 DO BEGIN
                XTIC [O] + XTIC [1] + (I+1) × 0.7874 + 1.936;
                BOO + I/2 = ENTIER (I/2);
                LINE (XTIC, YTIC, 2, BOO);   END;
                XNUM + 1.1;
                FOR I + 1 STEP 1 UNTIL 10 DO BEGIN
                YNUM + I × 0.7874 + 0.33;
                NBR +(2 × I - L) × Z3;
                NUMBER (XNUM, YNUM, 0.14, NBR, O, O);   END;
                YNUM + 0.095;
                FOR I + O STEP 1 UNTIL 3 DO BEGIN
                XNUM + I × 1.5748 + 1.9134;
                NBR + (4 × I + 2) × XZ + XST;
                NUMBER (XNUM, YNUM, 0.21, NBR, O, O);   END;
```

```
                FIZU N DO BEGIN
                XP[I] + (X[I] - XST)/XZ/2.54 + 1.935;
                YP[I] + (THETA[I]/Z3 + L)/2.54 + 0.4;    END;
                LINE (XP, YP, N, FALSE);
                        COMMENT DRAWS THE CURVE;
                PLOT (9.25, 0, -3);
        END GRAF ;


     PROCEDURE SMOOTH (DATA, N, C);
         ARRAY DATA[O];
         INTEGER N, C;
         BEGIN
             REAL FACTOR, TOP;
             INTEGER MAXI, I, J, K, O;
             ARRAY DELTA[O:N];
             FACTOR + 3.0/35.0;
             MAXI + N - 1;
             O + ENTIER (C/2);
             FOR K + 1 STEP 1 UNTIL O DO
               BEGIN
                 FOR I + O STEP 1 UNTIL MAXI DO
                  DELTA [I] + DATA [I+1] - DATA [I];
                 FOR J + O STEP 1 UNTIL 2 DO
                  BEGIN
                      TOP + DELTA[O];
                      MAXI + MAXI - 1;
                      FOR I + O STEP 1 UNTIL MAXI DO
                        DELTA [I] + DELTA [I+1] - DELTA [I];
                  END;
                 MAXI + N-2;
                 FOR I + 2 STEP 1 UNTIL MAXI DO
                  DATA [I] + DATA [I] - DELTA [I-2] x FACTOR;
                 DATA [O] + DATA [O] + TOP/5.0 + DELTA[O] x FACTOR;
                 DATA [1] + DATA [1] - TOP x 0.4 - DELTA [O]/7.0;
                 DATA [N] + DATA [N] - DELTA [N-3]/5.0 +
       DELTA[N-4] x FACTOR;
                 DATA [N-1] + DATA [N-1] + DELTA [N-3] x 0.4
       - DELTA [N-4]/7.0;
               END;
         END SMOOTH;


     PROCEDURE FIBSEARCH (T, Y, N, M);
         ARRAY T, Y[1];
         INTEGER N;
         ALPHA M;
         BEGIN
             REAL DELTA, SUMX, SUMY, SUMXY, SUMXX, L, R, FB, LFIRST,
         RFIRST, DIFF, SUMB, DENOM, SUM, MAXT, MINT, YFMAXT, YFMINT, MAXY,
         MINY, TFMAXY, TFMINY;
             INTEGER I, J, K, P, Q, DEGFRE;
             ARRAY X[O:N], A1, AO, V1, VO, F, V[O:15];
             LABEL LB47, LB8, LB11, LB12, LB2, LB1, LB3, LB46;
             FORMAT
             FM19 (//////"RESULTS OF COMPUTATION:"////X5,"FREE ENERGY--BE
       ST ESTIMATE",X8,"RANGE OF UNCERTAINTY",X14,"LIMITS OF UNCERTAINTY"//
             E19.3, E36.2, E26.4, E14.4),
             FM20 (///X5,"RA--BEST ESTIMATE",X19,"RANGE OF UNCERTAINTY"
             ,X14,"LIMITS OF UNCERTAINTY"//E19.3,E36.2,E26.4,E14.4),
             FM21 (///X5,"RB--BEST ESTIMATE",X19,"RANGE OF UNCERTAINTY"
             ,X14,"LIMITS OF UNCERTAINTY"//E19.3,E36.2,E26.4,E14.4),
             FM23 (//"FREE ENERGY DIFFERENCE APPEARS TO BE ABOVE", I9,
             " CALORIES.    CHECK YOUR DATA"/),
             FM24 ("DIVISION BY ZERO ATTEMPTED DURING ITERATION", I3//
             X15, "STOPPING CALCULATION"//"THE TROUBLE OCCURRED AT FREE ENE
       RGY", E12.3),
             FM30 (////"ROTATIONAL STRENGTH NOT MONOTONIC FUNCTION OF TEM
       PERATURE"),
             FM41 (X20, A6///X5,"TEMPERATURE DEG C      ROTATIONAL STREN
       GTH"/),    FM44 (I16, E26.4),
```

```
                   FM48 (//////"FIT OF DATA TO EQUATION:"////X5,"OVERALL VARIAN
CE",X9,"VARIANCE OF RA",X9,"VARIANCE OF RB"//E17,2,E24,2,E23,2);
                   DEFINE FINDO = FOR I + 1 STEP 1 UNTIL N DO#;
                   DEGFRE + N - 2;
                   WRITE ([PAGE]);
                   WRITE (FM41, M);
                   FINDO
                     BEGIN
                       WRITE (FM44, T[I], Y[I]);
                       T[I] + T[I] + 273.2;
                     END;
                   IF N < 3 THEN GO TO LB47;
                   MINIMAX (T, Y, N-1, MAXT, MINT, YFMAXT, YFMINT);
                   MINIMAX (Y, T, N-1, MAXY, MINY, TFMAXY, TFMINY);
                   IF NOT (MAXY=YFMAXT AND MINY=YFMINT) OR (MAXY=YFMINT AND
                 MINY=YFMAXT) THEN GO TO LB46;
                   LFIRST + 0;
                   RFIRST + 2000;
LB2:               J + 1;
                   L + LFIRST;
                   R + RFIRST;
                   F[1] + FB + (R - L) × 377.05/610;
LB8:               FINDO
                     X[I] + 1/(1 + EXP(-F[J]/1.9869/T[I]));
                   SUMX + SUMY + SUMXX + SUMXY + 0;
                   FINDO
                     BEGIN
                       SUMX + SUMX + X[I];
                       SUMY + SUMY + Y[I];
                       SUMXY + SUMXY + X[I]×Y[I];
                       SUMXX + SUMXX + X[I]*2;
                     END;
                   DENOM + N × SUMXX - SUMX*2;
                   IF DENOM = 0 THEN
                     BEGIN
                       WRITE (FM24, J, F[J]);
                       WRITE ([PAGE]);
                       GO TO LB47;
                     END;
                   A1[J] + (N × SUMXY - SUMY × SUMX)/DENOM;
                   AO[J] + (SUMY - A1[J] × SUMX)/N;
                   SUM + 0;
                   FINDO
                     SUM + (-A1[J]×X[I] - AO[J] + Y[I])*2 + SUM;
                   V[J] + SUM/DEGFRE;
                   V1[J] + V[J] × N/DENOM;
                   VO[J] + V1[J] × SUMXX/N;
                   IF J > 1 THEN GO TO LB3;
                   SUMB + SUM;
LB1:               J + J + 1;
                   F[J] + L + R - FB;
                   GO TO LB8;
LB3:               IF SUM ≤ SUMB THEN
                     BEGIN
                       IF F[J] < FB THEN
                         BEGIN
                           R + FB;
                           Q + K;
                         END
                       ELSE
                         BEGIN
                           L + FB;
                           P + K;
                         END;
                       FB + F[J];
                       SUMB + SUM;
                       K + J;
                     END.
                   ELSE
                     BEGIN
                       IF F[J] < FB THEN
```

```
                 BEGIN
                    L + F[J];
                    P + J;
                 END
               ELSE
                 BEGIN
                    R + F[J];
                    Q + J;
                 END
          END;
        IF J < 14 THEN GO TO LB1;
        IF FB < 0.98 × RFIRST THEN
          BEGIN
             WRITE (FM19, FB, F[Q]-F[P], F[P], F[Q]);
             WRITE (FM20, AO[K], AO[Q]-AO[P], AO[P], AO[Q]);
             WRITE (FM21, A1[K]+AO[K], AO[Q]+A1[Q]-AO[P]-A1[P],  AO[P]+
      A1[P], AO[Q]+A1[Q]);
             WRITE (FM48, V[K], VO[K], VO[K]+V1[K]);
             GO TO LB47;
          END
        ELSE
          BEGIN
             DIFF + RFIRST - LFIRST;
             IF RFIRST ≥ 2.8 × DIFF THEN
              BEGIN
                 WRITE (FM23, RFIRST);
                 GO TO LB47;
              END;
             LFIRST + RFIRST - 0.05 × DIFF;
             RFIRST + RFIRST + 0.95 × DIFF;
             GO TO LB2;
          END;
LB46: WRITE (FM30);
LB47: WRITE ([PAGE]);
      END FIBSEARCH;


    SWNO + 1;
AGAIN:
    RUNSTART (NUMR, THPRIM, CDNO[O], FINISH, SMCL);
    BEGIN
        ARRAY TEMP, ROT[1:NUMR];
        FOR I + 1 STEP 1 UNTIL NUMR DO
         BEGIN
            DATAROT (THETA, X, N, THPRIM, TEMP[I], XZ, XST, CDNO[1],
      ROT[I]);
            IF SMCL MOD 2 = 1 THEN
              BEGIN
                 CDNO[1].[42:6] + "D";
                 GRAF  (THETA, X, N, XZ, XST, CDNO, SWNO);
              END;
            IF SMCL ≠ 1 THEN
              BEGIN
                 SMOOTH (THETA, N, SMCL);
                 CDNO[1].[42:6] + "S";
                 GRAF   (THETA, X, N, XZ, XST, CDNO, SWNO);
              END;
         END;
        FIBSEARCH (TEMP, ROT, NUMR, CDNO[O]);
    END;
    GO TO AGAIN;
FINISH: END;  END.
```

97.   T. Masamune, M. Takasugi, M. Gohda, H. Suzuki, Sh. Kawahara, and T. Irie, J. Org. Chem., 29, 2282 (1964).

98.   (a) K. S. Brown and S. M. Kupchan, J. Am. Chem. Soc., 86, 4414, 4424, and 4430 (1964); (b) K. S. Brown and S. M. Kupchan, Tetrahedron Letters, No. 39, 2895 (1964); (c) S. M. Kupchan and W. L. Asburn, Tetrahedron Letters, No. 42, 3145 (1964).

99.   C. Djerassi and O. Halpern, Tetrahedron, 3, 255 (1958).

100.   E. J. Eisenbraun, J. Osiecki, and C. Djerassi, J. Am. Chem. Soc., 80, 1261 (1958).

101.   T. Okuda, Chem. Pharm. Bull. Japan, 7, 137 (1959).

102.   M. Suzuki, Y. Egawa, and T. Okuda, Chem. Pharm. Bull. Japan, 11, 582 (1963)

103.   T. Okuda, M. Suzuki, T. Furumai, and H. Takahashi, Chem. Pharm. Bull. Japan, 11, 730 (1963).

104.   K. L. Rinehart, V. F. German, W. P. Tucker, and D. Gottlieb, Ann. Chem., 668, 77 (1963).

105.   T. L. Harris, E. L. Hirst, and C. E. Wood, J. Chem. Soc., 848 (1937) and other papers of this series.

106.   Y. Tsuzuki, K. Tanaka, and K. Tanabe, Bull. Chem. Soc. Japan, 35, 1614 (1962).

107.   (a) Ch. Satoh, A. Kiyomoto, and T. Okuda, Chem. Pharm. Bull. Japan, 12, 518 (1964); (b) A. Satch and A. Kiyomoto, Chem. Pharm. Bull. Japan, 12, 615 (1964).

108.   See the leading references mentioned in Section 11-3.

109.   J. A. Schellman, in ref. 1., p. 210.

110.   (a) W. Gaffield, Chem. and Ind., 1460 (1964); (b) I. P. Dirkx and F. L. J. Sixma, Rec. Trav. Chim., 83, 522 (1964); see also the leading references mentioned in Section 11-9.

111.   V. M. Potapov, A. P. Terentiev, and Dang Ni Tai, Dokl. Akad. Nauk. S.S.S.R., 158, 1136 (1964).

112.   (a) J. Brahms and W. F. H. M. Mommaerts, <u>J. Mol. Biol.</u>, <u>10</u>, 73 (1964);
(b) D. W. Urry and H. Eyring, <u>J. Am. Chem. Soc.</u>, <u>86</u>, 4574 (1964); (c)
E. Iizuka and J. T. Yang, <u>Biochemistry</u>, <u>3</u>, 1519 (1964); (d) T. M. Hooker
and C. Tanford, <u>J. Am. Chem. Soc.</u>, <u>86</u>, 4989 (1964).

113.   (a) G. D. Fasman, E. Bodenheimer, and C. Lindblow, <u>Biochemistry</u>, <u>3</u>,
1665 (1964); (b) S. Beychok and G. D. Fasman, <u>Biochemistry</u>, <u>3</u>, 1675
(1964); (c) C. Y. Lin, D. W. Urry, and H. Eyring, <u>Biochem. Biophys.</u>
<u>Res. Commun.</u>, <u>17</u>, 642 (1964); (d) J. M. Calvo, C. M. Stevens,
M. G. Kalyanpur, and H. E. Umbarger, <u>Biochemistry</u>, <u>3</u>, 2024 (1964).

Index

368   Index

370   Index